Mechanical Engineering Design Notes

Theme: Automotive Engines

1st Edition

David J Grieve, CEng, MIMechE.

School of Engineering, University of Plymouth.

Published by: David J Grieve

Published by: David J Grieve
                   6 Parkers Green
                   PL18 9PG
                   UK

                   E mail: DaveJGrieve@aol.com

ISBN: 978-0-9560037-0-6

Printed and bound by TJ International Ltd, Padstow, Cornwall

Preface

The Institution of Mechanical Engineers has for many years recommended that engineering design be used to integrate the different subjects that comprise a degree course in mechanical engineering. We believe that a key to enthusing students in such a course is to use a suitable case study which involves some hands on work, a broad range of engineering analysis, an introduction to some areas of computer aided engineering (CAE) and which is somewhat open ended.

The above approach has been developed and used by the author and colleagues in the School of Engineering (SoE) at the University of Plymouth and has proved popular with students and has met with approval of external examiners.

A major factor in the success of such an approach is to select an appropriate case study. As I have had an interest in motor vehicles since I was a teenager, I found it very enjoyable thinking about and developing case studies based around automobiles and for most recent years we have used case studies based on car petrol engines.

(SoE also runs a BEng(Hons) course in Marine Technology and these students have a marine based case study, often on a topic around a remote operated underwater vehicle).

This book differs from most mechanical engineering design books in the following ways:

- The book has a clear theme of automotive engines, significant parts of the text relate to this theme as do many of the worked examples.
- There are a number of what I would describe as very approximate calculations, possibly little better than an order of magnitude approximation, see the example in Appendix 12.2. However, for finite element analysis (FEA) of anything other than a very simple configuration, engineers can only obtain approximate results by calculator to check computer analysis.
- There is significant content on simulation of performance. Although the examples relate to automobiles the approaches are transferable to any dynamic system and as customers expect ever better products, designers are increasingly going to be involved with simulation.

- The learning support material from which this book was developed are currently available on the Faculty of Technology web server, School of Engineering web pages: http://www.tech.plym.ac.uk/sme, start at 'Index to Online Documentation'

  The learning support material for the second year mechanical engineering design module (DSGN 215) including interactive resources, Java Applets, is currently at: http://www.tech.plym.ac.uk/sme/desnotes/desintro.htm, if readers inform me of any corrections or amendments needed, I will put a link from this web page.

  The index to the School interactive Java Applets and Javascript is at: http://www.tech.plym.ac.uk/sme/interacresources.htm

- To keep the cost of this book down I have published it myself. This means that I have not been able to include as many pictures as I would have liked and I have also made use of a number of sketches and some handwritten notes (hence the fourth word in the title). Each page carries the chapter number followed by the page within the chapter number, I found this convenient, I hope you do. This book is derived from web based notes, in .htm which has certain limitations in formatting - particularly as far as Greek letters are concerned, but I don't like Word and I find the htm editor I use much easier to use than Word. I think of these points as giving the book character!

As this book covers the learning support material used for the petrol engine case studies, it not only covers general mechanical engineering design, but also provides information and guidance about the principles and some aspects of designing automobile engines.

Modern automobile engines are highly sophisticated and are designed by teams of engineers, many of who have considerable expertise and experience, far more than can possibly be encapsulated in a single book. The topics considered in this book are those which the author and colleagues believe are appropriate for a second year course in mechanical engineering design.

To be a good engineering designer, it is essential to have a good understanding of materials and how they may be processed and some coverage of these topics is also included. For a thorough coverage of metals and materials the ASM publish a 20+ volume set about metals and a number of more specialist books - budget about £4000 + 2 m of strong shelving!

Although primarily written for mechanical engineering undergraduates, this book should also be of interest to technically minded people who wish to learn more about the design of automobile engines.

Acknowledgments
I would like to thank my colleagues in the School of Engineering for their support and for the many fascinating discussions over coffee. Particular thanks are due to professor Neil James, Pro Vice Chancellor and Dean of the Faculty of Technology, who has always had ideas about design and who has facilitated us in moving forwards.
For many years I was course co-ordinator and I have been grateful for the help and advice we received from our external examiners: Gary Hawley (who suggested I should write this book), John Bishop, Ajit Shenoi, David Eaton, Trevor Dean and Richard Penson.
Finally thanks to my wife Cathy, who has shown considerable forbearance as I increased my knowledge and understanding of automotive engineering while in our garage.

About the Author
David J Grieve, CEng, MIMechE, received a BSc and PhD from Birmingham University in 1967 and 1970 and then worked in a range of engineering related jobs in IMI, ICI and Degussa for several years before joining the now University of Plymouth. He has taught a range of engineering courses including mechanical engineering design.

He can be contacted by e mail currently at either: DaveJGrieve@aol.com or dgrieve@plym.ac.uk

Contents

9 Materials Selection

10 Mechanisms: Converting Piston (linear) Motion to Crank Rotation and Rotary Motion to Linear Motion - Using Cams. Springs

11 Engine Block, Crankshaft, Gudgeon Pins, Connecting Rods, Stresses in Mechanism Components, Buckling.

12 The Design of Bearings

Nomenclature

Below is a list of the symbols used, subscripts are frequently used to qualify the specific use. There are a few instances where different symbols have been used but I hope this will not cause confusion, sigma, S and the Greek symbol are all used for stress.
Note in calculations that E is used for Young's modulus and as on an engineering calculator, HP 32S, see below.
Most of this book was written in html where Greek letters are not readily available and this is the reason why some are used spelt out in English, ie: 'sigma' for stress.

A: area.
a: the velocity of sound in air. **Or** crack depth.
AISI: American Iron and Steel Institute.

BCC: body centred cubic (crystal structure).
BDC or bdc: bottom dead centre.
bmep: brake mean efective pressure, mep calculated from engine output at the flywheel, which was originally measured by a brake.
BS: British Standard.

C: spring index = mean coil diameter/wire diameter.
c: radial clearance
CAE: computer aided engineering - including design and simulation.
C_c: critical slenderness ratio.
C_d: drag coefficient.
C_p: specific heat of a gas at constant pressure (= 1000 J/kg°K for air at ambient conditions).
C_v: specific heat of a gas at constant volume (= 714 J/kg°K for air at ambient conditions).
CGI: compacted graphite iron.
CI: cast iron.
CR: compression ratio, $(V_s + V_c)/V_c$

D, d: diameter.
deltaT: temperature change.

E: Young's modulus
NB. E: is also used in calculations as in an engineering or scientific calculator: 10 to raised to the power of the number following the E.

F_c: critical load (buckling).
FCC: face centred cubic (crysral structure).

F_d: drag force.
FEA: finite element analysis.
FoS: factor of safety, preferably referred to as 'design factor'.

G: shear modulus.

gamma: ratio of specific heats, c_p/c_v. For air at ambient conditions γ is about 1.4, at elevated temperatures it is about 1.3.

HAZ: heat affected zone (either side of a weld).
HCP: hexagonal close packed (crystal structure).
h_o: minimum oil film thickness.

I: second moment of area.
ICE: internal combustion engine.

J: polar second moment of area.

K: end fixing factor for buckling calculation. **Or** stress intensity.
K_c: Critical stress intensity or fracture toughness.
k: radius of gyration.

mep: mean effective pressure.
MIG: metal inert gas (welding process).
mu: absolute viscosity.

N: number of engine revolutions per minute. **Or** number of load cycles.
n, n_d: design factor (fos).
NVH: noise, vibration and harshness.

omega: angular velocity, rad/s.

p: pressure.

Q and T: quenched and tempered.

The following when applied to the Otto cycle:

P_1: pressure at start of compression stroke (often ambient).
P_2: pressure at end of compression stroke.
P_3: pressure after instantaneous heat input.
P_4: pressure at end of expansion stroke.

P_c: critical load (buckling).
phi: (for Greek letter) angular position of maximum pressure in a hydrodynamic bearing.

PSE: principal structural element.
PTFE: polytetrafluoroethylene (a very inert plastic).

Q: shape factor for crack.

R: characteristic gas constant (= C_p - C_v), (= 287 J/kg°K for air).
r: compression ratio or radius.
rev/min and rpm: revolutions per minute
R_o: density.

S: Sommerfeld number (bearing characteristic number).
S_e: fatigue endurance strength of component.
S_e': fatigue endurance strength of smooth test piece.
shm: simple harmonic motion.
S_{ut}: ultimate tensile strength.
S_y: yield strength.
sigma: stress
slenderness ratio: length/k

t: time.

The following when applied to the Otto cycle:

   T_1: temperature at start of compression stroke (often just
   above ambient).
   T_2: temperature at end of compression stroke.
   T_3: temperature after instantaneous heat input.
   T_4: temperature at end of expansion stroke.

TDC or tdc: top dead centre.
TIG: tungsten inert gas (welding process).

U: surface velocity (of a shaft in a bearing).
u: internal energy (of a gas).
UTS: ultimate tensile strength.

All volumes are per cylinder unless otherwise stated.

   V_1 and V_4: volume when piston is at bdc.
   V_2 and V_3: volume when piston is at tdc.

v: velocity
V_c: volume when piston is at tdc, equal to V_2 and V_3.
V_s: swept volume
v_{pm}: mean piston speed.

x' and x": velocity and acceleration.

Z: Mach Index: gas velocity can be related to the Mach number (actual gas velocity/sonic velocity of the gas), however as the average velocity is only approximate, the term Mach index is used.
ZDDP: zinc dialkyldithiophosphate (an anti wear additive for engine oils).

Greek Symbols
δ: deflection

γ: ratio of specific heats, c_p/c_v. For air at ambient conditions γ is about 1.4, at elevated temperatures it is about 1.3.

η: efficiency. Subscripts are usually included to indicate which aspect is being considered.

σ_b: bending stress.

David J Grieve, 26th July 2008.

1. An Introduction to Design Methodology

1.1 Introduction

Below are some key points about design.

Design is an iterative process - at various stages it will be necessary to go back and re - consider some decisions. However at some point an agreed 'freeze' date must be specified, after which no changes will be permitted. Otherwise project deadlines will not be met and costs will rise - often catastrophically.

The following are major steps in the design process:

- recognition of a need, or idea for a new product
- brainstorm possible solutions
- if the proposed product already has competition in the marketplace, obtain examples, test them and reverse engineer them to determine possible weaknesses and aspects that could be improved.
- select a solution principle
- outline the solution
- market survey
- detailed design, selection of materials and manufacturing processes
- analysis of performance
- manufacturing plans
- sales promotion
- launch
- monitor progress
- develop mark 2 version.

Design problems are normally complex, even if they can be very simply stated, hence appropriate methodology needs to be understood and followed.

Almost invariably an important objective is to minimise time to market.

A serial approach has been traditionally used. Now simultaneous, or concurrent engineering is the standard, much more efficient approach involving simultaneous consideration of the design, the materials choices and the manufacturing processes.

The choice of manufacturing processes and materials must be considered as an integral part of the design process.

Communicating any design accurately and economically is vital. This can be done by drawing, CAD, 2D, or by having available a solid model data base - that can be shared (with appropriate access security) throughout the company and possibly with customers and suppliers.

Design problems are frequently multidisciplinary.

Some related important issues are:

> Safety needs to be designed in at the outset.
>
> Building in quality at the design stage is essential.
>
> Quality must be owned by every level of the organisation.
>
> A good understanding of the loads and operating conditions are essential.
>
> Design review is an important part of the design process to monitor progress.

Analysis and simulation using sophisticated computer software are increasingly used to speed design while making the process more accurate.
Using modern software it is possible to carry out a range of 'studies' to assist in achieving an efficient, or optimum, design. For example:

> **Design Optimisation:** Typically a component will be required to have a minimum mass while at the same time ensuring the maximum stress is below a specified value. The software can vary the sizes of features on a component while ensuring the specified conditions are met.
> **Sensitivity Study:** The effect on varying a particular dimension on the maximum stress occurring in a component may be of interest. Software can investigate this helping to determine how important particular dimensions are.

Design for manufacture / assembly / maintainability, is becoming increasingly important as consumers become more sophisticated. Modular design is an important way of meeting these requirements, however these benefits need to be balanced against an increase in weight which is a common consequence of introducing modularisation.

1.2 The First Stage: Brainstorming

This is often the first stage in the design process once a 'need' has been established. A variety of people meet to generate ideas. All ideas, however unlikely should be written down. At this stage, which is 'idea generation' not appraisal, care must be taken not to cast doubts on any idea. Such a meeting should be brief, half an hour may be sufficient. Once the meeting extends beyond about an hour, there is a danger that some of the people present may switch off.

The brainstorming session is followed up - a couple of days later - to allow some time for reflection on the generated ideas, by a meeting which assesses the ideas that were listed. At this stage the obviously non - feasible ideas are rejected. This then leaves a number of ideas or concepts that are potentially viable.

1.3 Evaluating the ideas: Evaluation Matrix

An evaluation matrix is used to select the best of the potentially viable ideas. At this stage an element of quantification is brought in. The concepts are listed accross the top of the matrix or table and down the left hand side are listed criteria by which the concepts are to be assessed. In a simple application of the evaluation matrix, each concept is awarded marks agaist the criteria and these are summed at the bottom of the matrix, the best concept having the highest total. There are several variations on this theme, weightings may be applied to criteria that are believed to be more important.

It should be noted that not only is an evaluation matrix used in assessing the concepts, such matrices may be used many times in the design of a system, for example when considering what transmission system or type of motor is to be used, or essentially anywhere where a choice has to be made between possible alternatives.

One difficulty with using the evaluation matrix approach is when some of the ideas that have emerged from the brainstorming session involve innovative technology. The newer such technology is the less data that will be available about reliability and durability which makes it difficult for designers to judge the suitability of such devices and systems without significant testing, which may well be expensive in money and time. However by opting for the safe proven technology, an organisation risks being overtaken by companies willing to take a more innovative - and riskier - approach.

Where innovative technology is being adopted it is desirable to have a back up plan developed in case the innovative technology proves unsuitable late in the day.

1.4 Quality Function Deployment (QFD).

In recent years manufacturers have become increasingly aware that if their designs are to be successful, their customers need to be carefully considered during the design process. Quality Function Deployment (QFD) is a way of achieving this.

There are four stages in QFD:

i) Customer requirements, gleaned from market research and technological forecasts, are translated into product characteristics.

ii) The product specification needed to meet the customer requirements for the product characteristics is derived. As well as assessing how the 'in house' design meets the customer requirements, it is common to assess rivals competitive products to gauge how the proposed product will fare in the market place.

iii) Manufacturing (including quality) plans identify the design and process parameters that are essential if the requirements are to achieved.

iv) Process sheets, derived from the manufacturing plans, provide instructions for the operators.

This QFD procedure is increasingly being used in automobile design and manufacture and is doubtlessly one of the reasons why cars are widely perceived as becoming 'better'.

1.5 Planning

One of the reasons that the UK motor industry lost out so badly to Japanese imports in the 1970s was that UK manufacturers did not have particularly good quality arrangements in place and were happy to sell cars which were not very well developed. This meant that they were unreliable. Japanese manufacturers realised that even a technically inferior (and aesthetically inferior!) car would sell in the UK if it was significantly more reliable than UK made vehicles. They therefore set about ensuring that their vehicles were reliable. This involved careful detailed design and careful detailed planning of manufacturing operations. This approach paid off. Spending money up front on design and planning was a much less costly approach than using customers as testers as the costs of correcting problems once manufacturing has started is very high and many identified problems were never corrected and the reputation of UK manufactured vehicles - and their market share - fell rapidly.

Quality is very important in the automobile industry and most of the time most of the companies maintain high standards, but occasionally there are still stories of slippage, usually to try and get more vehicles out of the factory in a hurry.

1.6 Late Changes to Designs

One obvious consequence of the need for meticulous planning is what happens when changes to a design are made after the 'freeze' date, even if the planning has previously been excellent. Any significant - even an apparently minor - late change is almost guaranteed to result in the project being delivered late and over budget, often considerably so. Most private sector industry has learnt this lesson and such mistakes are rare in this sector, however the government / civil service / Ministry of Defence amazingly appear not to have discovered this yet. It is not necessary to spend much time perusing the 'quality' newspapers before an article is found reporting on the latest debacle of a project that is hundreds of millions of pounds over budget and months / years late - and occasionally abandoned - because there is no longer any chance of it being completed successfully.
The British Library, Millenium Dome, Bowman radio are just three from a sadly long list of projects that have enjoyed only 'limited success'!

The lesson that once a design has been agreed it should not be modified has been known by a lot of engineers and designers since the middle of the last century, I certainly commend this lesson to readers, particularly if you are working or planning on working for the government / civil service / Ministry of Defence.

1.7 Sources and Use of Information

Design engineers spend a significant proportion of their time retrieving, studying and evaluating information - possibly about 20% of their working time. While the www has revolutionised the availability of all types of information and offers huge advantages in terms of quantity of information available and ease of access, the problem of evaluating the quality of the information is more difficult than in the days when it was all printed and the place where it was published offered good clues as to the quality. The list below gives some idea of the main sources.

- British and International Standards and company or industry standards
- Text and reference books
- Journal papers - proceedings of learned societies
- Professional journals
- Trade journals
- Trade associations
- Company brochures and www pages
- Colleagues

Because of the diversity of the quality of information it is now even more important to carefully evaluate information and check it from a different source if possible, before making use of it in any significant situation.

A major difficulty with most information (unless it is being read from an original journal paper) is that there is unlikely to be any background information about how the data was obtained. For example if it was obtained experimentally, what type of experiment was done, how were measurements made and how accurate were they, what was the range of experiments. All this is needed as background to enable the engineer to judge how valid the data is and how applicable it may be to the current project. A particular problem is where the available data does not quite extend to the matter of immediate concern, is it safe to extrapolate the data or not? Generally this should not be done unless there is very full background detail available and even then there is significant risk in extrapolation. As well as an understanding of engineering science, materials and manufacturing methods, engineering judgment is important. Such judgment develops as an engineer gains experience. An understanding of the engineering science should avoid mistakes of the type: 'This component requires heat treatment at x degrees for 1 hour, our furnace won't reach x degrees so we will use x/2 degrees for 2 hours'!

1.8 Factor of Safety - Design Factor

The 'factor of safety' (fos) should perhaps be called a 'factor of ignorance', however a more common name now is 'Design Factor'. The idea of this is that it takes into account the uncertainty of our knowledge about factors relating to a design.

We do not know exactly:

Full Details of Load(s)
The Nature of Defects Introduced by Manufacturing

It is common practice to size components so the maximum design stress is below the UTS or yield stress by an appropriate factor - the

Factor of Safety, based on UTS or Yield Strength (or in some cases involving fatigue, on the fatigue endurance strength).

Generally use a larger FoS if:

> There is little information about one or more of the factors above.
> Failure would have serious consequences, such as loss of life.

Increasingly now computers are being used to provide more accurate simulation of stresses that occur in components, particularly in the case of high value products where safety and saving weight is essential - aircraft and automotive.

In these critical applications, manufactured components will sometimes be tested to assess the reliability of the material and the manufacturing techniques. For some applications the efforts that go into large scale operations mean that much lower FoS are used for these than can be used for routine daily working.

The FoS, also sometimes known as the design factor of safety, n_d or n, may be determined in terms of the material's ultimate tensile stress (UTS) or the yield stress:

> n = strength / stress, or FoS = UTS / design stress

The above disussion is satisfactory for linear systems where the stress is proportional to the load. However for situations where buckling or instability is a possibility, the stress and load are NOT linearly related, then the design factor or factor of safety MUST be based on loads, ie:

> n or FoS = load to just cause failure/design load.

It is important to understand that different fos are appropriate for different components in a system.
If the example of a travelling crane on an overhead gantry is considered, in the event of overloading it is better that the hook or chain gives way dropping only the load, rather than the entire gantry gives way, dropping the load wrecking the entire crane and probably causing widespread damage in the workshop and greatly increasing the chance of casualties. The hook will have a low fos, the lifting chain a somewhat higher fos and the gantry a still higher fos. Additionally the hook is likely to have been annealed during the manufacturing process, so slight overload will result in the hook opening slightly and the resulting strain will cause some strain hardening which increases the strength (yield strength and UTS) of the hook, possibly enabling it to carry the slight overload. Obviously

regular inspection is carried out on cranes to check components for permanent deformation.

The ability of most metals, particularly those that have not already been strengthened by work (or strain) hardening, to increase their strength by work hardening, provides a useful safety characteristic which is used in many applications. Stub axles which carry the front wheels of cars are normally designed so excessive load will bend the axle but is unlikely to fracture it. A vehicle is likely to be easier to bring to safe stop with a bent axle than if the axle has broken leaving the vehicle with only 3 wheels.

One example where a fos of just over 1 is used is that an aero engine is held onto a jet aircraft wing by 3 bolts. Should a problem occur with the engine which results in sudden serious vibration, then these bolts will fail and the engine fall away before the vibration can damage the wing. These bolts are designed and manufactured with great care and low fos. They also have to be fitted with care. One accident was caused by using a fork lift truck to hold an engine approximately in place and then using the bolts to pull it finally into place (rather that the specified lifting jig) this overloaded the bolts which failed during normal flight.

An application where there is potential risk of loss of life is in lifts that carry humans. Such equipment has a back up emergency fail safe brake system, the critical components have high fos, typically between 6 and 12 and as a discouragement to overloading, if the stated maximum capacity is 10 people, the physical size of the lift will be such that is is a very tight squeeze to get 10 people in.

As vehicle manufacturing companies have in the past 40 years invested a great deal of money in research about loads vehicles undergo in different continents and in CAE facilities, this has enabled them to reduce the factors of safety they need to apply while at the same time increasing reliability and economy.

Discussion and examples using a statistical approach to design problems can be found in the reference below.

Reference
'Mechanical Engineering Design', J E Shigley and C R Mischke, McGraw-Hill, 6th Ed., 2001.

2 Principles, Fuels, Engine Configurations

2.0 A Health Warning for People Using CAE

If you are working on a hand calculator and are being very careless, pressing several incorrect keys, you will probably get about 7 wrong answers in a minute.

If you are using a piece of engineering software on a modern PC and press 1 incorrect key for a vital piece of input, the computer - with the aid of powerful post-processing and graphics card, which dress the results in attractive shaded plots and even animated videos - will with hardly any visible effort deliver you with wrong answers at the rate of at least 10,000 per minute.

> (The author explaining to applicants to the School of Engineering why although we do some teaching of CAE, it is vital that students gain a good understanding of the appropriate engineering science AND understand the importance of critically assessing the results from CAE.)

2.1 Principles

Engines work by heating a fluid so that pressure can be generated which can do work either by pushing against a piston or turbine blades. In the case of a steam engine the working fluid is steam which starts off as water, is heated in some type of boiler, undergoes a phase change to steam, which if not confined would occupy about 1000 times the original volume of the water, depending upon the temperature of the steam. The steam is confined under pressure in the boiler and supplied to the engine or turbine where it expands, doing work, providing a source of power. In engines using water / steam, where the heating of the fluid takes place away from the moving parts of the engine, the system is called external combustion. In petrol and diesel engines, the working fluid is heated by burning the fuel in contact with the moving part(s), usually a piston in petrol and diesel engines and these are called internal combustion (IC) engines.

As a general rule, the higher the temperature (and therefore pressure) of the working fluid, the greater the specific work that it can do and the greater the potential efficiency of the engine. This places rigorous requirements upon the materials to be used in engines. In external combustion engines, different zones of the system are at different (but reasonably) constant temperatures, but in internal combustion engines fresh (cool) fuel and air are introduced into the working zone (normally the cylinder) which provides brief cooling of the cylinder and piston. The mixture is then ignited, reaches a high temperature, well in excess of $1000°C$, for a short period of time, heating the surrounding components again while at the same time subjecting them to high pressure caused by the combustion. Although this alternate heating and cooling helps to keep the maximum temperatures below those that would be reached if the hot parts of the engine were continuously at high temperatures, the disadvantage is that the components are subjected to significant thermal fatigue.

2.2 Why Study Engine Design?

The design of automotive engines requires knowledge and understanding of all aspects of mechanical engineering and the competitive nature of the industry requires that those involved must engage in continuous development and improvement. This situation provides a huge range of challenges that many engineers find fascinating and who consequently wish to develop a career in this area.

Some engineers, among them the author, have empathy with the words of a Harley Davidson advertisement that appeared adjacent to a picture of one of their new models, several years ago: 'God did not create metal so man could make paper clips'.

To create the high temperatures needed to do the work in the engine, fuel has to be burnt. This has a number of consequences:

- i) If the fuel is obtained from a non renewable resource then finite resources of the planet are being depleted - it is obviously desirable that these resources are used as efficiently as possible.
- ii) Any burnt fuel will give rise to exhaust emisions, some of which may well have deleterious effects upon the atmosphere and planet.

It is widely accepted that when hydrogen is burnt, then only water vapour is produced which is benign, however energy will have been used on producing the hydrogen (and energy will have been used in constructing the plant, operating it and maintaining it) and transporting the produced hydrogen. These details should all be considered when assessing the environmental advantages and disadvantages of any fuel. If the hydrogen has been produced by electrolysis of water using electricity generated by a renewable energy source, then this will probably help, though again there is chemical plant involved.

Obtaining accurate data that includes all these details is difficult and much of it will be dependent upon specific plant type, location, age, condition and efficiency of operation. However as fossil fuels become depleted and technology develops, there will be greater drivers to determine these details and use the information effectively.

There are many challenges in designing efficient engines that minimise pollution, engineers have a vital role to play in all aspects of this work.

2.3 Fuels
2.3.1 Introduction
In the early days of powered machinery, boilers for steam engines were usually heated by coal, later coke and oil were used, but increasing public awareness of environmental issues has meant that gas is increasingly used to fire boilers.

However the ever increasing costs of petroleum related products means that significant research is being carried out to enable coal and oil to be either processed before combustion (eg the reduction of sulphur and vanadium in fuel oils) or pollution reduction systems fitted to boiler flues to reduce harmful pollutants in flue gases, particularly sulphur dioxide which easily converts to dilute sulphuric acid (which has in the recent past caused serious damage to woodland and forests in Europe).

Some power stations use nuclear energy to boil water for turbines to generate electricity, however there are environmental concerns about nuclear power and apart from electricity generation on land nuclear reactors are to date only used in aircraft carriers, ice breakers and submarines. There was a test aircraft engine built in the 1960s, but difficulties with control caused the work to be abandoned.

Although a number of alternative propulsion systems are being developed and tested for automobiles, the vast majority of power plants are internal combustion engines burning either petrol or diesel, with a small proportion burning natural gas or alcohol. It should be noted that in the past few years BMW has manufactured a small number of cars fitted with conventional IC engines powered by hydrogen and despite the problems posed by using hydrogen as a fuel BMW appear to be making significant progress. Their most recent cars can switch between petrol and hydrogen and exhibit the same performance on either fuel. In recent years the efficiency of both petrol and diesel engines has been significantly improved by techniques such as variable valve timing and sophisticated engine (and transmission) management. These developments, combined with the very extensive knowledge, experience and investment in manufacturing plants, means that IC engines, probably fueled by diesel or petrol, but possibly increasingly by hydrogen in the future, are likely to be manufactured for many years.

2.3.2 Petrol

Petrol contains four main groups of organic chemicals: paraffins, olefines, naphthenes and aromatics and in total consists of about 85% carbon and 15% hydrogen by weight, has a density of approximately 720kg/m^3 and a calorific value of about 46MJ/kg. A key property of petrol is its ability to resist self pre-ignition (ahead of the igniting spark and advancing flame front). This is defined by comparison with 'isooctane', C_8H_{18}, 100% isooctane having an octane rating of 100.

2.3.3 Diesel

Diesel fuel for high speed automotive engines is a 'gas oil' with a boiling range of 180 to 360°C and a density of 830 - 860kg/m^3. A key property of diesel fuel its readiness for self ignition on injection into the high pressure (and therefore hot) air in the cylinder. Diesel fuel is compared to a mixture organic liquid, hexadecane, known as 'cetane' with good self igniting properties and alpha-methyl-napthalene ($C_{10}H_7CH_3$) which has low ignition quality. The percentage of cetane which gives the same self ignition properties as the sample of diesel fuel is the 'cetane value' of the fuel.

A high octane number implies a low cetane number.

2.3.4 Hydrogen

To provide a reasonable range for a car, hydrogen needs to be stored either as a liquid, which requires extremely low temperatures (-253°C) and consequently a very well insulated storage tank, or alternatively it can be stored as a hydride combined with a suitable metal.

Hydrogen poses greater potential hazards than petrol or diesel as in natural form it is gaseous and the small molecule size means sealing joints is more difficult than with other gases and liquids. At temperatures of 1000°C or more steel is transparent to hydrogen. Of the flammable gases hydrogen has the widest range mixture ratios with air that will burn explosively.

2.4 Engine Configurations

Cylinders may be arranged in line, a very common arrangement as it is reasonably economic to manufacture and is well suited to four cylinder engines widely used to power medium sized cars, in 'V' formation or horizontally opposed. Other configurations have been used but are now uncommon: 'W' formation and radial arrangement - this was extensively used in propeller driven aircraft.

The only other design apart from piston in cylinder that is used is the approximately triangular rotor in an epitrochoidal housing, known as the Wankel Rotary Engine.

Early Wankel designs suffered from poor sealing, however this problem has been overcome, but it is not possible to overcome a fundamental aspect of the geometry which means that the combustion chamber has a greatly elongated shape. This means that it is almost impossible to burn the fuel efficiently resulting in poor fuel consumption and difficulties controlling exhaust emissions. On the plus side the purely rotary motion means that the engine is easy to balance and smooth running. There are three complete four stoke cycles per revolution of the rotor in the three working spaces formed by the rotor, all fired by the same spark plug as maximum compression is reached. This means the engine is very compact. However extensive development work has not overcome the disadvantages and this type of engine is only used in a few vehicles.

2.5 Two Stroke Compared to Four Stroke IC Engines.

In a two stroke engine there is one power stroke from each cylinder for every revolution of the crank shaft, whereas in a four stroke engine there is one power stroke from each cylinder for every two revolutions of the crankshaft.

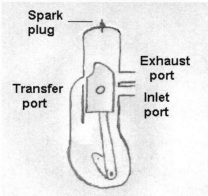

In a basic two stroke engine, see above, after the mixture has been ignited, the piston is pushed down and after the completion of about 80% of its stroke the exhaust port is uncovered. Very soon after the transfer port is uncovered and the compressed mixture in the crankcase rushes into the cylinder helping to scavenge the exhaust gases. The transfer port is closed by the rising piston slightly before the exhaust port so the final pressure in the cylinder depends to a significant extent upon the pulse effects of the exhaust pipe and silencer. The piston head is specially shaped to deflect the entering gases towards the top of the cylinder, this is known as cross flow scavenge. The rising piston then compresses the charge in the cylinder while drawing mixture into the crankcase. After ignition the gases expand and drive the piston down. However such a basic engine will only run efficiently in a limited band of engine speeds and outside this band fuel consumption is high and emissions are poor. Using fuel injection improves the efficiency but not the emissions as using crankcase compression makes it impossible to prevent oil entering the exhaust. External compression adds complexity and still does not overcome all emissions problems.

Some research is continuing on improving the emissions of two stroke engines as they have the potential to produce more power for a given engine weight which would be an important advantage if it could be achieved with emissions no worse than four stroke engines.

2.6 Current Trends
Three key drivers are:
i) The increasing cost of fuels, which long term seems almost certain to continue.
ii) The increasing demand from buyers who want higher levels of reliability (already much improved in recent years) better entertainment systems and more assistive technologies in their vehicles.
iii) Increasing government legislation imposing ever greater restrictions on vehicle emissions.

These demands mean that vehicle developments have involved, and are likely to continue to involve the following:

1. Improving streamlining to reduce drag, improving fuel economy.
2. Reducing mass which can improve fuel economy and / or performance.
3. Introducing better occupant and pedestrian safety in the event of an accident.
4. Introducing more accident avoidance technology.
5. Reducing vehicle noise both for occupants and people outside the vehicle.
6. Improving vehicle accessibility for older and less mobile users.
7. Increasing use of electrical actuation and reduced use of hydraulic systems.
8. Continuing research into alternative propulsion systems, fuels, combustion, fuel injection and engine and transmission management systems.

Item (1) requires computational fluid dynamics software and this has been available for several years and is now widely used and it's use has played a significant role in improving vehicle economy and there is little doubt that the application of such software will continue to increase in the future.

Items (2) and (3) require solid mechanics computational software, finite element analysis (FEA) is the standard approach to problems of assessing stress in components and optimising the components designs to reduce their mass while maintaining adequate strength. Specialist FEA software is used to investigate the performance of vehicle structures in various accident scenarios. The high costs (about £0.3 million) associated with carrying out an experimental crash of a prototype vehicle (compared with the costs of computer simulation) means that such computational work will increase in future.

Item (4) is a more controversial than the previous ones as here some element of control is removed from the vehicle driver, usually without warning. One of the first examples of this type of 'intrusive' technology was ABS (anti-skid) breaking. Although there was a little resistance initially to this technology, it is now fitted to a high proportion of vehicles sold in Europe and there are a few observations that have been made:
Some people who have only ever driven vehicles fitted with ABS have difficulty braking a vehicle in slippery conditions which is not fitted with ABS.
Some drivers seem to drive vehicles fitted with ABS as as if the system is able to suspend the laws of physics! One could argue that they would drive any vehicle without considering possible consequences - these arguments are, of course, impossible to prove one way or another.
Having an ABS system to moderate the brake when needed leads to the next stage where the vehicle is fitted with a drive system arranged so that the drive to any individual driven wheel can be interrupted should the wheel lose traction. Such traction control systems are fitted to many 'up market', 'executive saloons' and 'sports cars'.

Item (5) involves specialist CAE software which is able to predict sound and vibration levels. This is becoming widely used.

Item (6) in increasingly being investigated as the population ages and manufacturers seek to increase their market share.

Item (7) is inevitable as increasing use of microprocessors means that it is easier to make them interact with actuaters that are electrically powered rather than hydraulically powered. Already elctrically operated powered steering is replacing hydaulically assisted power steering. However, because of the high forces needed, it will probably be a while before electrically operated brakes are fitted to cars.

Item (8): A very small number of enthusiasts maintain that a modern steam engine would be a better choice than an IC engine. The fact that steam engines are external combustion does offer some advantages over IC engines, but the difficulties of rapid start up and building a compact light weight system still seem to most observers to rule such a system out for the short term future. The most likely alternative technology seems to be propulsion by electric motors. The debate is about how the electricity for the motors is provided: fuel cell - using petrol, LPG; battery power or electrical assistance to a small IC engine. There is then the complex discussion of how sustainable / environmentally friendly is the system used for generating (and possibly transmitting) the electricity to the vehicle.

Using alternative fuels for an IC engine is also a complicated subject, because although there are a number of possible alternative fuels there are complex issues of availability, infrastructure and ethics to be considered.
For example it is possible to use a very wide range of organic chemicals as a diesel fuel (although many are not efficient and not suitable for a modern sophisticated engine). Many of these are derived from crops, some of which are important foodstuffs. If a decision was reached that crop X was highly a suitable fuel source and large numbers of engines were to be produced to make use of such fuel, then demand could easily lead to large areas of deforestation so the crop could be grown in much larger quantities and foodstuff crops that provided staple diet for some third world countries could be abandoned in favour of growing the much more lucrative fuel crop, resulting in significant starvation.

2.7 Role of Computer Aided Engineering (CAE)
The introduction of computers, their rapid development and the development of CAE software has had a major effect on the design of almost all aspects of motor vehicles from simulation of chassis and suspension behavior, vehicle damage and occupant injuries likely to be suffered in accidents, engine performance and simulation of in cylinder combustion processes and of engine and transmission management systems.

All these developments have enabled manufacturers to produce better quality vehicles, with more features and better fuel economy while still keeping a competitive price.

Software used goes from simple spreadsheets, to highly sophisticated engineering simulation packages able to solve problems in stress analysis, vibration, acoustics, heat transfer and packages to simulate and predict the performance of dynamic systems. In many cases these software packages will include facilities for optimising aspects of the design, eg. generating a minimum mass design while keeping the maximum stress below a specific value.

As the costs of computers needed to run CAE software has rapidly fallen - now almost all CAE packages offer versions which can be run on high end PCs - the use of CAE packages is rapidly spreading into most areas of engineering including small companies with only limited resources.

See the health warning at the start of this chapter.

Some examples of computation are included in later chapters.

3 Comparison of Petrol (Spark Ignition) and Diesel (Compression Ignition) Engines

3.1 Comparison of Petrol and Diesel Engines

In a four stroke diesel engine the cycles can be described as follows:

- Just before the piston reaches top dead centre (TDC) the inlet valve opens and air is drawn into the cylinder by the descending piston. Just after the piston reaches bottom dead centre (BDC) the inlet valve closes
- The piston ascends, the air is compressed and increases in temperature, slightly before the piston reaches TDC the fuel injection starts and the temperature of the air ignites the fuel
- The piston passes TDC and starts to move down. The injection of fuel continues for a short time depending upon engine load, the fuel continues to burn raising the pressure and forcing the piston down. The combustion completes, the high pressure gases continue to expand, pushing the piston down and the pressure of the burnt gases decreases
- Shortly before the piston reaches BDC the exhaust valve opens and the ascending piston pushes out the burnt gases. The inlet valve opens just before the ascending piston reaches TDC and the exhaust valve closes just after the piston passes TDC.

The earliest diesel engines used air blast injection to propel the fuel (oil or finely powdered coal) into the cylinder which ignited due to the high temperature of the air in the cylinder having being compressed. The small but finite volume of the injecting air meant that the time taken for injection and combustion - as the piston was moving down from TDC - resulted in the combustion being at approximately constant pressure, point 2 to 3 on the diagram, below:

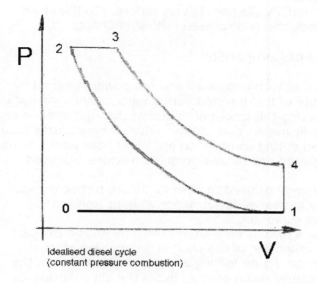

Idealised diesel cycle
(constant pressure combustion)

Fuel injection in modern diesels gives actual indicator diagrams quite similar to those obtained from petrol engines, but with rather higher peak pressure values.

The idealised PV diagram of the four stroke 'Otto', petrol cycle is shown in the sketch below:

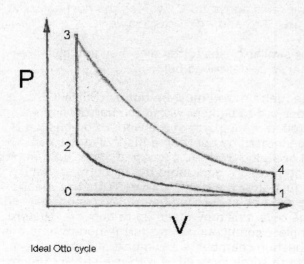

Ideal Otto cycle

Notes on the diagrams

A schematic of a 'real' PV diagram is very different to the above idealised schematics, this is discussed further in Chapter 8.

3.2 Other Points of Comparison

Diesel is always burnt with excess air and the power is varied by varying the quantity of fuel injected during each combustion cycle, this is done by varying the length of time that the injectors are kept open. The excess air means that the maximum temperatures (and pressures) reached during combustion are lower than would be the case if a stoichiometric or near stoiciometric mixture was used.

Virtually all diesel engines used to power cars are turbocharged, which significantly increases performance without significant increase in fuel consumption.
A tubocharger has a turbine on a shaft driven by engine exhaust gases and on the other end of the shaft is an impeller which compresses the incoming air forcing a larger mass of air into the cylinders. As the compression process heats the air, reducing its density, a cooler may be provided to cool the air.

A very wide range of organic liquids and gases can fuel a basic diesel engine, although often not very efficiently. Modern engines however may easily be damaged by non standard fuels.

Diesel fuel is much less flammable than petrol which makes it much safer and consequently it is preferred to petrol for military and marine applications. The flashpoint (the temperature to which a liquid has to be heated for the vapour to form a combustible mixture with air) of diesel is above 55°C, wheras the flashpoints of kerosene and petrol are 30°C and -40°C respectively.

The petrol engine has similar cycles to the diesel engine but there are important differences as described below.

In a petrol engine the fuel:air ratio must be tightly controlled, particularly if emissions are to be kept within the narrow limits which are now required in many parts of the world. Combustion is initiated by a spark generated by applying a high voltage to an electrode on the end of a plug which has a gap of about 0.8mm. For optimum efficiency the pressure generated by the burning fuel needs to be reached just after the piston passes TDC. This means that ignition must be initiated some time before the piston reached TDC. At higher engine revs. this may mean up to about 40° before TDC. To achieve complete combustion in a short period of time it is beneficial if the combustion chamber is a compact shape. In the past large cylinders were sometimes fitted with two spark plugs to initiate combustion in two places which would reduce the time for complete combustion however this is now rare except in engines used in light aircraft where having complete dual ignition systems is required to provide redundancy and hence additional reliability.

An important feature in improving engine efficiency is the compression ratio, CR, which is the ratio of the total enclosed volume when a piston is at BDC ($V_s + V_c$) to the enclosed volume when the piston is at TDC, V_c.

Where V_s is the swept volume per piston stroke = piston area x stroke.

$$CR = (V_s + V_c) / V_c$$

Compressing air (or any gas) heats it and this is the ignition source in a diesel engine. To reach a sufficiently high temperature requires a compression ratio of about 15:1 or greater, depending upon ambient air temperature. Increasing the CR increases the maximum temperature and pressure reached by the burnt fuel, yielding more work per kg of fuel burnt which improves efficiency, but at the expense of greater harshness, bearing loads and there are also emissions considerations. For these reasons diesel engines seldom use CR above about 22:1. Modern automotive diesel engines are fitted with a 'glow plug' in each cylinder head combustion chamber, which are activated as the ignition is turned on, a current of 12 amps or more provides extra heat to assist with rapid starting of the engine in cold conditions without excessive cranking which would otherwise be needed. Once the engine is running the glow plugs are not needed and are turned off as the temperature of compressed air is sufficient to ignite the injected droplets of diesel fuel.

In a petrol engine the mixture is ignited by a spark plug which requires a coil transformer to provide a high voltage, 15kV +, which ionises the gases in the vicinity of the gap enabling the spark to jump the gap (about 0.8 mm) and ignite the mixture as the piston approaches tdc towards the end of the compression stroke.

Originally in petrol engines the mixture of petrol and air was provided by a carburettor, however as the requirements for better control over the air:fuel ratio developed, the design of carburettors became more complicated and now fuel injection systems have superceded carburettors in virtually all new car engines and many medium and large motorcycle engines. In most engines the fuel is injected into the air stream just before it enters the cylinders although a few engines inject directly into the cylinders, often referred to as gasoline direct injection (GDI).

In a petrol engine it is difficult to use a CR above about 11:1 without causing 'detonation' or 'knock' at high loads. When this occurs, the fuel is not just ignited by the spark plug with the flame front advancing across through the mixture, but at several places almost simultaneously. This leads to very rapid rise in pressure, causing a knocking sound, which can very quickly destroy an engine. Some modern engines are fitted with knock detectors (accelerometers) which enable them to be operated close to the point at which knocking occurs, usually close to maximum efficiency.

The fact that the maximum CR of a petrol engine is typically about 10:1 and that of diesel engines is about 18:1, means that the diesel engine is inherently more efficient than the petrol engine. This is a major factor in the superior fuel economy of diesel engines compared to petrol engines.

4. Designing to Resist Failure
Failure Mechanisms, Failure Criteria,
Stress Concentration, Notch Sensitivity
Designing Against Cyclic Loading
Fracture Mechanics

4.1 Failure Mechanisms
The following types of failure are of interest to Mechanical Engineers:

Plastic Deformation / Fracture – Due to excessive load.

Excessive elastic deformation – Due to the structure being insufficiently stiff.

Plastic collapse, buckling – Due to instability.

Fracture – In a brittle material, or a normally ductile material that is behaving in a brittle manner (eg. because it is operating below its ductile / brittle transition temperature) - Due to load causing a stress intensity exceeding the critical stress intensity, or fracture toughness, of the component that contains a defect.

Fracture (fatigue failure) - typically in low strength metals - Due to cyclic load causing a crack to grow, usually from a defect at or close to the surface, reducing the area of material available to support the load until the remaining material is no longer able to support the load.

Fracture (fatigue failure) - typically in high strength metals - Due to cyclic load causing a crack to grow, usually from a defect at or close to the surface, so the maximum stress intensity at the crack tip exceeds the fracture toughness of the material.

Further reading - see ref. 4.1

4.2 Failure Theories
4.2.1 The Maximum Normal Stress Theory (Rankine)
Failure occurs when one of the three principal stresses equals the strength.

Assuming $\sigma_1 > \sigma_2 > \sigma_3$ then failure occurs when $\sigma_1 = S_t$ or $\sigma_3 = -S_c$

where S_t is the tensile strength and S_c is the compressive strength.

This criteria is often used when designing with brittle materials such as concrete or some cast irons.

4.2.2 The Maximum Normal - Strain - Theory (Also called St Venant's theory)

Applies only in the elastic range. States yielding occurs when the largest of the 3 principal strains becomes equal to the strain corresponding to the yield strength. If it is assumed that the yield strength in tension and compression are equal, conditions for yielding are:

$$\sigma_1 - \nu(\sigma_2 + \sigma_3) = \pm S_y$$

$$\sigma_2 - \nu(\sigma_3 + \sigma_1) = \pm S_y$$

$$\sigma_3 - \nu(\sigma_1 + \sigma_2) = \pm S_y$$

4.2.3 The Maximum - Shear - Stress Theory (Tresca)

This theory states that yielding begins when the maximum shear stress becomes equal to the maximum shear stress in a tension test specimen of the same material when that specimen begins to yield.

$$\tau_{max} \geq S_y/2 \text{ or } \sigma_1 - \sigma_3 \geq S_y$$

This theory also predicts that the yield strength in shear is $S_{sy} = 0.5S_y$

For principal stresses:

$$\tau_{1/2} = (\sigma_1 - \sigma_2)/2 \text{ etc}$$

Decompose the three normal principal stresses into the components -

$$\sigma_1 = \sigma_1' + \sigma_1'' \text{ etc so } \sigma_1'' = \sigma_2'' = \sigma_3'' \text{ these equal stresses are called hydrostatic components.}$$

If $\sigma_1' = \sigma_2' = \sigma_3' = 0$ then the three shear stresses would all be zero and there could be no yielding - regardless of the hydrostatic stress. The magnitude of the hydrostatic stress has no effect on the size of the Mohr circle, but move it along the normal stress axis.

This criteria may be used when designing with ductile materials (most commonly used metals) but gives somewhat conservative designs for some combinations of loadings.

4.2.4 Maximum Strain Energy Theorem

Suggests failure by yielding occurs when the total strain energy per unit volume reaches or exceeds the strain energy in the same volume corresponding to the yield strength in tension or compression.

The se / unit vol. when stressed uni-axially to yield: $u_s = S_y^2/2E$.

The energy in a unit vol. subject to multi-axial stresses:

$$u = \frac{\epsilon_1 \sigma_1}{2} + \frac{\epsilon_2 \sigma_2}{2} + \frac{\epsilon_3 \sigma_3}{2}$$

$$u = \frac{1}{2E}\left[\sigma_1^2 + \sigma_2^2 + \sigma_3^2 - 2\upsilon(\sigma_1\sigma_2 + \sigma_2\sigma_3 + \sigma_3\sigma_1)\right]$$

This is not much used presently.

4.2.5 The von Mises Theory (also known as the maximum distortion energy theory. This gives the same result as the von Mises-Hencky theory or the octahedral shear stress theory).

This states that yielding will occur when the distortion energy in a unit vol. equals the distortion energy in a unit vol. when uniaxially stressed to the yield strength. This was derived from the observation that yielding is not affected by a volume change caused by compression, so may be related to the angular distortion of a stressed element. With some algebra, the effective or von Mises stress is defined by:

$$\text{vms} = \frac{1}{\sqrt{2}}[(\sigma_1 - \sigma_2)^2 + (\sigma_2 - \sigma_3)^2 + (\sigma_3 - \sigma_1)^2]^{0.5}$$

and yielding occurs when $\text{vms} \geq S_y$

This criterion is commonly used when designing with ductile metals - it gives a better fit to experimental data than the Tresca criterion.

4.2.6 Coulomb Mohr or Internal friction theory

This theory and variants try to cover materials whose yield stress in compression is not the same as their yield strength in tension.

4.2.7 Failure Theories - Conclusion

- For brittle materials, eg grey iron, concrete, use the maximum principal stress theory
- For ductile materials, eg most steels and aluminium alloys, use the von Mises theory

4.3 Designing for Combined Loading

In many engineering situations components frequently have to withstand more than one type of load. Shafts often have to withstand torque and bending moments. To solve this type of design problem the components are assumed to behave in a linear manner and superposition is used. The stresses due to each type of loading are determined in turn and then combined using appropriate equations or Mohr's circle.

If the design is to be based on the maximum shear stress theory (Tresca) then the maximum shear stress in the component (after combining the contributions due to all the loads) must be found. In some configurations it will not be obvious where the maximum combined shear stress occurs, in these cases it will be necessary to check the combined stresses at a number of locations.

For the example of a uniform solid circular shaft, diameter d, subject to torsion T and tension P, the maximum shear stress is constant at all points at the maximum radius.

The direct stress due to P is $= 4\ P/(3.142\ d^2)$

The max. shear stress due to T (at the surface) is $= 16\ T/(3.142\ d^3)$

The maximum combined shear stress can be found from Mohr's circle to be:

max. shear stress $= [(\text{direct stress}/2)^2 + (\text{shear stress})^2]^{0.5}$

For a safe design the max. combined shear stress must be less than or = yield shear stress / factor of safety.

If the design is to be assessed against the distortion energy (von Mises) theory, then the von Mises stress needs to be calculated, which means the 3 principal stresses have to be determined.

In many cases of three dimensional solid components, it will often be adequate to carry out a 2D stress analysis. An example of this is in the design of most shafting, where there are no interference fits and consequently the radial stresses are usually insignificant compared to axial stresses caused by bending and / or tension / compression and shear stresses (on axial and circumferential planes) caused by torques transmitted.

An example of calculation to design a shaft against failure under combined loading is given in Appendix 4.1.

4.4 Stress Concentration

4.4.1 Introduction

Basic stress analysis calculations assume that the components are smooth, have a uniform section and no irregularities.

In practice virtually all engineering components have to have changes in section and / or shape. Common examples are shoulders on shafts, oil holes, key ways and screw threads. Any discontinuity changes the stress distribution in the vicinity of the discontinuity, so that the basic stress analysis equations no longer apply. Such 'discontinuities' or 'stress raisers' cause local increase of stress referred to as 'stress concentration'.

The 'theoretical' or 'geometric' stress concentration factor K_t or K_{ts} is used to relate the actual maximum stress at the discontinuity to the nominal stress.

K_t = max direct stress / nominal direct stress and

K_{ts} = max shear stress / nominal shear stress.

In published information relating to stress concentration values the nominal stress may be defined on either the original 'gross cross section' or on the 'reduced net cross section' and care needs to be taken that the correct nominal stress is used.

The subscript 't' indicates that the stress concentration value is a theoretical calculation based only on the geometry of the component and discontinuity.

4.4.2 Notch Sensitivity

Some materials are not as sensitive to notches as implied by the theoretical stress concentration factor. For these materials a reduced value of K_t is used: K_f. In these materials the maximum stress is:

max. stress = K_f x nominal stress

The notch sensitivity, q, is defined as: $q = (K_f - 1) / (K_t - 1)$ where q is between 0 and 1.

This equation shows that if q = 0, then $K_f = 1$ as the material has no sensitivity to notches.

If q = 1, then $K_f = K_t$ and the material is fully notch sensitive.

When designing, a frequent procedure is to first find K_t from the geometry of the component, then specify the material and look up the notch sensitivity, q, for the notch radius from a chart. Then by rearranging the above equation, determine K_f.

$$K_f = 1 + q(K_t - 1).$$

Curves for q values are normally plotted up to notch radii of 4mm. For larger notch radii, the q value at 4 mm can be used.

Most cast irons have a very low q value. This is because their microstructures contain many notches, so additional machined ones make little difference. A value of q = 0.2 will be on the safe side for all grades of cast iron.
In the absence of specific information high strength steels can be assumed to be fully notch sensitive with q = 1.

4.4.3 When to Use Stress Concentration Values

To apply stress concentration calculations, the part and notch geometry must be known. However where a part is known to contain cracks, the geometry of these may not be known and in any case as the notch radius tends to zero, as it does in a crack, then the stress concentration value tends to infinity and the stress concentration is no longer a helpful design tool. In these cases 'Fracture Mechanics' techniques are used.

Where the geometry is known, then for brittle materials, stress concentration values should be used.

In the case of ductile materials that are subject only to one load cycle during their lifetime (fairly unusual in Mechanical Engineering) it is not necessary to use stress concentration factors as local plastic flow and work hardening will prevent failure provided the average stress is below the yield stress.

NB Not all ductile materials are ductile under all conditions, many become brittle under some circumstances. The most common cause of brittle behavior in materials normally considered to be ductile is being exposed to low temperatures.

For ductile materials subjected to cyclic loading the stress concentration factor has to be included in the factors that reduce the fatigue strength of a component.

4.5 Cyclic Loading - Fatigue
4.5.1 Introduction
Fatigue involves crack initiation followed by crack growth

> Requires cyclic - repeated stressing - normally cracks only develop under tensile stresses.
> Fatigue is only a problem when the failure is unexpected
> Fatigue contributes to 80 - 90 % of all failures
> Offshore fatigue contributes to 20 - 25% of failures

Fatigue has been recognised and researched for 120 years - so - why is it still a problem?

> A major reason is that it is complex.
> Welding now used extensively - and is a potent source of defects
> Higher mechanical efficiency is being required, leading to more highly stressed components.

Comparatively recent techniques enable calculations to be made predicting the life or remaining life of a structure containing defects.

Two stages: crack initiation and crack growth. For some materials, ferrous metals being an important group, low cyclic stresses, below the 'threshold limit', do not lead to crack initiation.

Fatigue damage normally starts where cyclic stresses are most severe, this will often be at somewhere on a component surface where there is some imperfection or notch. For smooth specimens with a gradually changing section impurities or inhomogeneities in the grain structure provide crack initiation points. For these reasons it is important to take care when designing components which contain changes in section and features such as - key ways, screw threads, 'O' ring grooves, etc. to ensure that their effects are properly assessed. For components subjected to very high cyclic stresses, high purity steels may be used to minimise potential crack initiation locations, an example of this is the steel used by some manufacturers of ball and roller bearings.

4.5.2 Design philosophies:
4.5.2.1 Safe life:
Developed in the late 1950s and 1960s for the aircraft industry. Still widely used, based on S-N curves, but although mean values are available for many materials, experimental curves contain a lot of scatter.
Some effects are important and fairly well understood, effects of surface roughness, components size, notches.
The effects of mean stress may need to be considered as most data

has been generated for R = - 1 (zero mean stress). Some data is available for R = 0 (zero - tension - zero loading). For other loadings a transformation may need to be carry out.

There were however two significant problems with this approach:

- The structure was not protected if it contained a manufacturing or maintenance induced defect.
- Owing to the spread of results, a conservative safety factor was required and many components were prematurely retired. Even testing to 4 times the required life did not prevent some aircraft losses.

4.5.2.2 Fail Safe:
Developed in the 1960s for aircraft design to overcome limitations of the 'Safe Life' methodology.
The idea is to multiple load path structures, such that if an individual element should fail, the remaining elements would have sufficient structural integrity to carry the additional loads from the failed element until until the damage is detected through scheduled maintenance.
Designers and operators live safely with cracks. This was not a feasible approach until the 1960's when fracture mechanics started to be able to provide a quantative description of the residual life of a cracked component.

In addition to the multiple load paths, crack stoppers are often used. These may consist of materials with a high fracture toughness used to supplement the residual strength of the surrounding structure and to prevent cracks propagating to failure.
An example of a crack stopper is a stringer in a pressurised aircraft fuselage.

4.5.2.3 Defect (or Damage) Tolerant Approach:
Developed in the 1970s for aircraft design and based upon fracture mechanics techniques, see section 4.5, below.
This is useful for complex structures with inherent defects, it is assumed that all structures contain growing cracks and failure can occur when actual conditions are different to those modelled.
For this approach to be used facilities must be available for measuring crack lengths. Generally defects need to be bigger than the grain size of the metal for the fatigue strength to be lowered.

For aircraft the objective is to detect cracks in 'Principal Structural Elements' (PSE) before they propagate to failure. By establishing inspection intervals for the PSEs based on the time it takes for a crack to grow from an initial detectable size to the critical crack length, safe operation can be maintained. This computation is quite complex and will involve working from the detailed usage programme of the plane.

Having determined the number of flight hours to failure, this is normally divided by two to give an inspection interval, this means that should a PSE develop a crack it should be inspected at least once before the crack propagates to failure.

This methodolgy means that undamaged components are not retired and factors of safety can be reduced as fracture mechanics provides a more precise characterisation of crack behaviour, the large scatter factors associated with fatigue results and methods are not required.

4.5.3 Factors Affecting the Fatigue Strength of Components
4.5.3.1 Introduction

Most fatigue testing is carried out on cylindrical specimens with a central section of uniform diameter and end of larger diameter, the ends being blended with the central section by a large radius and the entire surface smooth or polished. Details are available in the appropriate standards. One end is fixed in a rotating chuck and a rolling element bearing is fitted to the other end and the required load hung from the bearing. The specimen is rotated at 2000 - 3000 rpm which subjects it to fully reversed bending giving a maximum tensile and compressive stress every revolution and a zero mean stress.

A large number of tests on each material at different loads (and therefore different stress levels) are needed to determine the fatigue strength at different stress levels and the fatigue endurance strength (S_e') of the test pieces. This is the stress amplitude, in a fully reversed loading test, that the material can withstand for a very large number of cycles, see schematic plot below, on log - log axes:

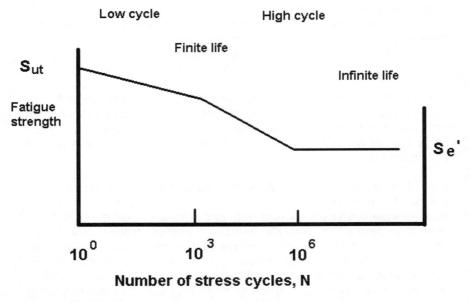

Typical schematic S - N diagram, log - log axes

It should be noted that only ferrous materials have a finite fatigue endurance strength, with all other materials the fatigue strength continues to fall as the number of cycles increases.

A common 'rule of thumb' for many ferrous materials where a value of the fatigue endurance strength is not available is to make a preliminary assumption that if the S_{ut} is 1400MPa or less, then the $S_e' = 0.5 \times S_{ut}$ and where if S_{ut} is greater than 1400MPa, the $S_e' = 700MPa$.
It should be noted that for different types of steel the 0.5 ratio suggested above varies. Ferrous materials with more ductile structures have a higher ratios, whereas more brittle structures have lower ratios.

Most S - N curves are derived from tests involving fully reversed bending with zero mean stress. Where the mean stress is not zero then the curve derived from zero mean stress can be entered with a value of equivalent completely reversed stress amplitude, S_{ar} to obtain the life. A number of expressions are used but the most common is derived from the modified Goodman diagram equation:

$$S_{ar} = S_a / (1 - (S_m / S_{ut}))$$

4.5.3.2 fatigue Endurance Strength Modifying Factors

Most engineering components do not have either smooth surfaces or different diameters blended by large radii fillets. Consequently the results from smooth specimens need to be corrected by applying:

- surface roughness factor (k_a)
- component size factor(k_b)
- load factor (k_c)
- temperature factor (k_d)
- miscellaneous effects factor (k_e)

Different formulae and values for these factors are found in different texts, the information below is indicative.

i) Surface Factor, k_a

$k_a = a\,(S_{ut})^b$ with the values below suggested for some surface conditions:

Surface Finish	Factor 'a'	Exponent 'b'
Ground	1.58	-0.085
Machined or cold drawn	4.51	-0.265
Hot rolled	57.7	-0.718
As forged	272	-0.995

References: 2, 3 and 4.

ii) Size Factor, k_b.

A lot of testing data has been accumulated for 7.62mm diameter (0.3 inch) specimens. It has been noted that larger diameter test pieces tend to have lower S_e' values when tested in rotating bending and the formula below (due to Mischke) is often suggested for bending and torsion:

$k_b = (d/7.62)^{-0.1133}$ where d is the diameter in mm and this is valid for d between 2.79 and 51mm.

There is no size effect for axial loading, so $k_b = 1$ in this case.

For other configurations the approach is to consider the proportion of the section where the stress is 95% or more of the maximum and evaluating an equivalent diameter. This is illustrated below:

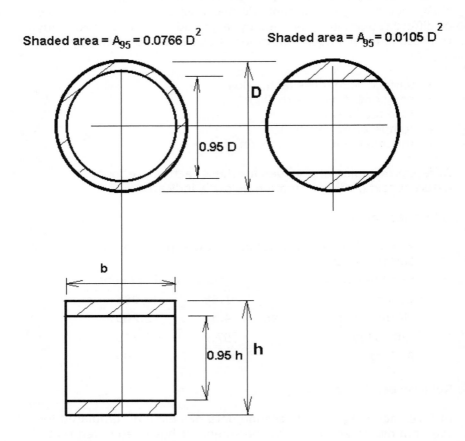

Shaded area = A_{95} = 0.0766 D^2 Shaded area = A_{95} = 0.0105 D^2

Shaded area = A_{95} = 0.05 h b

Geometry of sections for calculating A_{95} area

For the rotating circular specimen in reversed bending, the area subject to 95% or more of the maximum stress is given by the shaded area between the two circles in the top left diagram. The area is given by:

$$A_{95} = (3.14159/4)[D^2 - (0.95D)^2] = 0.0766\ D^2$$

For a non rotating circular section in repeated reversed bending, the top and bottom shaded segments, in the diagram top right, $A_{95} = 0.0105\ D^2$

The equivalent diameter, D_e for this stationary configuration can be determined by equating the two A_{95} areas:

$$0.0766 \, D_e^2 = 0.0105 \, D^2 \text{ giving}$$

$$D_e = 0.370 \, D$$

For a rectangular section in reversed bending, equating the A_{95} areas:

$$0.0766 \, D_e^2 = 0.05 \, h \, b \text{ giving}$$

$$D_e = 0.808 \, (h \, b)^{0.5}$$

Other shapes can be analysed in a similar manner.

iii) Load Factor, k_c
The following values for k_c are often given:

- 0.923 Axial loading, S_{ut} less than 1500MPa
- 1 Axial loading, S_{ut} greater than 1500MPa
- 1 Bending
- 0.577 Torsion and shear

iv) Temperature Factor, k_d
When operating at temperatures below 20°C, brittle fracture is a possibility and should be considered.
When temperatures are above 20°C yielding should be considered as yield strength decreases with increasing temperature. It is possible that materials have zero fatigue endurance strength at elevated temperatures and as most materials creep when under stress at elevated temperatures, the time of exposure to stress and temperature as well as the number of load cycles is probably important. For steel the reduction in S_{ut} is only 2-3% at 300C, but increases more rapidly thereafter, the loss being about 10% at 400°C.

v) Miscellaneous Effects Factor, k_e
The miscellaneous effects factor is intended for all the other effects and some of these can not normally be quantified.

Residual stresses are frequently significant, particularly for components or structures that have undergone welding or heat treatment. In some highly stressed components compressive stresses are deliberately imparted to the surface in critical location, by for example shot peening or fillet rolling as these processes can significantly improve the fatigue lives of treated components. The reason being that cracks can normally only develop and grow in and area subject to tensile stresses. If residual compressive stresses are formed in critical areas, then for a given load causing tensile stresses, the tensile stress level is lower as the first part of the load is needed to bring the residual compressive stress to zero, leaving less load to develop tensile stress.

Directional Structures. Rolled or drawn sheets and bars have a fatigue endurance strength in the transverse direction which is 10 - 20% lower than in the longitudinal direction. Similarly the superior structure of rolled as compared to cut threads means that bolts with rolled threads have a higher fatigue endurance strength than those with cut threads.

Electrolytic Plating. Although zinc plating does not effect the fatigue endurance strength of steels, most plating processes cause a significant reduction, often by as much as 50%.

Corrosion reduces fatigue resistance, and in a corrosive atmosphere the fatigue endurance strength of steel is zero. Normally in fatigue failure is independent of the frequency, however in a corrosive enviroment (and at elevated temperatures) The lower the frequency the greater the crack growth per load cycle and the fewer the number of load cycles that a part will be able to withstand.

Stress Concentration Effect is the often the key component of this factor. The geometric stress concentration factor is determined (from tables or graphs, see ref. 4) and this is multiplied by the notch sensitivity of the chosen material, this will give a number greater than 1, the reciprocal of this is taken and used as the k_e factor - if any other effects need to be considered these are used to further reduce the above result.

4.5.4 Determining Whether a Design for Component Subject to Cyclic Loading is Safe
4.5.4.1 Introduction
There are a variety of mainly similar approaches to determining if a design is safe or not.

This section shows how an assessment is made of a proposed design against the 'Modified Goodman Criterion'. This criterion is usually represented graphically, see below:

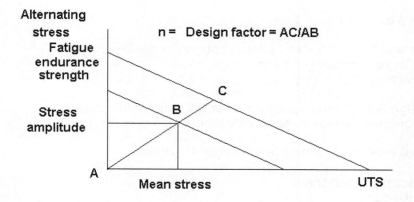

Fatigue diagram showing Goodman line

The UTS of the material (S_{ut}) is marked on the horizontal axis and the fatigue endurance strength of the actual component, S_e (after the fatigue strength reduction factors have been applied to the smooth specimen fatigue endurance strength, S_e') is marked on the vertical axis and the modified Goodman line connects these two points.
A point 'B' is put on the diagram so that the mean stress, S_m the part is subjected to is indicated along the horizontal axis and the alternating stress amplitude, $Sigma_a$, along the vertical axis.

It should be noted that in real components the fatigue endurance strength will be reduced below that achieved with polished test specimens (due to surface, size, load, temperature and miscellaneous effects) and the theoretical endurance strength must be multiplied by these fatigue strength reducing factors before being marked on the vertical axis as the one end of the modified Goodman line.

Components subjected to cyclic stress regimes which when plotted on this diagram are below and to the left of the modified Goodman line are safe designs whereas those subjected to stresses that when plotted are above / to the right of the modified Goodman line are unsafe designs.

If the stresses on a safe design are marked (for example as point B) on the diagram and a line drawn through this point and parallel to the modified Goodman line, the distance this line is away from the modified Goodman line is a measure of the factor of safety, or the design factor, n = AC/AB, of this particular part.

By writing the equation of a straight line in intercept form:

$$(x / a) + (y / b) = 1$$

where a and b are the x and y intercepts respectively, the factor of safety can be represented by the equation:

$$(Sigma_a / S_e) + (Sigma_m / S_{ut}) = 1 / n$$

The design factor usually assumes that the ratio of the stress amplitude/mean stress remains constant.

A worked example is shown in Appendix 4.2, below.

4.6 Fracture Mechanics
4.6.1 Introduction
In the 1960s when higher strength steels started to be introduced, it was noted that components often failed suddenly at loads that were well below those that would have caused yielding. Investigations into these failures led to the development of 'fracture mechanics'.

Changes in component geometry such as those caused by grooves, give rise to stress concentration effects. As long as the geometry is known, these effects can be computed and taken into account during design. However many components contain defects, often cracks, where the end of the crack is very sharp, its radius is not known and can not be measured. For situations like these, the stress concentration can not be determined and an alternative approach is needed. The approach is to use 'fracture mechanics'.

The way in which a cracked component is loaded can be idealised in one of three ways, see diagram below:

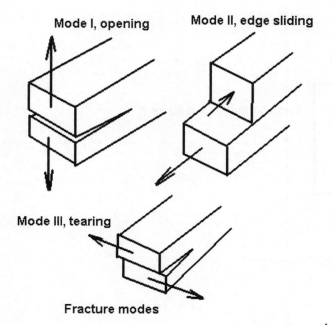

Mode I, opening   Mode II, edge sliding

Mode III, tearing

Fracture modes

For the vast majority of engineering applications it is 'mode I', the 'opening mode', which is of interest.

The stress near a crack tip can be characterised by a single parameter, the stress intensity factor, $K = Q\sigma\sqrt{\pi a}$ where Q is a factor depending of specimen and crack geometry ('geometry correction factor'), a is the crack depth (or half the crack length).

Fracture occurs when the value of K reaches K_c the fracture toughness of the material.

4.6.2 Geometry Correction Factors - for configurations shown below.
These are for mode I loading and normally are only valid when b>>a. For a short single edge through crack of depth a, Q also = 1.12

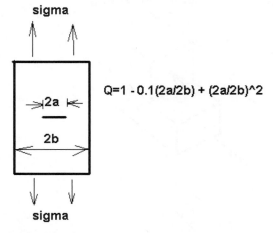

Q=1 - 0.1(2a/2b) + (2a/2b)^2

Centre, through thickness crack

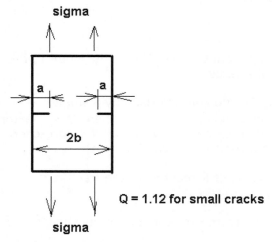

Q = 1.12 for small cracks

Edge, through thickness cracks

Geometry Correction Factors - Q

K_c can be found from laboratory tests and applied to real structures of different geometries. K_{Ic} (the subscript 'I' meaning mode I) is a function of the material thickness and reaches a minimum when the material is thick enough to provide full restraint (plane strain). Extensive values can be found in the literature (see below).

Although strictly the stress intensity applies only to linear elastic fracture mechanics (LEFM), some crack tip plasticity is common in structural materials. Provided this plastic zone is only small <a/15 or < B/15 (where B is the specimen thickness) then the stress intensity is not significantly affected away from the crack tip and LEFM and K can be used.

Structural materials absorb significant energy in the plastic zone near the crack tip which makes them tough, however brittle materials have no, or a very small crack tip plastic zone and have low toughness.

A worked example is given in Appendix 4.3.

4.6.3 Leak Before Burst

An important application of fracture mechanics is in the design of pressure vessels. It is preferable that should a defect be present and a crack growing in a pressure vessel wall that the crack is able to grow sufficiently for it go all the way through the wall, allowing the gas to escape rather than the vessel to suffer catastrophic, explosive, failure.

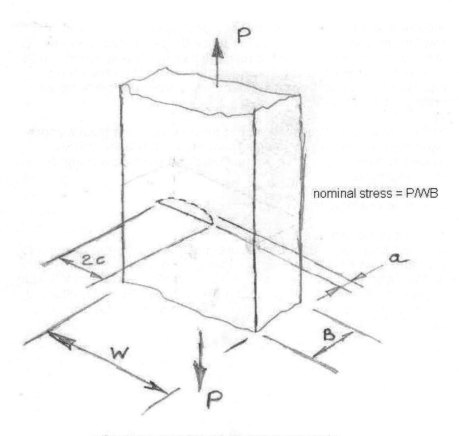

nominal stress = P/WB

Geometry of an eliptical crack in a finite plate

Consequent to the above, one configuration which is often of interest to designers is a surface breaking semi elliptical crack perpendicular to the axis of a finite rectangular component subject to tension, as shown above.

For an elliptical crack buried in an infinite body an analytic solution exists involving an elliptic integral of the second kind. While values of this are tabulated in mathematical texts, good approximations can be made with simple formulae. As the case of interest is an elliptic crack bisected by a surface, there is a modifying factor to be included which is slightly more than 1 depending upon the a / B ratio. (It is common to use 't' to indicate wall or plate thickness so this ratio will appear as a / t in some texts). This information can readily be presented in a simple formula:

$$K = Y \text{ sigma } (3.14159\ a)^{0.5} / Ø$$

with some tabular values and this is done, with some further explanation, in the worked example in Appendix 4.4.

4.6.4 Crack growth rates in components subjected to cyclic loading

Fracture mechanics is now widely used to analyse crack growth under cyclic loading. Many materials have been investigated and all structural metals have the same 'sigmoidal' shaped crack growth curves when the crack growth is plotted against the stress intensity range (K_{max} - K_{min}) on log axes.

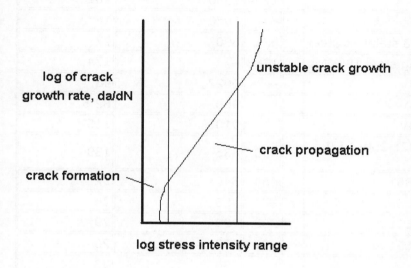

Typical fatigue crack growth curve showing 3 stages

Data and equations based on these curves are used to predict residual lives of cracked components.

4.6.5 How Fracture Mechanics is used in Design and Maintenance Operations

Fracture mechanics may be used to assess if a defect present in a structure will cause failure during the load application or for cyclic loading, how many load cycles will be required to grow the crack to the critical length that causes failure.

For any engineering material it is frequently the case that increasing the UTS or yield strength results in a lowering of the fracture toughness.

Material	UTS	Yield strength, MPa	K_{IC}, MPa(m)$^{0.5}$
A533B Alloy steel	--	500	175
4340 steel	2332	1450	51
4340	1827	1503	59
4340	1764	1530	201
52100	--	2070	14
AISI 403 stainless steel	821	690	77
Maraging steel 18% Ni	1783	--	174
Ti-6Al-4V	--	1022	43
Ti-6Al-4V	--	960	82.5
Ti-6Al-4V	--	910	115
Ti-6Al-4Zr-2Sn-0.5Mo-0.5V	890	836	139
2219-T851 Al	454	340	32
2024 Al	--	455	26
6061-T651 Al	352	299	29
7079-T651 Al	569	502	26
7178 Al	--	490	33
7056-T6 Al	--	516	28.6
7056-T6 Al	--	440	33

4.6.6 Residual Life Assessment:

Stage II of the sigmoidal crack growth curve can be represented by a 'power law' relationship giving the fatigue crack growth rate da/dN of a material in terms of the range of the applied stress intensity factor as:

$$\frac{da}{dN} = C(\Delta K_I)^m$$

where C and m are constants for a particular material, environment and loading condition and

$$\Delta K_I$$

is the range of the stress intensity factor occurring at the crack tip.

The power law eqn. can be integrated:

$$\Delta N = \int \frac{da}{C(\Delta K)^m}$$

between the limits of the initial (present) crack length and the final (maximum safe) crack size. Substituting for K:

$$\Delta N = \left[\frac{1}{C(\Delta\sigma)^m \, \pi^{m/2}}\right] \int \frac{da}{Q^m \, a^{m/2}}$$

as Q generally depends upon the crack depth and shape, numerical integration is normally needed.

For very small cracks, which are described by the initial part of the sigmoidal curve, the above results, which are based on the main, middle part of the sigmoidal curve, are conservative.

The effects of temperature may need to be considered. As the temperature rises the yield stress decreases and for a given load the size of the plastic zone will increase, so even though LEFM may be applicable at ambient temperatures, it may not be applicable at elevated temperatures.

It is generally preferable for pressure vessels to leak before they fracture. Fracture mechanics is used to check that when an eliptical crack in the wall has grown so that its depth extends through the wall, allowing leakage, the crack length is still below the critical length that would cause sudden rupture.

4.7 Conclusion
S - N tests of components show considerable scatter, particularly for finite life results. Fracture Mechanics tests give much narrower scatter. Where calculations on safety critical components are being carried out, some test results to support the calculations are highly desirable if not essential.

Further reading and references.

- 1) 'Case Studies in Engineering Design', by C Matthews.
- 2) 'Mechanical Engineering Design', Shigley, J E and Mischke, C R., McGraw-Hill, 1989.
- 3) 'Mechanical Behaviour of Engineering Materials', Marin, J., Prentice Hall, 1962.
- 4) 'Allowable Working Stresses', Noll, C G and Lipson, C., Soc. for Experimental Stress Analysis, vol III, no. 2, 1946, p49.
- 5) 'Mechanical Behaviour of Materials', by N E Dowling, Prentice-Hall, 1993.
- 6) 'A Compendium of Stress Intensity Factors', by D P Rooke and D J Cartwright, HMSO, London, 1976.
- 7) 'Fatigue Design: Life Expectancy of Machine Parts', by E Zahavi, published by CRC Press, 1996.
- 8) 'Stress Concentration Design Factors', by R E Peterson, J Wiley & Sons, New York, 1953.

Appendix 4.1

Sample calculation to design against failure under combined loading
A uniform circular shaft is to be subjected to a bending moment, M, of 8000 Nm and a torque of 24000 Nm. Assuming the shaft is made from a material with a UTS of 700 MPa and a design factor of 4 is to be used, determine the shaft diameter required using:

   a) The maximum shear stress failure criterion.
   b) The von Mises failure criterion.

NB: No account is taken in this solution of any stress concentrations or of cyclic loading and fatigue effects.

Solution:

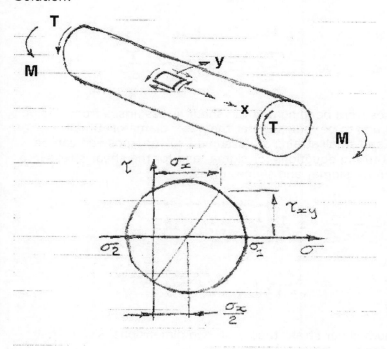

The top diagram shows the layout of a small element in the 'top' (where the bending stresses are assumed to be a maximum) part of the shaft.

The next diagram shows the Mohrs circle representation of the 2D state of stress in the element shown in the first diagram.

Stresses perpendicular to the small element (in a radial direction) are negligible so the problem is reduced to two dimensions. So:

$$\sigma_{1,2} = \frac{\sigma_x}{2} \pm \sqrt{\left(\frac{\sigma_x}{2}\right)^2 + \left(\tau_{xy}\right)^2}$$

or:

$$\sigma_{1,2} = \frac{\sigma_x}{2} \pm \frac{1}{2}\sqrt{\sigma_x^2 + 4\tau_{xy}^2}$$

Bending stress:

$$\sigma_x = \frac{My}{I} = \frac{64\,M\,d}{\pi\,d^4\,2} = \frac{32M}{\pi\,d^3}$$

Shear stress due to torsion:

$$\tau_{xy} = \frac{Tr}{J} = \frac{Td}{2}\frac{32}{\pi d^4} = \frac{16\,T}{\pi\,d^3}$$

Sigma$_x$ arises from bending and the shear stress arises from torsion and is assumed to be maximum at the outer diameter. Small deflections and small strains are assumed so superposition can be used. Substituting equations for sigma$_x$ and for the shear stress into the equation for sigma$_1$ and sigma$_2$ gives:

$$\sigma_1, \sigma_2 = \frac{16M}{\pi\,d^3} \pm \frac{1}{2}\sqrt{\left(\frac{32\,M}{\pi\,d^3}\right)^2 + 4\left(\frac{16\,T}{\pi\,d^3}\right)^2}$$

or:

$$\sigma_1, \sigma_2 = \frac{16}{\pi d^3}\left(M \pm \sqrt{M^2 + T^2}\right)$$

The maximum shear stress theory, in two dimensions, states that failure will occur when:

Absolute value(sigma$_1$ - sigma$_2$) = sigma$_{yield\ stress}$

and in this example the maximum allowable shear stress is the absolute value of:

(sigma$_1$ - sigma$_2$) = sigma$_{uts}$/Design Factor

Absolute value(sigma$_1$ - sigma$_2$) = 32(M^2 + T^2)$^{0.5}$/(3.14159 d^3)...(i)

b) The von Mises failure theory states that failure will occur when:

(sigma$_1$ - sigma$_2$)^2 + (sigma$_2$ - sigma$_3$)^2 + (sigma$_3$ - sigma$_1$)^2 = 2 sigma$_{yield}$^{2}

As only two dimensions are being considered this reduces to:

sigma$_1$^{2} - sigma$_1$sigma$_2$ + sigma$_2$^{2} = sigma$_{yield}$^{2}

Substituting values for sigma$_1$ and sigma$_2$ and replacing sigma$_{yield}$ with sigma$_{uts}$/Design factor, etc. and re-arranging:

$$\left[\frac{16}{\pi d^3}\left(M + \sqrt{M^2 + T^2}\right)\right]^2 -$$

$$\left[\frac{16}{\pi d^3}\left(M + \sqrt{M^2 + T^2}\right)\right]\left[\frac{16}{\pi d^3}\left(M - \sqrt{M^2 + T^2}\right)\right] +$$

$$\left[\frac{16}{\pi d^3}\left(M - \sqrt{M^2 + T^2}\right)\right]^2 \leq \left(\frac{\sigma_{uts}}{Design\ factor}\right)^2$$

$$\left(\frac{16}{\pi d^3}\right)^2 \left(4M^2 + 3T^2\right) \leq \left(\frac{\sigma_{UTS}}{\text{design factor}}\right)^2$$

So:

$$\frac{\sigma_{UTS}}{\text{des. fac.}} \geq \frac{16}{\pi d^3}\sqrt{4M^2 + 3T^2} \quad (ii)$$

For (a) subst. values in (i):

$$d^3 \geq \frac{32 \times 4}{\pi \times 700 \times 10^6}\sqrt{(8000)^2 + (24000)^2}$$

$$d^3 \geq 0.001472$$

$$d \geq 0.1138 \text{ m} , \quad \text{or} \quad 114 \text{ mm}$$

For (b) subst. values in (ii):

$$d^3 \geq \frac{16 \times 4}{\pi \times 700 \times 10^6}\sqrt{4(8000)^2 + 3(24000)^2}$$

$$d^3 \geq 0.001296$$

$$d \geq 0.109 \text{ m} \quad \text{or} \quad 109 \text{ mm}$$

For ductile metals the value from (b) can be used.

Appendix 4.2

Sample calculation, designing against fatigue loading using modified Goodman Diagram

A cold drawn tie bar 40mm diameter in AISI 1018 steel is subjected to a fluctuating tensile stress between 0 and 50270N. What is the design factor assuming:

- 1) the stress amplitde and mean stress rise pro-rata.
- 2) the mean stress remains constant and only the stress amplitude can vary.

Solution:

Data for this steel gives typical values as: S_{ut} = 440Mpa and S_y = 370MPa.

In the absence of information about the fatigue endurance strength of smooth test specimens, S_e' it is assumed that S_e' = 0.5 x S_{ut} = 220MPa.

The stress reduction factors factors need to be calculated, using the methods shown in section 4.4.3:

Surface factor, k_a = a $(S_{ut})^b$ and using the suggested values from the table in section 4.4.3.2,

Substituting values: k_a = 4.51 $(440)^{-0.265}$ = 0.8988 or 0.9

Size factor, k_b = $(d/7.62)^{-0.1133}$

Substituting 40 mm diameter: k_b = $(40/7.62)^{-0.1133}$ = 0.8287 or 0.83

Load factor, k_c, it is suggested that for a steel with a S_{ut} of 1500MPa or less, 0.923 be used.

Temperature Factor, k_d. As there is no specific information about this it is assumed a value of 1 can be used.

Miscellaneous Effects Factor, k_e. The information given is that a stress concentration factor of k_f = 1.38 occurs due to fillet radii. There is no information about other miscellaneous effects so taking k_e = 1/k_f

k_e = 1/1.38 = 0.725

Using the equation relating real components to polished smooth test pieces:

$$S_e = k_a \times k_b \times k_c \times k_d \times k_e \times S_e'$$

Substituting values:

$$S_e = 0.9 \times 0.83 \times 0.923 \times 1 \times 0.725 \times 220 = 110 \text{MPa}.$$

Mean Stress and Stress Amplitude: As the load fluctuates from zero to 50270, the mean stress = stress amplitude = 0.5 x max. stress.

$$\text{sigma}_m = \text{sigma}_a = 50270 \times 4 / 2 \times (3.14159 \times (0.04)^2) = 20 \text{MPa}$$

Point 'A' on the modified Goodman diagram below, indicates the 20Mpa mean stress and stress amplitude the tie rod is subjected to.

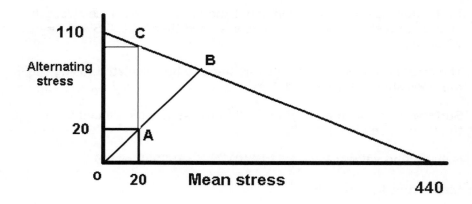

1) Assuming pro-rata increases in mean stress and stress amplitude, the ration of lengths BO/AO gives the design factor or factor of safety, n.

Using the equation: $(\text{Sigma}_a / S_e) + (\text{Sigma}_m / S_{ut}) = 1 / n$ and substituting values:

$$(20 / 110) + (20 / 440) = 1 / n = (2 / 11) + (1 / 22) = 5 / 22$$

so n = 4.4

2) If it is assumed that the mean stress remains constant and only the amplitude can increase, then the design factor is given by the ratio: ordinate value of C / 20

By inspection this can be seen to be: 105 / 20 = 5.25

Appendix 4.3 - worked example - critical stress intensity

A steel ship deck plate with a thickness of 35mm has a width of 10m and a length of 20m (in the tensile loading direction) and is being operated below its ductile-to-brittle transition temperature, with a $K_c = 25MPa(m)^{0.5}$
If a 80mm long central transverse crack is present, calculate the tensile stress for catastrophic failure. The steel has a yield strength of 220MPa.

Solution: 2a = 80mm, 2b = 10m and 2h = 20m

So a / b = 40 / 5000 = 0.008 and h / b = 10 / 5 = 2
As a/b is so small the plate may be considered to be infinite and the geometry correction factor, Q, can be assumed = 1

Before proceeding further with this solution, it is necessary to check that the approach is satisfactory. This is because the results of fracture toughness tests depend upon the thickness of the specimen. The thicker the specimen the greater the restraint provided by adjacent metal in the thickness direction and the lower will be the K_c value. At some thickness, further tests with increased in thickness produces no further reduction in K_c value and this is taken as the correct value. A study of results from tests (ref. 5) showed that for high strength materials, the test is valid when this empirical relationship is met:
t and a are greater than or equal to $2.5*(K_c$ / yield strength$)^2$

For this example: $2.5*(25 / 220)^2 = 32.3$mm so the approach is valid. When this approach is not valid, then other corrections need to be made and a more detailed text should be consulted, see ref. 5.

So tensile stress at failure is given by: sigma = K_c / $(3.14159 * a)^{0.5}$
= 25 / $(3.14159 * 0.04)^{0.5}$ = 70.5MPa.
Thus catastrophic failure will occur at a strength/stress ratio of 220 / 70.5 = 3.1

Appendix 4.4 - Semi -elliptical crack in the surface of a plate

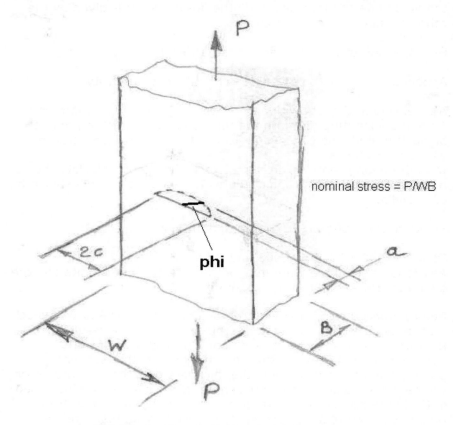

Geometry of an eliptical crack in a finite plate

The equation below is a simplified formula for the stress intensity in the semi - elliptical crack shown in the above diagram.

$$K = Y \, sigma \, (3.14159 \, a)^{0.5} / \emptyset$$

The table below gives values of Y depending upon the a / c and a / B ratios of the crack.

By studying the table it can be seen that initially, when the a / B ratio is small, if the a / c ratio is also small, ie the crack is highly elliptical, then the maximum stress intensity will be at phi = 90° and the crack will grow more rapidly to increase 'a' than 'c'. Once the a / c ratio reaches about 0.8 the stress intensity does not vary much with the angle phi and the the crack will tend to grow with an a / c ratio of about 0.8, as can be seen by examining the tabulated values. Once the crack is through most of the wall, for higher values of a / B, the equilibrium a / c ratio is nearer 0.6. This is due to the fact that the thinning remaining wall at phi = 90° exerts less restraint than was the case when the wall was thicker, slightly reducing the stress intensity.

Ø	a / c	phi		Y		
				a / B		
			0.2	0.4	0.6	0.8
		0	0.617	0.724	0.899	1.190
1.051	0.2	45	0.990	1.122	1.384	1.657
		90	1.173	1.359	1.642	1.851
		0	0.767	0.896	1.080	1.318
1.151	0.4	45	0.998	1.075	1.247	1.374
		90	1.138	1.225	1.370	1.447
		0	0.916	1.015	1.172	1.353
1.277	0.6	45	1.024	1.062	1.182	1.243
		90	1.110	1.145	1.230	1.264
		0	1.174	1.229	1.355	1.464
1.571	1.0	45	1.067	1.104	1.181	1.193
		90	1.049	1.062	1.107	1.112

Problem
If a cylindrical steel pressure vessel with wall thickness of 20 mm, a radius of 200 mm and a length of 2 m is to contain gas at a pressure of 20 MPa what is the minimum required fracture toughness of the steel so that it will leak before bursting.

Solution
The hoop stress in the cylinder is given by:

$sigma_{hoop}$ = pressure x radius / thickness.

Substituting values: $sigma_{hoop}$ = 20 x 0.2 / 0.02 = 200 MPa

Assuming the crack grows with an a / c ratio of 0.8 and interpolate Ø values to give 1.424 and extrapolate a / b entries and for phi = 90° take Y = 1.157

Then: K = 1.157 x 200 (3.14159 x 0.02)$^{0.5}$ / 1.424 = 40.7 MPa(m)$^{0.5}$

The minimum fracture toughness required is 41 MPa(m)$^{0.5}$

5 Losses in Reciprocating Engines - Efficiency

5.1 Introduction

IC engines involve many components moving relative to one another, separated by varying amounts of lubrication. All this relative motion, whether lubricated or not, causes of friction which results in work being wasted and converted into heat. As high temperatures are generated when the fuel is burnt, which in any event necessitates cooling, the additional heating caused by friction losses, adds to the required cooling that must be provided. Some calculations using approximate data are given in the sections below, but while these are approximate and vary to differing degrees according to the engine speed, they do give reasonable order of magnitude results.

5.2 Efficiency

One problem when discussing efficiency is that there is not complete agreement on the definitions of the different efficiency terms used to describe various aspects of IC engine performance.

Engineers commonly use the brake specific fuel consumption (bsfc) which is the fuel flow rate divided by the brake power.
The brake power is the power available at the crankshaft or flywheel and therefore available to do useful work. The name arose because it was measured by applying a brake to the flywheel of the engine. The bsfc is inverseley proportional to the engine efficiency.

Volumetric Efficiency
This is defined as the mass of fuel and air inducted into the cylinder divided by the mass that would occupy the displaced volume at the density in the intake manifold. Note that the volumetric efficiency is a mass ratio **NOT** a volume ratio.

5.3 Efficiency of Combustion

The theoretical work available from burning the fuel can be calculated from an idealised indicator diagram, using the engine compression ratio and the initial air temperature and pressure as starting point. However the idealisation assumes that there is no heat of combustion lost, no gas leakage and no residual products of combustion remaining in the cylinder at the start of the induction cycle. Also that the air behaves as an ideal gas with specific heats c_p and c_v remaining constant and $c_p/c_v = 1.4$ and that the heat input due to combustion is instantaneous at the point of maximum compression.

In technical terms the four stages are:

- isentropc compression (an isentropic change is adiabatic, heat is neither added nor dissipated and it is frictionless i.e. reversible). Point 1 to point 2 on diagram.
- isochoric heat input (constant volume). Point 2 to 3 on diagram, followed by
- isentropic expansion. Point 3 to 4, and
- isochoric reversion of the gas to its initial condition. Point 4 to 1.

In the diagram below 1 - 0 is the exhaust stroke and 0 - 1 is the induction stroke. The mean pressures during these strokes are typically 10 - 15 kN/m^2 above and below atmospheric pressure respectively, which when drawn to the same scale as the other strokes appears as a thick line.

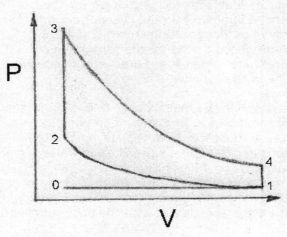

Ideal Otto cycle

The efficiency of this ideal cycle, the Air Cycle Efficiency, is defined as the work produced divided by the heat added. This calculation, see Chapter 8, gives:

$$\eta_{ac} = 1 - (1/r)^{k-1}$$

where k is the ratio of specific heats at constant pressure and constant volume, k = c_p/c_v

For a diatomic gas at normal temperatures k = 1.4

In reality the combustion process starts slowly, proceeds rapidly in the mid - phase then slows down towards the end, the entire process being spread over something like 40° of crank rotation. This has the effect of significantly lowering the peak pressure reached and it is not reached till 10 - 20 degrees of crank rotation after TDC. The fact that the exhaust valve opens before BDC and the inlet valve does not close till after BDC means that the sharp corners on an idealised diagram are well rounded on an actual indicator diagram, see Chapter 8.

Modern computer aided engineering tools in computational fluid dynamics have enabled engine designers to improve the efficiency with which the air and fuel are mixed in the cylinders and consequently the combustion process. However there will inevitably be very small quantities of fuel - air mixture will be trapped in narrow spaces between piston and the cylinder walls and will not burn. Inevitably even if the idealised indicator diagram was achieved, the work theoretically available is less than the total energy released by burning the same quantity of fuel. the efficiency of combustion, η_c, is less than 100%.

The indicated efficiency η_i is determined from a device that measures pressures and volumes within the cylinder during the engine cycle. (In the days of reciprocating steam engines an indicator diagram was produced by the mechanism and a planimeter used to determine the enclosed area which was then scaled to the work done in the cylinder).

The following sections describe the main causes of friction losses, it is common to quantify the losses in terms of mean effective pressure that the losses account for, however for most of the approximate calculations in this book a power loss in watts is given for a specific engine speed.
Friction losses are normally determined by 'motoring' an engine, driving it with an electric motor, monitoring the power needed. This is be done at different engine speeds and with the engine in various stages of dis-assembly.

5.4 Piston - Cylinder interface
5.4.1 Introduction
Sliding friction between the piston and the cylinder is the biggest cause of waste heat in most reciprocating engines. As the motion is intermittent, the piston is momentarily stationary as it reverses direction at TDC and BDC, it is difficult to develop and maintain an oil film to keep the surfaces from metal to metal contact, especially at low engine speeds. One complicating factor is the need to have a good seal between the piston and the cylinder to prevent gas

leaking past the piston and not doing useful work. This is minimised by having two or three piston rings (compression rings) to help seal the gap between the piston and cylinder wall - which the rings do by exerting a normal force on the cylinder wall, thus generating frictional heating when the piston is moving. The pressure of the burnt gas above the piston pushes the rings down in their grooves and allows gas in behind them to increase the radial outward pressure that they exert, improving sealing when the burnt gases above the piston are exerting high pressures which is when good sealing is needed.

To prevent oil being left on the cylinder wall after the piston has descended - which would be burnt during the combustion stroke - an oil control or scraper ring is fitted below the bottom compression ring, these have a completely different design to compression rings. If an oil control ring was not fitted the use of oil and the exhaust gas emissions would be unacceptable.

To help formation of the appropriate oil film on the cylinder walls virtually all cylinder walls are honed in a criss cross pattern at a specific angle,

5.4.2 Stresses in Piston Rings

This section provides a simplified way of calculating the stresses in a piston ring. A example (from a Nissan 2 l engine) is analysed, see below, and the results compared with a finite element analysis (FEA).

The material is assumed to be cast iron, E = 100GPa

The main assumption in the hand calculation is that the ratio of the depth of the beam to its radius of curvature is small and the error in assuming that the beam is initially straight will only be small.

Ring width = 0.00115m

Ring depth = 0.0031m

Free ring radius approx. = 45mm

Free ring gap approx. = 10mm

Angle subtended at centre of ring by gap = 10/45 = 0.222radians

Installing the ring, almost closing the gap (there is still a small gap when the ring is installed, between 0.2 and 1mm) causes a rotation of one end of the ring relative to the other of 0.22 rad.

Starting with the bending equation: $EId^2y/dx^2 = M$

Then integrating: $EIdy/dx = Mx + C$

$$EI \frac{dy}{dx} = EI\theta = Mx + C$$

length of beam = 0.09 π m

substitute this length for x

$$0.22\ EI = 0.09\ M$$

$$M = \frac{0.22\ E\ I}{0.09}$$

$$= \frac{0.22 \times 100\ E9 \times (0.00115)(0.0031)^3}{0.09\ \pi \times 12}$$

$$= 0.222\ Nm$$

$$\sigma = \frac{My}{I}$$

$$= \frac{0.222 \times 0.00155 \times 12}{0.00115 \times (0.0031)^3}$$

$$= 120\ MPa$$

The simple analysis, above shows that if it assumed that a uniform bending moment is applied to the ring 0.222 Nm is required to close the gap, with this moment applied, the maximum stress in the ring is 120 MPa.

An FEA model of the ring was produced, one end restrained and one end loaded with a moment of 0.222 Nm. This gives essentially a uniform moment throughout the ring however the deflection of the free end does not result in the gap being 'neatly almost closed' as would occur on actual installation.

The computed von Mises stress was 123 Mpa on the ring bore and 117 MPa on the outer periphery of the ring.

The minimum principal stress, on the ring bore was -123 MPa and the maximum principal stress, on the outer periphery was 117 Mpa.

These computed results are in close agreement with the hand calculations and the stresses are well below the strength of grade 30 cast iron - approximately 200 MPa.

Further FEA indicates that to almost close the gap (by 9.2 mm of the 10 mm gap in the 'x' direction requires a radial inward pressure on the ring of just under 75000 N/m^2 which corresponds to a total inward radial force of about 21.6N. However there is still a shift of the free end in the inward radial (-'y') direction.
Moreover this loading does not give a reasonably uniform stress on either the bore or the OD - von Mises stresses vary betwen 110 and 190 MPa, so this is also not a satisfactory loading.

Rotating the free ring end by 0.2 radians also does not work, closing the gap by only 5 mm and moving the free end in by 4.5mm.

This example shows that modeling even an apparently simple configuration and carrying out FEA can be problematic.

5.4.3 Very Approximate Calculation of Friction Losses From Piston Ring - Cylinder Walls
5.4.3.1 Calculation involving only the residual stress of the installed piston ring

Assuming that the engine is 2 litre capacity and 80mm bore, the stroke is determined from:

Swept vol. = stroke x 3.14159 (bore)^2/4
giving the stroke as close to 100mm.

Assume there are 3 compression piston rings for each piston (+1 oil control ring which is a different design).

The nominal contact area per cylinder is 3 x ring width x outer periphery (80mm bore):

3 x 0.00115 x 3.14159 x 0.08 m^2 = 867E-6 m^2
If the normal pressure is 75000N/m^2 the total radial (or normal) force per cylinder is
867E-6 x 75000 N = 65N

Assume the coefficient of friction between the piston rings and the cylinder wall is an average of 0.2

Then the friction force opposing the motion of each piston will be about 0.2 x 65N = 13N

Assuming the engine crank is rotating at 4000rpm, this equals 4000/60 = 66.7 revs per s.

In 1 second each piston travels 0.1 x 2 x 66m = 13.2m

In 1 second the work done against friction by each piston is 13.2 x 13 = 171.6Nm

Total for four pistons in engine is 686Nm/s = 686 watts.

5.4.3.2 Effect of Gas Pressure Behind Piston Rings

In reality the design of pistons and rings directs gas pressure arising from combustion on to the top and to behind the piston rings, pushing them against the cylinder with much higher pressure, improving their sealing, but causing greater friction losses.

If it is assumed that the brake mean effective pressure in the cylinders is about 0.9MPa, then this pressure can be assumed to be the mean pressure pushing the top rings against the cylinder walls and some leakage past the top rings will result in lower pressures pushing the lower rings against the cylinder. In the calculation below it is assumed that 0.4MPa is acting on the second compression rings.
This gives rise to a force between each top piston ring and cylinder of:

$$0.00115 \times 3.14159 \times 0.08 \times 900000 \text{ N} = 260\text{N}$$

and for each second ring of:

$$0.00115 \times 3.14159 \times 0.08 \times 400000 \text{ N} = 115.6\text{N}$$

Assume coefficient of friction = 0.2, then friction force per ring is:
Top ring: 260 x 0.2 = 52N, second ring: 23.1N

For a four cylinder engine the total friction force is 4(52 +23.1) = 300.5N.

This is acting only during the power stroke. Work done per second by this friction is given by:

$$300.5 \times 0.1 \times 0.5 \times 66 = 992 \text{ watts.}$$

5.4.3.3 Effect Side Force on Piston due to Connecting Rod Orientation

The figure below shows schematically the forces acting on the piston during the combustion stroke:

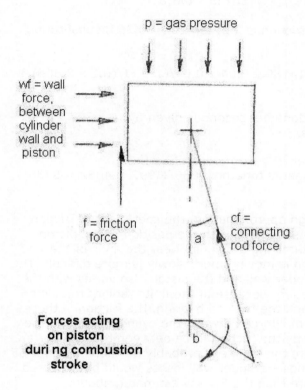

p = gas pressure

wf = wall force, between cylinder wall and piston

f = friction force

a

cf = connecting rod force

b

Forces acting on piston during combustion stroke

If it is assumed that the 'average' angle of inclination of the connecting rod to the line joining the centre of the crank to the piston pin ('a' in diagram) is about 20°, then resolving vertically gives:

$$p \times \text{piston area} = cf \times \cos(a) + f \ \dots \text{(equation i)}$$

and resolving horizontally gives

$$wf = cf \times \sin(a) \ \dots \dots \text{(equation ii)}$$

The Coefficient of friction between cylinder wall and piston:

$$mu = f/wf$$

substituting for wf in (ii)

f/mu = cf x sin(a) .... so cf = f/(mu x sin(a))
Substituting back into (i):
   p x piston area = f x cos(a)/(mu x sin(a)) + f
Rearranging:
   p x piston area = f x (1 + 1/(mu x tan(a)))

   f = p x piston area/(1 + 1/(mu x tan(a)))

Assume coefficient of friction is 0.2, tan 20° = 0.364, substituting values:

   f = 900000 x 3.14159 x 0.04 x 0.04/(1 + (1/(0.2 x 0.364)))
   = 307N

For 4 cylinders, work done per second is given by: 4 x 307 x 0.1 x 0.5 x 66 = 4052 watts.

Very Approximate Total:
Adding these 3 components together: 686 + 992 + 4052 = 5730 watts

NB: This is a very rough approximation, the coefficient of friction varies with the engine speed and with the position of the piston during the stroke, maintaining an oil film near the ends of the stroke where the piston is moving more slowly is more difficult. The force between the cylinder wall and the piston also varies with the connecting rod orientation. Because of the finite radii of the piston pin (or gudgeon pin) and the big end bearing, the friction in these will also effect the normal force between the cylinder wall and the piston, and consequently the friction force between the cylinder and the piston. At 4000 rpm the engine is probably developing about 65 kW and the piston - rings - cylinder wall losses would be expected to be considerably more than the 5.7 kW estimated above.
These calculations serve only as a very rough order of magnitude approximation. A slightly more accurate calculation could be done by adding this onto the spreadsheet described in Chapter 8 allowing for the variation in pressures and the changing angle during the power stroke.

As a rough approximation, the friction losses are proportional to the swept cylinder surface area, hence for a given engine capacity, increasing the number of cylinders, commonly done to reduce the individual reciprocating masses and allow higher engine speeds, results in greater frictional losses. Consequently increasing the number of cylinders also tends to increases the fuel consumption. There is also the issue that where cylinders are very small, the 'standard' clearances will allow increased leakage. Engines with very small cylinders tend to be less efficient, however this is not noticeable in automotive engines, but it is with very small engines for model boats and aeroplanes.

The friction losses due to the friction between the pistons, piston rings and cylinders and the pumping losses are approximately proportional to the piston speed and account for about 50% of the total friction.

The other half of the friction losses, due to the valve train, crankshaft, seals, alternator, oil and water pumps, is more nearly proportional to the engine rotational speed than the piston speed.

5.5 Camshaft / Followers / Tappets
Almost all automobile engines use cams to positively open the (reciprocating) valves, either acting directly on the end of the valve stem or via a rocker, with springs to push the valves shut. The spring must be able to exert sufficient forces to provide sufficient acceleration to close the valves at the maximum speed of operation. Obviously this means that at lower speeds excess spring force is present and at all engine speeds there will be friction between the camshaft and the followers or tappets.
The alternative of using a cam to open and another cam to close the valves (desmodromic valve gear) is significantly more complicated and currently only used by Ducati in their motorcycle engines. This approach does reduce the friction losses.

There have been experiments using electro-hydraulic and electro-magnetic operation of valves, but there are no automotive applications other than research engines. However this type of electrical control of operation of engine valves has recently been introduced in commercial application of large low speed (about 250 rpm) marine diesel engines.

Typical losses at mid range engine speeds are about 23% of the total losses but this will vary quite widely depending upon the type and detail design of the valve train.

5.6 Hydrodynamic Bearings
The main and big end bearings (see Chapter 12) in a IC engine have oil pumped to them. The bearing is designed to ensure that under normal operation the metal surfaces are separated by a hydrodynamic oil film. The oil film is under continuous shearing and due to the viscosity of the oil (without which the bearing would not operate) the oil absorbs mechanical work and this is converted to waste heat. In engines of moderate performance, this heat can be dissipated from the oil sump without difficulty, but in high

performance engines an oil cooler is often provided - and additional power will be needed to pump the oil through the cooler.

In recent years improvements in manufacturing accuracy mean that bearing clearances can be controlled better and this has enabled manufacturers to lower viscosity engine oils which has slightly reduced such losses.
Different types of bearings and their design is discussed in Chapter 12 and an example of approximate calculation to losses is included. Typical mid - range losses due to crankshaft bearings and seals is about 12% of the total losses.

5.7 Oil and Water Pumps, Air Conditioning
In addition to the need to pump engine lubricating oil to the main and big end bearings, lubricating oil is supplied through narrow passages and pipes to other parts of the engine, eg camshaft(s), sprayed onto the underside of the pistons to aid their cooling and the lubrication of the gudgeon pins. Also parts of the engine - mainly the cylinder head and cylinders - require specific cooling. This used to be done by pumping water through passages or by blowing air accross fins on the cylinder barells and head. Air cooling does not do much to reduce engine noise and owing to the increased legislation to reduce vehicle noise levels, air cooling is now limited to some motorcycles - usually relying on natural air flow. Some motorcycles that are nominally air cooled also rely to a significant extent on the cooling effect of the circulating engine lubricating oil.
It is perhaps of historical interest that the 5.7 litre air cooled flat 12 Porsche engine of the 1970s that powered the 917 sports / racing model produced over 500 hp and the fan used to blow the cooling air round the engine absorbed 24 h.p!

Water after circulating through the engine and cooling it gains heat and this must be dissipated to the airstream that the car is moving through - or if the car is stationary, air must be drawn through a radiator to cool the water. For many years cars had fans driven constantly by the engine, which was inefficient, now nearly all cars have electric fans actuated thermostatically that only operate when the water reaches a predetermined level.
Normally engine coolant impellers run all the time with the coolant flow being controlled by a thermostat, this is not efficient.
Electrically driven pumps are available for some vehicles which only operate when needed, this is more efficient, but more costly and is only in very limited use.

The introduction of air conditioning (which is now very widely fitted to new cars) has introduced another load on the engine. Some people claim that the loss of power caused by running air conditioning is no greater than driving with either the windows or the sun roof open - but there does not seem to be much evidence for this. At one stage many US cars fitted with air conditioning had a switch that turned it off when the throttle was floored to provide the maximum power to accelerate the vehicle - this suggested that the load on the engine was significant.

Typical mid range losses are about 6% for the oil pump and about 13% for the water pump and alternator.

5.8 Pumping Losses - during induction

A petrol engine has to operate in a narrow band for the air:fuel ratio and an engine with a carburetor when the throttle closed (either because it is idling or going downhill or slowing down) the engine has to do work to draw in air. However modern fuel injection systems shut off the fuel supply when the throttle is closed at higher engine speeds on the over run and only turn the fuel back on when the engine revs drop to a specified value (eg 1600 rpm). Measures such as this mean fuel injected engines are more efficient than engines with carburettors.

The pumping losses appear in the lower loop of indicator diagrams, 1 - 0 and 0 - 1, however as these are normally diagrams for full throttle operation, there is negligible pressure drop across throttle plate and although there will be a significant pressure drop across the inlet valves, the pumping losses are small and the lower loop appears merely as a horizontal line on the diagram. However operation at small throttle openings result in significant pressure drops across the throttle and the pumping losses will absorb a significant portion of the engine power.

Diesel engines operate with excess air and the air flow into the engine is not throttled which leads to better efficiency than a petrol engine when doing a lot of stop start and slow speed driving.

5.9 Exhaust Gas Losses

The exhaust gas will be considerably hotter than ambient, a few hundred degrees centigrade, and at a pressure consideranly above ambient when the exhaust valve opens. This exhaust gas will contain a proportion of the energy of the burnt fuel which will do no useful work. Turbo-charging extracts some work from the exhaust gas, but at the expense of greater back pressure in the exhaust manifold, reducing the work the gas can do in the cylinder.

A hundred years ago large reciprocating 'triple expansion' steam engines used in ships and land based applications had a small cylinder where the high pressure steam (at about 1.2MPa and 300°C) underwent some expansion and then exhaustsd to a medium sized cylinder where the steam expanded further and was then exhausted to a large low pressure cylinder, where the steam expanded further and which in some cases exhausted to a condenser at below atmospheric pressure. Such engines were very large and heavy for the power produced compared to modern IC engines. For IC engines the turbocharger, which is a very compact and light unit, is the best way extracting the maximum residual energy from the exhaust gas.

5.10 Efficiency η

From the losses dicussed above it is clear that the overall efficiency of any engine will fall short of 100%. While it is possible to convert totally mechanical work to heat, usually by varying forms of friction, it is not possible in a heat engine to convert the heat supplied totally to work. The proportion converted is defined as the thermal efficiency.

In a modern large diesel engine it is possible to convert just over 50% of the supplied heat to work. In a 1.9 litre automotive diesel engine the maximum thermal efficiency is about 44% and in a petrol engine the maximum thermal efficiency is typically between 30 and 35%.

6 Predicting Vehicle Performance and Losses to Consider 'Matlab Simulink'

6.1 Introduction
Because of the very high costs of introducing a new vehicle, either with an existing or a new engine, it is critically important that manufacturers are able to make accurate predictions of performance. This chapter shows a number of simple approaches to simulating vehicle performance by using the 'Simulink' toolkit that that is an add on to the 'Matlab' mathematics package. This chapter starts with a brief discussion of some of the factors which reduce vehicle performance and need to be considered.

6.2 Rolling Resistance of Tyres
The coefficient of rolling resistance increases with vehicle speed and depends upon the road surface type and the type of tyre.
Rolling resistance is proportional to the amount of tyre deformation and inversely proportional to the tyre radius. Hence increasing the tyre load or reducing the tyre inflation pressure will increase the rolling resistance.
'Radial ECO' tyres have slightly lower rolling resistance than radial HR, SR and VR tyres.

The vehicle rolling resistance = coefficient of rolling resistance x vehicle mass x gravity.
Typical values of the coefficient of rolling resistance for correctly inflated car tyres vary between about 0.01 and 0.015.

6.3 Drag caused by Air Resistance
Aerodynamic drag is calculated as:
$F_d = 0.5$ x air density x C_d x $A(v + v_o)^2$

> where: C_d = Drag coefficient, determined either by testing in a wind tunnel or by computational fluid dynamics.
> A = Largest frontal cross section area of the vehicle
> v = Vehicle speed
> v_o = Headwind speed

At low speeds the aerodynamic drag is small, but it increases as the square of the speed and high speeds the effect dominates other effects such as rolling resistance.
In the middle of the 20th Century only four car manufacturers were consistently making cars with low drag coefficients: Bristol, Porsche,

Citroen and Saab. As fuel prices have rapidly increased, along with concern for the environment, fuel economy is now a big factor when most potential buyers are thinking of purchasing a car and serious efforts are being made to minimise the drag coefficients of virtually all new cars.

Typical C_d values for most modern cars are between 0.3 and 0.4, but estate cars and convertibles have higher C_d values and motorcycles have C_d values of 0.5 or more.

6.4 Efficiency of Transmission

Losses in the transmission occur in both the gearbox and in the differential unit. For a vehicle fitted with a hydrodynamic converter there will be additional losses (of a few percent - if fitted with 'lock up' the losses will be virtually zero once steady conditions are reached and it is locked up).

Transmission, or drivetrain efficiency for a longitudinally mounted engine is typically 0.88 - 0.92 and for a transversely mounted engine 0.91 - 0.95. (Ref 6.1).

6.5 Modelling and Simulation

6.5.1 Introduction

In this chapter a signal flow, block diagram approach is used. This is referred to as 'causal' as each block requires a signal flowing in one direction as an input. It also requires that the person constructing the model, not only has information about the properties of the components in the system being modelled, but also knows the equations representing the behaviour of the different components and how they interact. This is needed to enable the correct elements or blocks to be selected, with the correct parameters inserted so that the correct connections of the blocks can be made. The 'Simulink' toolkit of the 'Matlab' software package is causal and is used in this chapter.

However most engineering systems consist of physical components connected together. It is more intuitive to model such a system by using blocks to represent components and connecting lines to represent the relationships between the components. This approach is called 'acausal' and is used by 'MapleSim', a software package associated with the 'Maple' mathematics software package. This simplifies the modelling as the underlying physical laws describing the behaviour of the components are incorporated within the blocks representing components and the links or connections determine the system behaviour.

6.5.2 Matlab and Simulink - Introduction

Matlab is a mathematics package which originally focussed on manipulating matrices, but has developed into a powerful mathematics package with a broad range of capabilities, many of which are supported by specialist 'toolkits'. A useful introductory guide is ref. 6.2.

This section will look briefly at using the Simulink simulation toolkit part of the package. This is intended for analysing the dynamic performance of engineering systems in general and of control systems in particular.

Using Matlab to solve dynamic problems involves deriving the appropriate equations describing the system then writing the appropriate code (as an 'm' file) to solve the equations. The great benefit of using Simulink is that it is not necessary to write any code. Once the appropriate equations have been derived and the relationships between them understood, a block diagram model is built up by dragging and dropping appropriate types of elements into a model window and connecting them as needed to simulate the interactions. The code is then automatically generated, solved and results produced without operator intervention.

6.5.3 Before you Start Modelling With Matlab and Simulink
6.5.3.1 Always start simple.
As a first stage develop a very simple model and get some results from it, see if these are remotely reasonable. Then improve the model, get more results, refine the model further, etc. Trying to start straight away on a complex model is almost guaranteed to cause huge difficulties which will probably require excessive time to sort out.

6.5.3.2 Work in SI units.
Although it may superficially appear to give easier numbers if work is done in mm rather than m, it immediately becomes very easy to get things wrong, often by a factor of 1000.

The first stage of the process is vital and needs careful thought. This is because it involves considering the system and finding out about all the elements within it, what functions they perform and the relationship between the input(s) and output(s). The process is rather similar to reverse engineering a product. Errors made at this stage mean all future work will contain the consequences of these errors and the results will be incorrect.

6.5.3.3 Determining System Characteristics
For purely mechanical systems it is usually reasonably straightforward to carry out the necessary measurements to determine dimensions, weights, moments of inertias, stiffnesses, etc.

An exception to this is when analysing hydrodynamic bearings which normally operate with small clearances and determining these with sufficient accuracy will demand accurate measurement facilities. Other exceptions are gears, where low levels of noise are required and very close tolerances are specified which require specialist measuring machines. Splines are also difficult to measure accurately.

It is difficult to estimate the moments of inertias of irregular bodies unless a digital solid model is available, in which case most CAD/CAE systems will provide these. Where a digital solid model is not available, compound pendulum theory can be applied to results from simple experiments.

Values of coefficients of discharge (for example relating to engine valves) may not be available, although some data can be found in Ref. 6.3.

Where a system is a combination of electrical and mechanical components, the problem becomes more difficult. Thirty years ago it was normal to use discrete electronic components, which would often have values marked on them, or else they could be cut out and their properties measured with appropriate instrumentation. Current practice is to put a large number of functions on a single chip and specialised sophisticated test equipment is needed to establish the properties and performance of such sub systems. Indeed it may be almost impossible to determine the characteristics of such a sub system without access to appropriate documentation. In many cases it will be necessary to use a combination of information supplied by manufacturers, measurements taken and to make a number of assumptions.

Once all the characteristics of all the elements have been determined, it should then be possible to write an equation for every element (similar to the process of writing system equations for the free body diagrams of every element in a mechanical system). However, even with manufacturers documentation, there are still likely to be difficulties with electro-mechanical components, such as fuel injectors. To determine the characteristics of fuel injectors specialist equipment is needed. Where this is not available, assumptions and estimates must be made. For some electro-mechanical components, such as solenoids and some electric motors, performance characteristics are often available.

6.5.3.4 Developing the Model
Once all the element characteristics are available - or it has been decided which will not be available and about which some assumptions must be made, a start can be made on building the model.

Sorting out how even a simple model should be put together requires thought and it is advisable to make some carefully labeled sketches. Start on a large piece of paper, spacing everything out, as inevitably there will be elements and links to add in later as the model develops.

6.5.3.5 Errors and Unexpected Behavior

Once a start has been made building the model in Simulink, a simulation should be run after each element and link is added. A 'scope' from the 'Sinks' group of blocks should be used to see the output. This will ensure that any unexpected behavior will be spotted quickly and can be investigated immediately.

Where unexpected behavior does occur, the block characteristics and the calculations done to determine the characteristics should be checked. The simulation parameters should also be checked, as inappropriate time steps can give completely incorrect results. The use of 'Auto' settings in the simulation parameters may also give incorrect results in many cases. Normally an incorrect value or simulation parameter will send the output very rapidly towards + or - infinity.

It is more difficult to detect and correct errors where the output only slowly diverges, this could be due to a poor estimate of some element characteristic.

6.5.4 Practical Details

Once Matlab is started from the icon, Simulink is started by typing simulink [rtn] in the command window.

Systems are modeled by dragging and dropping appropriate elements into a modeling window. A range of elements are available from libraries including:

- 'continuous' elements - derivative, integrator, transfer function
- functions and tables - look up table, polynomial
- math - algebraic constraint, gain, sum, math function
- non linear - backlash, switch
- signals and systems - function call generator
- sinks - to workspace, to file, scopes (to view signals)
- sources - clock, signal and pulse generators, ramp and sine wave signals, from file
- subsystems

Once elements are dropped into the modelling window they are connected output to input - this is done by placing the cursor over the output port of one element, pressing the left mouse button and moving the cursor to the inlet port on the appropriate element and releasing the mouse button. A link will appear with an arrow indicating the direction of signal flow.

Element parameter values are set by right clicking with the cursor over it then clicking on Block parameter and entering the appropriate value in the parameter form that is shown and then clicking OK.

For example if a torque is to be applied as an input to a rotary system and the value of the angular acceleration is the required output, then a gain element is required and the parameter needed - the gain constant - is equal to the inverse of the equivalent moment of inertia. If the angular velocity is required then the angular acceleration is fed as the input to an integrating element which provides velocity as the output.

To connect a link into an existing link (e.g. to provide a feedback link) place the cursor over the position on the link where you want the branch to start then press [cntrl] and the left hand mouse button and take the link to the required input port or summing point and release the mouse button.

For anything other than a simple model it is a good idea to include a number of oscilloscopes at different places in the model so that any unexpected results can be investigated.

Check the Start and Stop times are appropriate by clicking on the Simulation tab and clicking on the Simulation parameters sub - menu. The time step settings should be left set to auto initially.

The simulation is run by picking the Start command from the Simulation menu.

To view results click on the auto-scale icon (the binoculars) on all the oscilloscope windows.

Think - do the results look believable? Carry out some sort of check if at all possible.

Some simple examples are shown in the following sections.

6.5.5 Spring - Mass - Damper Model
i) Introduction
As a simple introduction a single degree of freedom spring - mass - damper system, see figure below left, is modelled:

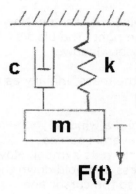

The Simulink block diagram representing this system is shown below:

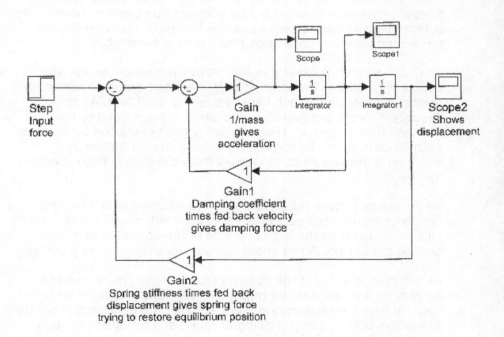

ii). Building the Model

When Matlab has started, the prompt of two arrows pointing to the right is displayed in the right hand window. At this prompt type in: simulink then press Enter.

A new window opens containing a list of block types.

From the 'File' menu (at top left of this new window) click on 'New' then 'Model'. An empty window appears on the right. The blocks needed ere dragged and dropped into this model window.

It is assumed that a force is being applied to the mass, initially as a step input of 1 N.

iii) Double click on the 'Sources' group block and a window containing block diagram representations of several sources appears. The 'Step' source can be recognised from its symbol. Move the mouse so the cursor is over this block, press and hold down the left hand mouse button and move the mouse so the cursor and block are in the empty model window at the left hand side.

iv) This externally applied force will be opposed by the spring force, proportional to the displacement of the mass, and the damper force which is proportional to the velocity of the mass. These opposing forces will need to be included by putting two summing points, each subtracting the appropriate opposing force, thus leaving the net force acting on the mass to go into the next element.

v) The summing points are in the 'Math Operations' group, so double click on this group to open it, drag and drop two summing points. Initially these each have two + signs in them. As the 'feedback' forces are negative, the signs in them need to be changed from ++ to +-.This is done by positioning the cursor over each block in turn, clicking the right hand mouse button and selecting Summing Point Properties from the menu. Then change the ++ to +-.

vi) To connect these together position the cursor over the right hand side of the step generator, press the left mouse button and move the cursor to the left hand side of the summing point then release the button. A link should appear as shown in the diagram.

vii The step force, less the opposing forces from the spring and damper, will accelerate the mass, the net force is divided by the mass to give it's acceleration. This is done by a gain block from the 'Math Operations' group. Having dragged and dropped this gain block into the diagram, right click with the cursor over the block and select the block parameters menu item. In the box enter 1/mass value in kg. Assume a mass of 1 kg so enter 1.

viii) The mass acceleration is integrated once to give its velocity and a second time to give its displacement. The integration blocks are found in the 'Continuous' group. Drag and drop two of these into the model window.

ix) The force generated by the displacement of the mass stretching the spring has to be fed back and converted to a force by using a gain block with the gain set to the stiffness of the spring (in N/m). Leave as 1 initially.

x) The force generated by the velocity of the mass moving the piston through the dashpot has to be fed back and converted to a force by using a gain block with the gain set to the damping coefficient of the damper (in Ns/m). Leave as 1 initially.

xi) Drag and drop two gain blocks to provide these 'feedback' loops. The blocks have to be 'flipped' to point to the left. With the cursor over the gain block, click the right hand mouse button and from the 'Format' heading select 'Flip Block'.

xii) Enter the appropriate gain values into the gain blocks - leave as 1 initially.

xiii) To connect up the feedback loops a connection will have to be made to the existing main line. Do this by putting the cursor over the point on the line where the connection is required to start, press and hold down the 'Ctrl' key and move the cursor to the position that the line is required to run to and release the mouse button and the Ctrl key. The link should appear.

xiv) To see how the displacement fluctuates, an oscilloscope will be used. Oscilloscopes are in the 'Sinks' group. Run a connecting link from the displacement line to the scope input.

The model should now appear similar to the schematic shown in Figure 2.

xv) Run the simulation by clicking on 'Simulation', 'Start'. Double click on the scope to show its screen, then click on the binocular icon at the top of the scope screen to auto-scale the scope display.

xvi) To get a better display it may be necessary to set a specific maximum time step. From the 'Simulation' menu, click on Simulation Parameters' and change the maximum time step from 'auto' by entering 0.01 seconds.

xvii) The effects of changing the spring stiffness, damping coefficient and mass can easily be assessed by altering the values (parameters) set in the three gain blocks.

xviii) To investigate the effects of a sinusoidal input, click over the Step icon in the circuit and press delete. from the 'Sources' group drag in a 'Sine' source and connect it up.

xix) To investigate the effects of a non-standard input the 'Signal Builder' source must be used. Having dragged and dropped this source into the model window it will need to be opened and modified to give the required signal. To do this place the cursor over the 'Signal Builder Block' click the right hand mouse button then click on 'Open', from the top of the menu list. The default signal is a pulse input, this can be edited to a more complex signal by:

- adding new points
- moving points up and down
- moving line segments up and down

These operations are done as follows:

- adding new points: place to cursor over the existing line at the time a specific point is wanted, press the shift key and then the left hand mouse button, a new point appears.
- moving points up and down: place the cursor over the point, press the left hand mouse button and move the mouse till the point is in the desired position.
- moving line segments up and down: put the cursor over the line segment, press the left hand mouse button and move the cursor up and down till the line is in the desired place.

Once the appropriate signal has been 'drawn', it must be 'saved' before it will operate.

6.5.6 To Simulate the Acceleration of a car Subject to a Step Input of Torque and air 'drag' Resistance, Proportional to Velocity Squared
i) Assumptions

- the engine produces a constant torque of 170 Nm
- the calculation is done assuming the car remains in one gear
- the overall gear ratio is 9:1
- the diameter of the wheels (= 2 x radius, r) is 600 mm
- the mass of each wheel is 10 kg
- the vehicle (less wheels) mass is 1000 kg
- the moment of inertia of each wheel is 0.4 kgm^2
- the vehicle frontal area, A, is 2 m^2
- the vehicle drag coefficient, Cd, is 0.33

ii) Developing the model
From the gear ratio and the engine torque, the torque at the driving wheels is 9 x 170 Nm = 1530 Nm.

To determine the vehicle acceleration, the equivalent inertia of the car at the wheels the expression derived in Appendix 6.1 can be used to give:

acceleration = $T/(r[4(I/r^2 + m) + M])$ where: T = torque acting on the driving wheels,
m = mass of each wheel,
I = moment of inertia of each wheel
M = mass of vehicle less the wheels
r = radius of wheel periphery (this is NOT the same as the tyre size, which is the diameter of the metal wheel rim the tyre fits).

As air drag and rolling resistance are usually in terms of force, it is preferable to work in terms of force rather than torque. The Force acting at the tyre periphery to drive the car is given by:
        Driving force = Torque at wheels/radius of tyre periphery
The expression for acceleration becomes:
        acceleration = $F/[4(I/r^2 + m) + M]$

where F = Driving Force = T/r

However the above expression is only valid if air resistance is ignored. Some part of the total force will be required to overcome the air resistance in this simulation.
The vehicle drag force, Fd, is given by Ro A Cd $v^2/2$, where Ro is the air density and v is the vehicle velocity.
The force required to overcome this air drag resistance, Fd, is given by:
Fd = Ro A Cd $v^2/2$
The net force available to accelerate the vehicle will be F - Fd, hence the above expression for acceleration needs to be modified:
        acceleration = $(F - Fd)/[4(I/r^2 + m) + M]$

This can be represented in a Simulink model as shown:

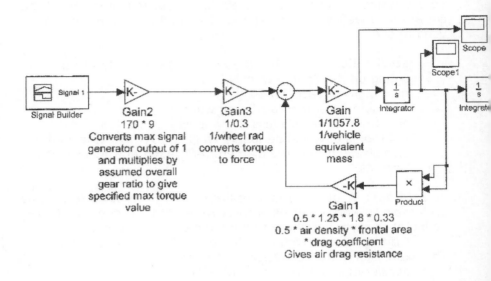

The gain block is given the value $1/(r[4(I/r^2 + m) + M])$

$$= 1/[4(0.4/0.3^2 + 10) + 1000]$$
$$= 0.0009454$$

The drag varies with the velocity squared and there is a feedback loop after the acceleration has been integrated to give the velocity. The gain value in this loop is:

Ro A Cd/2 = 1.25 x 1.8 x 0.33/2 = 0.371

60 mph is equal to approximately 26.4 m/s.
The results from oscilloscope traces (not included here) indicated that the vehicle takes about 7.5 seconds to reach 60 mph, which appears reasonable, but bear in mind that only a single gear ratio is used and the signal builder was set up so full torque was not reached till 4 seconds after the simulation started (with a linear increase from zero torque at zero time).

6.5.7 Implementing Gear Changes in Models
A significant problem with the previous model is that there is no gear change, which would be required in most vehicles when simulating acceleration up to 60mph.

In the model below gear changing is simulated with switch elements, with thresholds set at velocities of 13m/s for changing from 1st gear to 2nd and 19m/s for changing from 2nd to 3rd gear. A velocity line feeds back to both of these switches. Another improvement is to assume that the engine torque is a function of the engine rpm and this is simulated by using a one dimensional look up table where the input is engine rpm and the output is engine torque, assuming that the throttle is fully open. This table is assembled from data in the drivers handbook for a 1983 Porsche 944, see approximate schematic sketch below:

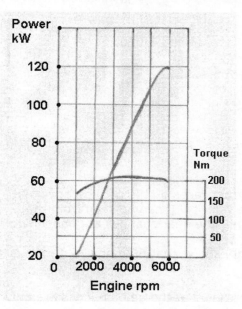

Because the engine rpm have to be fed back to the look up table, the effects of gear changes need to be considered in the feed back loop so there are 2 switch elements in this loop. Again the switches are activated by velocity thresholds, 13m/s for 1st to 2nd and 19 m/s for 2nd to 3rd.

Although the overall ratios are given as 3.889 x 3.6 = 14; 3.889 x 2.125 = 8.264 and 3.889 x 1.458 = 5.67, for simplicity 12, 8.5 and 5 were used. Also the equivalent mass used should probably be nearer 1200 kg.

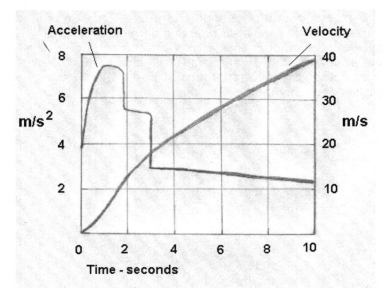

The sketch above is taken from the traces on the oscilloscopes that display the acceleration and the velocity. It can be seen from the step decreases in acceleration that the gear changes are happening as expected.

The sketch of the trace of velocity shows that 60 mph (26.4 m/s) is reached in about 5.5 seconds.

It should be noted from the sketches that the gear changes are only just discernible from the velocity trace, as slight changes in gradient, whereas they are very clear on the acceleration trace as large steps. This illustrates the importance of making full use of oscilloscopes for diagnostics and for checking that the model is doing what it should be doing.

The 0 - 60 mph time of about 5.5 seconds in this model is too brief. One reason for this discrepancy is that there is no time allowed for actually changing gear, this would probably add about another second. Also the gear ratios were not exactly correct and the mass in the model is probably about 10 % low which would perhaps cause the result to be about 0.5 second below correct.

The published 0 - 62.5 mph figure for the 1983 Porsche 944 was about 8.5 seconds.

The model diagram is shown below:

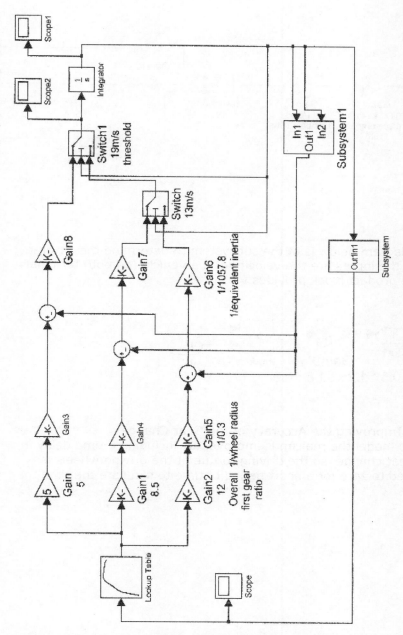

The diagram below is the subsystem for determining the engine rpm to be fed back to the look up table, the input is the vehicle velocity.

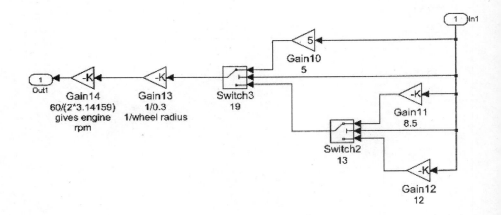

The diagram below is of the subsystem to determine the air drag force, the inputs are the velocity of the vehicle (on both terminals so the product block provides v^2).

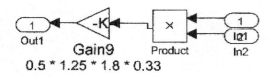

6.5.8 Improving the Accuracy of the Gear Change
In this model the realism is improved by including a time delay in the gear change, so the driving torque at the driving wheels is reduced to zero for a short period of time to simulate the time that

the vehicle is in neutral between gears.

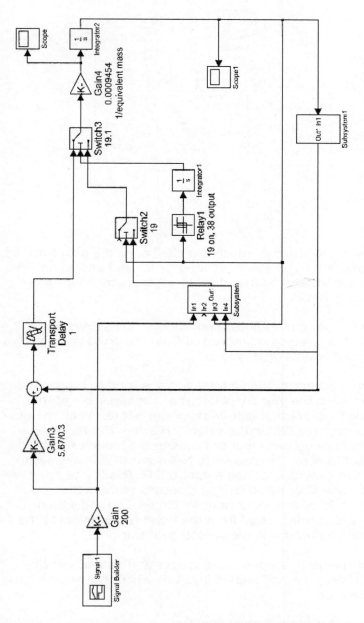

The subsystem, below, shows how the gear change, using two switch blocks and a relay, implements the period of time between gears when zero torque is transmitted.

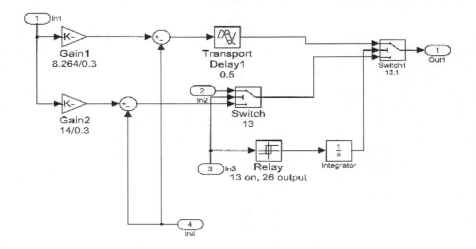

Input 1 is the engine torque, which is multiplied in the gain block by the overall gear ratio (1st along the lower track and 2nd along the upper track) and divided by the wheel tread diameter which gives the gross driving force.

Input 4 is the air drag resistance, derived as in the subsystem of the previous model, which is subtracted from the gross driving force to give the net available driving force.

Input 3 is the feedback of the velocity which is used to trigger the gear change. When the velocity is less than the threshold of the lower left switch, the output is from the lower left terminal, the net first gear driving force. When the velocity reaches 13m/s, the switch threshold value, the input switches to the top left hand terminal, which is zero. The relay also has a switch on point set to 13 and starts to give its specified output of 26. This is integrated by the integrator and after just over half a second reaches the specified threshold of the upper right switch on 13.1. This then switches the signal transmitted from the lower left terminal to the upper right terminal which is the second gear track.

By looking at the oscilloscopes showing acceleration and velocity (not included here) the half second intervals where the driving force is zero can be seen.

6.5.9 Approach Based on Air and Fuel Flow
In this section different approach is suggested (but the model is not developed) using engine rpm and throttle opening as the inputs to a 2d look up table and this table is then used to give as the output

the air mass flow rate into the engine. The air mass flow rate was the primary control in many early fuel injection systems.

The initial assumption for this model could be that the engine has a peak output of 120kW at 5800 rpm (approximately that of a 1983 Porsche 944, above) and if it is assumed that the efficiency is 30%, this means that the fuel burnt must provide 120/0.3 = 400kW.

400 kW requires a fuel mass flow rate of:

400000/46000000 = 0.00869 kg/s

Assuming stoichiometric mixture, this requires an air flow rate of 0.00869 x 14.7 = 0.128 kg/s

6.5.10 Pressure Drop Across the Throttle
6.5.10.1 Introduction

In this model the pressure drop across the throttle, the effect this has on the air mass flow rate and the cross section area opened by the throttle for the air to flow through are all considered. Again a single gear is assumed.

This model initially makes the assumption that the air flow is incompressible and that Bernoulli's equation can be applied. This simplification means the modeling is not excessively difficult, but is not very accurate as the flow should be considered as compressible, which is more complex to model.

It is assumed that the inlet tract is 0.06 by 0.05 m and that the throttle plate when fully open blocks 3% of the inlet tract csa.

To apply Bernoulli the velocity in the inlet tract, v_1, and across the throttle plate, v_2 are required. As there is assumed no change in level, the equation can be written:

$$v_1^2/2 + P_1/Ro = v_2^2/2 + P_2/Ro$$

which when re-arranged, assuming $P_1 = 100000 N/m^2$, to give P_2 reads:

$$P_2 = Ro.v_1^2/2 + 100000 - Ro.v_2^2/2$$

(Ro is assumed to be 1.25, so Ro/2 = 0.625)

At a later stage in the model it is assumed that the density is proportional to the absolute pressure.

The block diagram for this model is shown below:

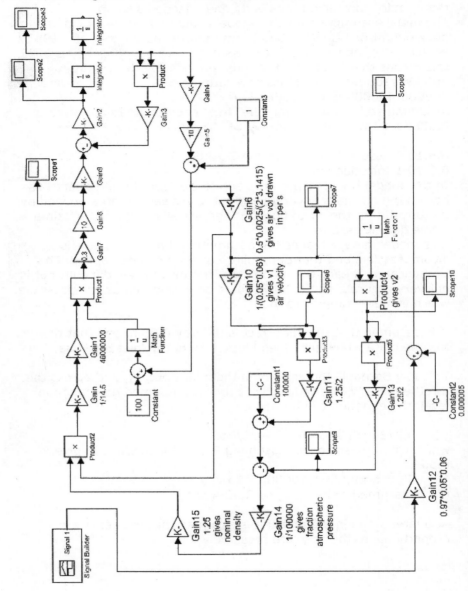

6.5.10.2 The Model

Starting from near the top left, the output from the 'Product2' block is the air mass flow rate. This is multiplied by the Gain of 0.068 (assuming a stoichiometric mixture) to give the fuel mass flow rate. 'Gain1' multiplies this by 46000000 to give the gross power produced by burning the fuel. 'Gain7' is an assumed efficiency of 30% to give the assumed net power.

The 'Product1' block multiplies the assumed net power by 1/engine angular velocity to give the assumed engine torque. There is a 'Constant' of 100 added into this feedback loop to prevent division by zero and simulate the engine speed when letting out the clutch.

'Gain8' is the assumed overall gear ratio, assumed to be 10, and 'Gain9' is 1/wheel radius to give forward thrust generated by the driving wheels. The summing point takes away the air resistance to give the net force available to accelerate the vehicle which goes into 'Gain2' which is 1/equivalent mass of the vehicle, giving the acceleration. This goes through the 'Integrator' to give the vehicle velocity.

The vehicle velocity is squared in 'Product' and in 'Gain3' is multiplied by:

frontal area x drag coefficient x air density/2

This gives the air resistance opposing the forward motion.

The velocity is also fed back through 'Gain4', 1/wheel radius, to give the drive shaft angular velocity, then through 'Gain5', the overall gear ratio, to give the engine omega value. 'Constant3', value 1, is added to get the model started from rest and 'Constant', value 100 is to simulate the effect of letting the clutch out at about 1000rpm. This engine omega is then fed back via the 'Math Function' reciprocal into the 'Product' block to obtain the net engine torque, Torque = Power/omega.

The engine omega is also multiplied in 'Gain6' by:

swept volume/(2 * 2 * 3.14159) NB - do NOT omit the brackets in expressions of this type.

to give the volume flow rate into the engine.

This value is then multiplied (in 'Product2') by the air density of the inducted air, to give the air mass flow rate.

The volume flow rate is multiplied in Gain10 by 1/(0.05 * 0.06) to give the velocity in the inlet tract, v_1, which is squared in Product3 and in Gain11 multiplied by 1.25/2 and 100000 added from Constant1.

The volume flow rate is also multiplied (in 'Product4') by 1/inlet tract open area to give the speed of the air past the throttle. This is squared in 'Product5' and multiplied by 1.25/2 to give pressure drop. This is subtracted from 'Constant1', 100000 and from ($Ro.v_1^2$) to give the absolute pressure, P_2 and this is multiplied by 1/100000 in 'Gain14' to give the air pressure as a fraction of atmospheric. This is multiplied by 'Gain15', 1.25, to give the air density which is then multiplied in 'Product2' by the volume rate flow to give the mass flow rate.

The 'Signal Builder' source provides the throttle opening, between zero and one, which is multiplied in 'Gain12' by 0.97 * 0.05 * 0.06 to give the open cross section area past the throttle plate. This is inverted (a small constant added, 'Constant2' to avoid division by zero when starting) and this goes to 'Product4' to give the air velocity, v_2, across the throttle plate.

6.5.10.3 Results
Running this model gives a 0 - 60 mph time of just over 7 seconds. Again because of the single gear ratio the engine revs at this speed are an unrealistically high 7700 rpm.

6.5.11 Pressure Drops Across the Throttle and the Inlet Valve
6.5.11.1 Introduction
In previous models account has only been taken of the pressure drop across the throttle plate. This model will consider the pressure loss across both the throttle plate and the inlet valve.
A single gear is assumed.
Like the previous model this model initially makes the assumption that the air flow is incompressible and that Bernoulli's equation can be applied.
The block diagram for this model is shown below and subsystem block diagram is shown on the following page:

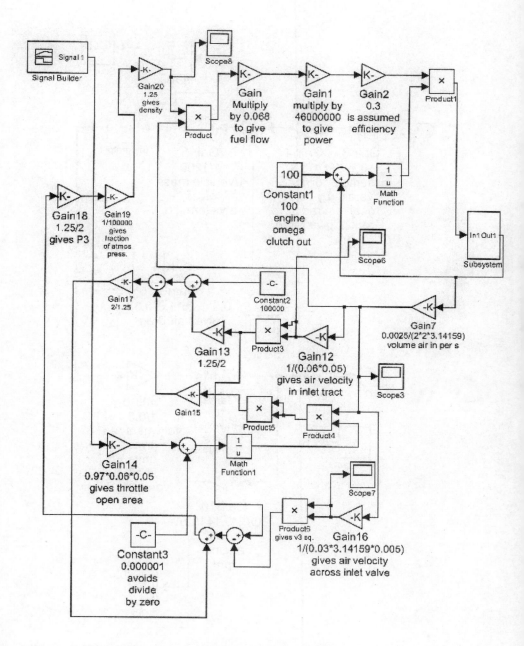

The subsystem below is very similar to parts of the previous models, the input is the engine torque, oscilloscopes display the vehicle acceleration, velocity, engine rpm and engine angular velocity. The output is the engine angular velocity.

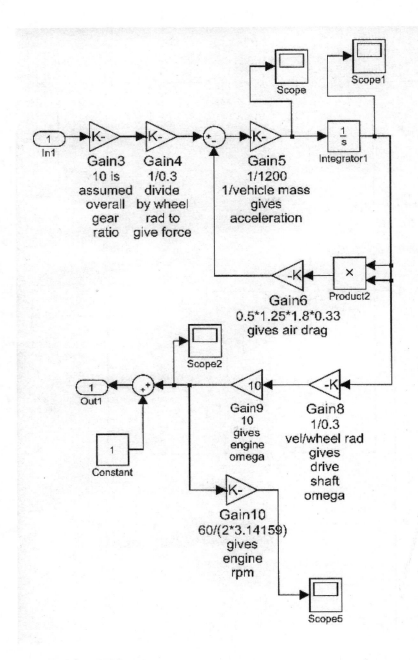

6.5.11.2 The Model

Starting from near the top left, the output from the 'Product' block is the air mass flow rate. This is multiplied by the 'Gain' of 0.068 (assuming a stoichiometric mixture) to give the fuel mass flow rate. 'Gain1' multiplies this by 46000000 to give the gross power

produced by burning the fuel. 'Gain2' is an assumed efficiency of 30% to give the assumed net power.
The 'Product1' block multiplies the assumed net power by 1/engine angular velocity to give the assumed engine torque. There is a 'Constant' of 100 added into this feedback loop to prevent division by zero and simulate the engine speed when letting out the clutch.

In the subsystem 'Gain3' is the assumed overall gear ratio, 10, and 'Gain4' is 1/wheel radius to give forward thrust generated by the driving wheels. The summing point takes away the air resistance to give the net force available to accelerate the vehicle which goes into 'Gain5' which is 1/equivalent mass of the vehicle, in this model assumed to be 1200kg, giving the acceleration. This goes through the 'Integrator1' to give the vehicle velocity.

The vehicle velocity is squared in 'Product2' and in 'Gain6' is multiplied by:

frontal area x drag coefficient x air density/2
This gives the air resistance opposing the forward motion.

The velocity is also fed back through 'Gain8', 1/wheel radius, to give the drive shaft angular velocity, then through 'Gain9', the overall gear ratio, to give the engine omega value. 'Constant1', value 1, is added to get the model started from rest.

This output from the subsystem has a constant, of 100, added (from Constant1) to simulate the engine angular velocity when the clutch is let out. This is then fed back via the 'Math Function' reciprocal into the 'Product' block to obtain the net engine torque.

The pressure drop calculations are carried out in the blocks in the lower left hand part of the main system diagram.

The engine omega is also multiplied by:

swept volume/(2 * 2 * 3.14159)
to give the air volume flow rate per second into the engine.

This value is then multiplied (in 'Product') by the calculated density, Ro_3, of the inducted air, to give the air mass flow rate.

To determine the velocity through the open inlet valve, v_3, the diameter is assumed to be 30mm, the average open height is assumed to be 8mm and each valve is assumed to be open for 1/2 of each crankshaft revolution, it is a 4 cylinder engine, with 1 inlet valve per cylinder, so the velocity across the open inlet valve, v_3 is given by:

$$v_3 = \text{volume drawn in per second}/(0.03 * 3.14159 * 0.008)$$
This is calculated by 'Gain16' and squared in 'Product6'.

To apply Bernoulli the velocity in the inlet tract, v_1, and across the throttle plate, v_2 are required. As there is assumed no change in level, the equation can be written:

$$v_1^2/2 + P_1/Ro = v_2^2/2 + P_2/Ro$$
which when re-arranged, assuming $P_1 = 100000N/m^2$, to give P_2 reads:
$$P_2 = Ro.v_1^2/2 + 100000 - Ro.v_2^2/2$$
(Ro is assumed to be 1.25, so Ro/2 = 0.625)

The volume flow rate is also multiplied (in 'Product4') by 1/inlet tract open area to give the speed of the air past the throttle. This is squared in 'Product5' and multiplied by 1.25/2 ('Gain15').
The volume of air drawn in per second is also multiplied by 1/(full inlet tract cross section area) ('Gain12') to give the v_1 value, which is squared in 'Product3'. This is multiplied by 1.25/2 in 'Gain 13'.
'Constant2', 100000, gives the assumed atmospheric pressure.
The two adjacent summing points are then used to evaluate P_2.
The value of P_2 is fed into 'Gain17' and the adjacent summing points together with 'Gain18' applying Bernouilli to determine P_3.

At this point the assumption of incompressible flow is changed and it is assumed that the air density is proportional to the absolute pressure (P_3) and P_3 is multiplied by 1/100000 (in 'Gain19') and by 1.25 (in Gain20'). This gives a value for the air density across the inlet valve, Ro_3.

The air density, Ro3 is then multiplied in 'Product' by the volume rate flow to give the mass flow rate.

The 'Signal Builder' source provides the throttle opening, which is multiplied in 'Gain14' by 0.97 * 0.05 * 0.06 to give the cross section area of inlet tract opened by the throttle. The 0.97 is to allow for a slight obstruction of the tract even when the throttle is fully open. This is inverted (a small constant added, 'Constant3' to avoid division by zero when starting) and this goes to 'Product4' to give the air velocity, v_2, across the throttle plate.

6.5.11.3 Results
Running this model gives a 0 - 60 mph time of almost 7 seconds. Again because of the single gear ratio the engine revs at this speed are an unrealistically high 9000 rpm.

This model is however very sensitive to the constant value in 'Constant', the assumed rad/s at which the clutch is let out.

However the airflow is exceeding the maximum after about 5 seconds, which should be limited for accuracy.

The engine torque does not reach its maximum stated value (of 205 Nm) but reaches a maximum of about 175Nm after about 4 seconds, then falls away. These effects may be due to the fact that the throttle cross section area is not accurate.

As a check on the model the computed P3 value is compared with another possible assumption that the pressure drop across the inlet is proportional to the engine speed and at 5000 rpm P_3 is $0.8P_2$. The value of P_3 calculated in this way when displayed on 'Scope10' was quite similar to the display of P_3 on 'Scope11', suggesting that the model is reasonable in this respect.

6.6 Conclusions
By combining the different aspects illustrated in the models above, it should be possible to develop a model which will simulate a real vehicle with a fair degree of accuracy. Obviously the more comprehensive the model the better the results should be.

6.7 References
6.1 'Automotive Handbook', Bosch, 5th ed., 2000, ISBN: 0-7680-0669-4.
6.2 'An Introduction to Matlab', by D M Etter and D C Kuncicky, Prentice Hall, 1999.
6.3 'Internal Combustion Engines', C R Ferguson and A T Kirkpatrick, John Wiley and Sons, Inc., 2001, 2001, ISBN: 0-471-35617-4.

Appendix 6.1 - The Interaction of Linear and Rotary Components in a System

1. Introduction
Many dynamic systems involve both linear translation and rotary motion. These problems are commonly solved by applying Newton's law, where components are undergoing translation only then the equation of linear motion is used:

Force = mass x acceleration

Where a body is rotating about a fixed pivot point then the equation:
Torque = Moment of Inertia about the Pivot point x angular acceleration

can be used.

NB Where a body is translating **and** rotating, the best approach is to consider the linear motion of the centre of mass and the rotation about the centre of mass. There will also be at least 1 equation linking the rotation and the translation. This is shown in the following example where the rotation of the wheels on a vehicle need to be related to the translation of the entire vehicle. In this example it is required to determine an expression for it's acceleration in terms of the torque applied to the driving wheels, their radius, mass and moment of inertia and the mass of the vehicle body. It is assumed that the wheels do not skid.

The approach used is to draw a layout diagram, then the free body diagrams (FBD). As the two rear wheels are identical, only 1 FBD is shown. The same applies for the front wheels. It is assumed that the vehicle is travelling on horizontal ground so only forces and motion in the horizontal direction are considered. Having drawn the FBDs the 5 system equations are can be written down - translation for the vehicle body (eqn. 2) rear wheel (eqn. 1) front wheel (eqn. 3) and rotation of the front (eqn. 5) and rear (eqn. 4) wheels.

Car with four wheels

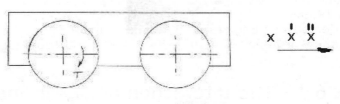

Body mass (less wheels) = M   Wheel radius = r
4 wheels, mass each = m
Total torque applied to 2 rear wheels = T
Each wheel, moment of inertia = I

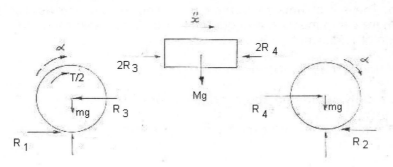

Linear motion:

$$R_1 - R_3 = m\ddot{x} \qquad (1)$$

$$2R_3 - 2R_4 = M\ddot{x} \qquad (2)$$

$$R_4 - R_2 = m\ddot{x} \qquad (3)$$

Rotary motion:

$$\frac{T}{2} - R_1 r = I\alpha \qquad (4)$$

$$R_2 r = I\alpha \qquad (5)$$

Using (5), substitut for R_2 in (3):

$$R_4 = I\frac{\alpha}{r} + m\ddot{x} \qquad \text{then } \frac{\ddot{x}}{r} = \alpha$$

$$R_4 = \ddot{x}\left(\frac{I}{r^2} + m\right)$$

Substitute for R_4 in (2)

$$2R_3 - 2\ddot{x}\left(\frac{I}{r^2} + m\right) = M\ddot{x}$$

$$2R_3 = \ddot{x}\left[2\left(\frac{I}{r^2} + m\right) + M\right]$$

Substitute for R_3 in (1):

$$R_1 - \ddot{x}\frac{\left[2\left(\frac{I}{r^2} + m\right) + M\right]}{2} = m\ddot{x}$$

$$R_1 = \ddot{x}\left\{\frac{\left[2\left(\frac{I}{r^2} + m\right) + M\right]}{2} + m\right\}$$

substite for R_1 in (4)

$$\frac{T}{2} = r\ddot{x}\left\{\frac{\left[2\left(\frac{I}{r^2} + m\right) + M\right]}{2} + m\right\} + I\alpha$$

Multiply by 2 and substitute for α:

$$T = r\ddot{x}\left[2\left(\frac{I}{r^2} + m\right) + M + 2m + 2\frac{I}{r^2}\right]$$

collecting terms:

$$\ddot{x} = \frac{T}{r\left[4\left(\frac{I}{r^2} + m\right) + M\right]}$$

Equivalent inertia $= 4\left(\frac{I}{r^2} + m\right) + M$ **kg**

7 Engine Design - First Decisions

7.1 First Decisions
Before any detailed design work is undertaken a number of fundamental decisions need to be made and some basic calculations carried out. These are described in this section.

7.2 Configuration - Number of Cylinders and Arrangement
One of the key limiting factors in the design of a petrol powered internal combustion engine is the maximum advisable mean piston speed, v_{mp}. This is the piston speed averaged over one cycle.

- 15.25 m/s - 1983 Porsche 944 2.5 litre at 5800 rpm, the engine speed for maximum power output of 120 kW.
- Under 17.5 m/s - reliable
- 17.5 - 20 m/s - somewhat stressed
- Over 20 m/s - may well be short lived
- 20.4 m/s - 2007 Harley Davidson Softail motorcycle 1.584 litre at 5500 rpm, the maximum specified sustained engine speed.
- 22 m/s - Year 2008 Honda Fireblade motorcycle 1 litre at 12000 rpm, the engine speed for maximum power output (130 kW).
- 22.8 m/s - F1 engine

From the table above it can be seen that quite a small increase in mean piston speed can change a design from reliable to short lived. For a reliable design it is necessary to have a aim for a design where the maximum value of the mean piston speed is below 17.5m/s. There are a number of reasons why this guidance is appropriate for a very wide range of engine sizes.

Virtually all engines use piston rings made of similar materials sliding in cylinders which are also made of very similar materials with the same surface finishing operations.

Increasing the piston speed increases the loads and stresses on the bearings due to inertia of the reciprocating parts.

Volumetric efficiency will also suffer due to pressure losses caused by the increased velocity (causing pressure drops and decrease in density) of gases through the valve passages. The ultimate limit to the gas flow through the valve aperture is the occurrance of sonic flow in the valve aperture which occurs at a critical pressure drop and 'chokes' the flow so that increasing the pressure drop does not result in any further increase in flow.

At low engine speeds the mechanical efficiency is about 0.85, whereas at high speeds this will only be about 0.6.

All 8, 10 and 12 cylinder engines, and many 6 cylinder engines, have their cylinders arranged in V formation to avoid an excessively long crankshaft which is vulnerable to torsional vibration and to help make the engine more compact.

7.3 Mean Effective Pressure (mep)
The mep is the notional average pressure exerted on the piston during the combustion, or working, 'stroke'.
The mep or 'p' below, is dependent primarily upon the compression ratio and the volumetric efficiency and has a definite limit that can not be exceeded without recourse to forced induction, either super-charging or or turbo-charging.
The mean effective pressure (mep) of a modern petrol engine will typically be 1 to 1.5 MN/m^2. (The maximum pressure in the cylinder during combustion being about 5MPa).

7.4 A Comparison of the Effects of Different Numbers of Cylinder and Sizes

The effects of changing some of the design parameters are summarised in the table below.

It is possible to compare the effects of the size and number of cylinders by considering 3 engine configurations, each working at the same mean effective pressure (mep) and each having the same piston speed.

Variable	Engine A	Engine B	Engine C
Number of cylinders	1	1	4
Bore	1	2	1
Total Piston Area	1	4	4
Stroke	1	2	1
Mean Torque	1	8	4
Rev/Minute	1	0.5	1
Power	1	4	4
Capacity	1	8	4
Weight	1	8	4
Power/Weight	1	0.5	1

Maximum Inertia Stress	1	1	1
Mean Gas Velocity	1	1	1
Piston/ring/cylinder Friction Losses assumed proportional to swept area/unit time	1	2	4

The power of an engine is proportional to the number of cylinders, other variables being held constant and also proportional to the square of the cylinder diameter.

If it is assumed that all dimensions increase in proportion to the cylinder diameter, then for a given piston speed and mean effective pressure the power is proportional to the square of the linear dimensions, however the weight will vary as the cube of the linear dimensions (proportionally to the volume of metal) so the weight increases more rapidly than the power.

If the number of cylinders of a given size is increased then the power and weight go up in approximately the the same proportion and there no increase of weight per unit power. However piston/ring/cylinder friction (the largest friction loss in IC engines) increases in proportion to the number of cylinders.

Although 4 cylinder engines are very popular for small and medium car engines, for the above reason some manufacturers have introduced 3 cylinder engines of about 1 litre or slightly smaller capacity where fuel economy is a more important consideration than producing high power.

It can be shown that for a given piston speed, varying the size of the engine will leave the maximum stresses and intensity of the bearing loads, due to inertia, unaltered.

7.5 Work, Power and Torque
The engine capacity and number of cylinders selected will depend upon maximum power, torque and rpm required. The available space, location and required vehicle characteristics will influence the engine configuration.

The average force acting on the piston during the combustion stroke will be the product of the mep x Piston Area.

If p = mep, N/m^2
D = diameter of cylinders, m
L = length of stroke, m

n = number of cylinders
N = engine revolutions per minute
f = number of combustion strokes per cylinder per engine
revolution, = 0.5 for a four stroke engine and 1 for a two
stroke engine.
Then the force acting on one piston during the combustion stroke:
= $3.14159 D^2 p/4$

The work done during the combustion stroke by the force acting on
one piston = $3.14159 D^2 p L/4$ joules

The work done during 1 crankshaft revolution by all 'n' cylinders:
= $n f (3.14159 D^2 p L/4)$ joules

The power produced by the engine, $P = N n f 3.14159 D^2 p L /(4 \times 60)$ joules per second = watts

The original English unit for power (= rate of doing work) was
'horse power' (h.p.) and 1 h.p. = 746 watts.
The definition of h.p. originated from experiments by James Watt
but he added a 50% allowance because of the nature of the
experiments and very few horses are actually able to work at a rate
of 1 h.p. for any length of time!

The indicated horse power (i.h.p) is the rate of work done inside the
cylinders by the pressure produced by the the burning of the
mixture. A significant proportion of the energy produced by burning
the fuel goes out of the exhaust and in non turbo-charged engines
is wasted.
The parts of the spreadsheet described in chapter 8 which deal with
finite heat release attempts to model the pressures in the engine
from which the i.h.p. is calculated.
The useful power will be less than the i.h.p. as a significant
proportion of this has to be used overcoming the friction losses
before the useful power, brake horse power (b.h.p) is available at
the engine output, usually one end of the crankshaft.
The name 'brake' horse power originates in that this useful work
could be measured comparatively easily by applying a brake (a
friction brake, fan or water turbine brake) to the end of the
crankshaft.

The mechanical efficiency is defined as the b.h.p./i.h.p. In a modern
engine this may be about 70%, varying somewhat with engine rpm.

Chapter 8 contains a more detailed description about combustion
within the cylinders and how effectively the fuel can be burnt.

The expression for power, above, can be re-written in terms of the mean piston speed:

Mean piston speed, v_{pm} = 2 N L/60
$P = v_{pm}$ n f 3.14159 D^2p/(4 x 2)
The piston area A_p = 3.14159 D^2/4
$P = v_{pm}$ n f p A_p/2
Power per piston area: $P/(n\ A_p) = p\ f\ v_{pm}/2$

7.6 Valves - Number, Layout and Size

Originally engines were fitted one inlet and one exhaust valve in each cylinder, in most early engines 'side valves' were used. In this configuration valves were at the sides of the cylinders in one side of the engine block actuated from a cam shaft low down in the block. This was not efficient and it was realised that it was more efficient to have valves in the cylinder head ('over head valve' - ohv), see diagram below:

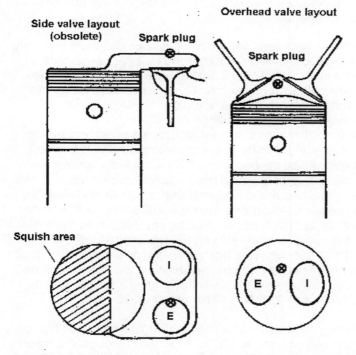

The ohv layout facilitated higher compression ratios and the ability to have more than 1 inlet and 1 exhaust valve per cylinder. The ohv layout offered advantages of shorter flame paths leading to improved combustion facilitating higher speed engines and efficiency.

Almost all modern automotive engines have valves operated by one or more overhead cam shafts located in the cylinder head. The best known exception is Harley Davidson whose V twin air cooled engines operate valves via push rods running up the sides of the cylinders and actuating rockers mounted in the cylinder heads. Overhead cam shaft engines may have cams with lobes that contact the valve stems via shims or alternatively via rockers which incorporate adjustment mechanisms. Some engines use engine oil under pressure to ensure that valves are operating with appropriate clearances. Actuation of the valves by rockers is usually needed when only one overhead cam shaft is fitted and there are four valves per cylinder.

To facilitate higher engine speeds and power without increasing the engine size, there is a tendency in modern engines to have 2 inlet and 2 exhaust valves per cylinder. Although this increases complication, the individual valves and associated springs etc., have lower masses reducing the inertia loading on the individual cam lobes for any given speed.

Cylinder heads fitted with four valves per cylinder can normally only be satisfactorily cooled by water. As currently all cars and many motorcycles are water cooled this is not an issue for such vehicles, however there are still a number of air cooled motorcycle engines manufactured and these are normally limited to two valves per cylinder to achieve satisfactory cooling.

There are a number of reasons for increasing use of water cooling, even among motorcycles. Firstly it is increasingly difficult to meet ever more stringent noise restrictions with air cooled engines. A second factor which applies particularly to sports motorcycles is that very high power densities are developed and to maintain reliability water cooling is needed. As an example the 2008 Honda Fireblade develops 130 kW at 12000 rpm and 112 Nm at 8500 rpm from a 1 litre engine with a compression ratio of 12.3:1 and the bike has an a dry kerb weight of 199 kg. This has a four valve per cylinder head and is water cooled. This can be contrasted with the 1983 Porsche 944 with a 2.5 litre, two valve per cylinder engine that produced 120 kW at 5700 rpm and 205 Nm of torque at 3000 rpm.

A key factor limiting the ability of a modern engine to rev at higher speeds is that the velocity of the air (or mixture) through the open inlet valve reaches sonic velocity, the flow is then choked as any further drop in downstream pressure is not communicated upstream. Having more than one inlet valve provides additional area for air or mixture flow assisting with raising the maximum engine revs. Even when the flow is not choked, the volumetric efficiency will be improved. The velocity of sound in air is given by:

$$a = (\gamma\ R\ T)^{0.5}$$

In ambient conditions this is about 343m/s.

The average air velocity across a valve can be related to the Mach number (actual gas velocity/sonic velocity of the gas), however as the average velocity is only approximate, the term Mach index is used, Z.

Experimental plots of volumetric efficiency against inlet valve Mach index show an approximately linear decrease of volumetric efficiency with increasing Mach index. To maintain a volumetric efficiency of about 80% the Mach index should not exceed about 0.6.

As the exhaust gas is significantly hotter than the inducted air (or mixture) about 1000°K, it can be seen from the equation above for 'a' that the sonic velocity of the exhaust gases is significantly higher than for the inducted air. Therefore exhaust valves are normally smaller than inlet valves in the same engine (assuming either one of each or two of each).
It is also necessary to allow for spacing between valves and the bore and between valves. The third picture in Chapter 14 shows how close valves can be in the cylinder head.

The number and size of the inlet valves per cylinder should be chosen to give a Z value of about 0.6 at the maximum desired piston speed.

A small number of engines have 2 inlet and 1 exhaust valve per cylinder and some have 3 inlet and 2 exhaust valves per cylinder.

As a good starting point assume the new engine design will have 2 inlet and 2 exhaust valves in each cylinder.

Virtually all engines use a cam lobe to open the valve and a coil spring (sometimes 2 concentric coil springs) to shut the valve. Only Ducati currently have desmodromic valve operation (valve opening and closing carried out by cams) on their V twin motorcycle engines, though this approach has occasionally been used in car engines in the past e.g: the Mercedes 300SL 'Gullwing' sports car of the 1950s and the Fiat S52 motor of 1914. The mechanism needed for desmodromic operation is complex to maintain.

More detailed information about the design of valves and valve trains is given in Chapter 14.

7.7 Suggested Procedure
An outline approach is given below:

Type of vehicle	Number of Cylinders	Approximate engine capacity	Power, kW
City, economy compact car	3, or possibly 4	up to 1 litre	30 - 40
Mid range, family	4	1.4 - 1.8 litre	60 - 80
Sports, luxury	6, 8, 10, 12	1.8 - 3 litre or 4.5 for high end luxury, performance	100 up

Decide on whether the fuel is to be petrol or diesel.

Having decided on the power required, for a petrol engine assume a best overall engine efficiency of 30% and for a turbo-charged diesel engine assume 40% (in both cases it should be a little higher, but designing for these figures gives a margin for error).

Using the above efficiency values determine the mass of fuel per second needed and assuming stoichiometric mixture, the mass and volume of air needed per second.

Assuming the inlet valves will be open for approximately 25% of the time, determine the necessary diameter and lift to ensure the air velocity is not excessive at the proposed maximum engine rpm. The exhaust valves can be slightly smaller.
From the sizes of the valves, the minimum bore needed can be determined. As a reasonable starting point the bore may be a similar or slightly large than the stroke.

Decide on the number of cylinders, their arrangement and check this gives a capacity of the order suggested in the table above and a maximum piston speed of 17.5 m/s or less..

Check the proposal does not contradict any findings from focus groups and market surveys, eg number of cylinders expected in a luxury car.

Check if any existing engines might enable the market to be met at lower cost than putting another engine into production.

A great deal work now needs to be done on: planning, detail design, analysis, simulation and detail process specifications.

8 Thermodynamic Considerations, Modelling Engine Performance

8.1 Work, Temperatures and Efficiency

Based on the idealised Otto cycle it is possible to calculate the theoretical work input and output per cycle. The four phases in the cycle are summarised in the table below:

Phase	Process	Heat transfer per kg	Work out, pdv
Point 1 to 2	Reversible adiabatic compression (Isentropic)	0	$-(u_2-u_1)$ $=-C_v(T_2 - T_1)$
2 to 3	Heat addition, due to burning fuel (Constant volume)	$C_v(T_3 - T_2)$	0
Point 3 to 4	Reversible adiabatic expansion (Isentropic)	0	$+ (u_3-u_4)$ $=+C_v(T_3 - T_4)$
Point 4 to 1	Heat rejection, hot gas exits through exhaust (Constant volume)	$- C_v(T_4 - T_1)$	0

8.2 Air Standard Cycle

Based on the simple assumptions shown in the table above (and ignoring the presence of fuel) it is possible to determine the net work output per cycle per kg of working substance:

$$= C_v [(T_3 - T_4) - (T_2 - T_1)]$$

$$= C_v [(T_3 - T_2) - (T_4 - T_1)]$$

Thermal efficiency, η_c = Net work output per cycle / Heat added per cycle

$$= C_v[(T_3 - T_2) - (T_4 - T_1)]/[C_v(T_3 - T_2)]$$

$$= 1 - [(T_4 - T_1)/(T_3 - T_2)]$$

Also

$$v_1 / v_2 = v_4 / v_3 = r, \text{ the compression ratio}$$

$$T_2 / T_1 = (v_1 / v_2)^{\gamma-1} = r^{\gamma-1}$$

$$T_3 / T_4 = (v_4 / v_3)^{\gamma-1} = r^{\gamma-1}$$

and

$$T_3 = T_4 \, r^{\gamma-1} \ldots \text{ and } .. \, T_2 = T_1 \, r^{\gamma-1} \ldots \text{ so } ..$$

$$T_3 - T_2 = T_4 \, r^{\gamma-1} - T_1 \, r^{\gamma-1}$$

$$(T_4 - T_1)/(T_3 - T_2) = 1 /(r^{\gamma-1})$$

Therefore
$$T_4 / T_3 = T_1 / T_2 = (T_4 - T_1)/(T_3 - T_2)$$
So the thermal efficiency is given by
$$\eta_c = 1 - 1 /(r^{\gamma-1})$$

8.3 Implications
There are some important implications from the above equations:

i) To increase the efficiency the $(r^{\gamma-1})$ needs to be as large as possible, which means that r, the compression ratio needs to be as large as possible. In a petrol engine this is limited by the quality of fuel available and the need to prevent pre-ignition or 'knocking'. Most car petrol engines have a compression ratio of about 10:1.

The pressures in an Otto cycle are linked by the relationship:

$$p_2 / p_1 = p_3 / p_4 = r^{\gamma}$$

Diesel engines have a much higher compression ratio as this is required to heat the air to a temperature which will ensure ready ignition of the fuel oil. There is no issue of pre-ignition with diesel engines, however excessively high compression ratios cause noisy and rough operation, often emitting a knocking sound, which is not the same as 'knocking' when referring to a petrol engine. Typically diesel engines have a compression ratio between 18 and 20. This means that they are inherently more efficient than petrol engines.

Another consequence of increasing the compression ratio is that the maximum temperature, T_3, is increased as is the maximum pressure, p_3. This combination of increased temperature and pressure means that while aluminium pistons are almost universal in petrol engines, cast iron pistons are still commonly used in diesel

engines as cast iron maintains higher strength at higher
temperatures than aluminium and its alloys.

The table below shows how the 'air standard cycle efficiency' and
temperature, T_2, after compression, varies with compression ratio,
assuming that the initial air temperature T_1 = 30°C or 303_0K:

Compression ratio, r	7:1	8:1	9:1	10:1	11:1	18:1	20:1	22:1
Nominal air cycle efficiency, %	54	56	58	60	61.7	68.5	70	71
Temperature after compression, T_2, in °C	387	423	457	488	518	690	731	770
Pressure after compression, p_2, in MPa	1.5	1.8	2.2	2.5	2.8	5.7	6.6	7.6

The maximum temperature (T_3) in the idealised air cycle can be
calculated by assuming only air is being heated and ignoring the
products of combustion and their properties. Assuming a
stoichiometric mixture (the theoretical correct amount of air just to
give complete combustion) then 1 kg of air will require 1/14.7 kg of
fuel, or 0.068 kg. This when burnt will produce 46000000 x 0.068 J
= 3130000 J.
Assuming air has a specific heat at constant volume, C_v, of 716 J/kg
K, then the increase in temperature (from T_2) on combustion is
given by: 3130000/716 = 4370°K, giving an actual value (assuming
a compression ratio, r = 8) of 4370 + 423 + 273 = 5066°K =
4793°C.

The characteristic equation for a perfect gas: pV = mRT, shows that
p is proportional to T,
so $p_2 / T_2 = p_3 / T_3$ giving $p_3 = T_3 p_2 / T_2$

So p_3 = 5066 x 1.8 / 696 = 13.1 MPa

8.4 Fuel - Air Cycles
The very high temperatures (T_3) and pressures (p_3) obtained from
calculations based on the air standard cycle are much greater than
actual values. The fact that these values are clearly incorrect can be
deduced from the fact that for a compression ratio of 8:1, the air
standard cycle efficiency of an IC engine is 56.5%, whereas the

best thermal efficiency from petrol engines is between 30 and 35%. The simple air standard cycle overestimates the engine efficiency by a factor of approximately 2. Some of the reasons for this disparity will be considered in this section.

Diesel engines which have higher compression ratios, have higher efficiencies, some large marine engines have achieved a maximum efficiency of 50%. The best efficiency achieved by an automotive diesel engine (about 2 litres) is 44%.

The next stage in calculating more accurate values is to consider the effects of the fuel as well as the air. This is then referred to as the 'Fuel - Air' cycle. As well as allowing for the fuel, it is necessary to allow for the fact that the properties of the gases in the combustion chamber are not constant but vary with temperature. At high temperatures the products of combustion are subject to some dissociation. It may also be noted that in a real engine there are likely to be some residual gases from the previous combustion cycle present diluting the fresh mixture.

Allowing for these factors results in theoretical calculations of mep and efficiencies being only a few % higher than results from actual tests.

Such an analysis takes into account the following:

1) Gases in the combustion space contain fuel, air, water vapour and residual gases. The fuel:air ratio varies with the engine operating conditions and so consequently do the relative quantities of the gases.

2) The specific heats of gases (except for mono-atomic) increase with temperature. The value of C_p / C_v, gamma, γ also varies with temperature.

A simple assumption which may be used in the range 300 - 2000 K is that $C_p = a_1 + k_1T$ and $C_v = b_1 + k_1T$

$$R = C_p - C_v = a_1 - b_1$$

Above 1500 K the specific heat increases much more rapidly and the following may be used:

$$C_p = a_1 + k_1T + k_2T^2 \text{ and } C_v = b_1 + k_1T + k_2T^2$$

$C_p - C_v$ is constant so C_p / C_v decreases with increasing temperature.

If the variation in specific heats is considered during the compression stroke, the final temperature and pressure will be lower than if constant values of specific heat are used.

A ɣ gamma value (k) allowing for the above of 1.35 is sometimes used.

3) At higher temperatures, above about $1600^{\circ}K$, there is some dissociation and CO, H_2, and O_2 are present as well as H_2O and CO_2.

Dissociation starts at about $1000^{\circ}C$ for CO_2

$2 CO_2 -- 2CO + O_2 + heat$

and about $1300^{\circ}C$ for:

$2 H_2O -- 2H_2 + O_2 + heat.$

At lean air fuel ratios there is little dissociation mainly as the temperatures produced are too low.

The presence of CO and O_2 in the gas suppresses dissociation of CO_2, limiting dissociation in rich mixtures. Maximum dissociation occurs in burnt gases of the chemically correct air fuel mixture when the temperatures are high. Typically the reduction in maximum temperature is about $300^{\circ}K$ at the chemically correct air fuel ratio.

Dissociation is less pronounced in CI engine due to the presence of excess air, which tends to reduce the peak temperature attained in a CI engine.

4)The number of molecules present after combustion depends upon the air - fuel ratio and pressure and temperature after combustion.

$pV = NR'T$ The pressure depends upon the number of molecules. This has a direct effect on the amount of work that the gases in the cylinder can impart to the piston.

However the fuel - air cycle still assumes instantaneous complete combustion, no heat transfer and reversible compression and expansion which result in the work output being over estimated.

8.5 Finite Heat Release
8.5.1 Introduction

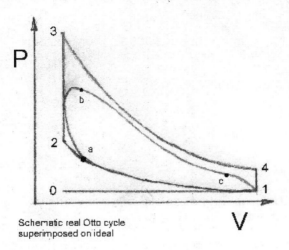

Schematic real Otto cycle
superimposed on ideal

The lower loop in the diagram (induction, point 0 to 1) appears as a horizontal line as the pressure range is small compared to the main loop. The pumping pressures - drawing in the air and expelling the burnt exhaust gases - are only slightly below and above atmospheric, a few kPa, whereas the peak combustion pressures are a few MPa. This lower loop is ignored in the further discussion and calculation.

The rounded corners of the 'real' diagram are caused by the fact that at some stage both inlet and exhaust valves are open and that the combustion takes a finite time to initiate and develop, there are heat losses and leakage:

- Point a - Ignition commences
- Point b - End of combustion
- Point c - Exhaust valve opens

To obtain a more accurate estimate of the power produced during the combustion cycle than is possible with the previous ideal cycles it is necessary to carry out a detailed computer simulation including consideration of the crank position when ignition is initiated, the duration of the combustion, as well as the manner in which it proceeds and the fact that the number of molecules of gas after combustion is greater than at the start. Such a model can best be presented in a spreadsheet and this is described in the appendix to this chapter and in Chapter 10.

To avoid complication the dissociation of the gases will be ignored as will the variation in C_v and C_p with temperature.

The first assumption concerns the way in which combustion proceeds:

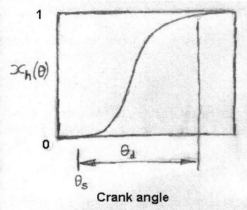

Crank angle

The diagram above shows schematically how combustion proceeds, after ignition the combustion is slow at first, followed by a period of rapid growth then gradual decay. These three regions appear as an 'S' curve which can be conveniently modelled by a Weibe function, see below, which is similar to a Weibull function.

$$x_h(\theta) = 1 - exp\left[-a\left(\frac{\theta - \theta_s}{\theta_d}\right)^n\right]$$

where

theta = crank angle
$theta_s$ = crank angle at ignition
$theta_d$ = duration of combustion in degrees of crank angle rotation
n = Weibe form factor
a = Weibe efficiency factor

The parameters a and n are chosen to fit experimental data. At the point of ignition theta = $theta_s$ so f($theta_s$) = 1 - exp(0) = 0

The cumulative heat release curve asymptotically approaches 1 so the end of combustion is arbitrarily chosen as x_h = 0.9 or 0.99. Corresponding values of the efficiency factor a are 2.3 and 4.6 respectively. Values of a = 5 and n = 3 have been reported to fit well with experimental data.

The spreadsheet entries are listed in Appendix 8.1

8.5.2 Assumptions for Spreadsheet

i) All results (unless otherwise stated) are per cylinder.

ii) The air mass drawn in during each inlet stroke is given by the swept volume x air density.

iii) The mass of fuel combusted is given by the air mass drawn in, divided by the air:fuel ratio specified in cell F8 (14.7 for the results given below) multiplied by a factor less than 1 to indicate the volumetric efficiency, in cell H7, 0.8 used for the results below.

iv) As combustion proceeds it is assumed that petrol is octane (C_8H_{18}) and after combustion the number of molecules increases by a factor of 1.0756 and this is considered to be an added mass when calculating the pressure and temperature changes occurring after the start of combustion.

v) The spread sheet starts at BDC (in row 10) and proceeds via 360 steps of $1°$ to TDC and on to BDC.

vi) To determine the velocities and accelerations of the piston, the piston displacements were differentiated numerically using a 5 point moving average formula:

$$v_i = [x_{i-2} - 8x_{i-1} + 8x_{i+1} - x_{i+2}]/12dt$$

where v is piston velocity, x is piston displacement from BDC and dt is the time for $1°$ of crank rotation.

The equivalent formula was used to determine the accelerations from the velocities.

It should be noted that the following columns were inserted to check some aspects and the results from some of these are not accurate. In particular column in L the pressure was calculated based on that of the previous step ($1°$) but this approach leads to error build up and the approach used in column N is more accurate. Columns prior to O assume instantaneous heat input at TDC. Columns O onwards assume heat release as described in section 8.5.1.

8.5.3 Results from Spreadsheet Applied to 1.1 litre K-Series Rover Engine

	Engine Specification	Computed Values
Max. Power (at 5700 rpm)	45 kW (at flywheel)	84 kW (on pistons)
Max mep	0.91 MPa (bmep)	1.7 MPa (mep)
Otto Efficiency		60.2 %
Engine efficiency	31.8 %	59.3 %

The computed results, in the right hand column, are significantly higher than those for the actual engine. That is because a significant proportion of the energy put in is lost to the exhaust gases, cooling water and engine oil by conduction and these losses are difficult to quantify accurately. Friction effects, some of which heat the cooling water and oil, are discussed in Chapters 5 and 12.

The finite heat release model involved burning petrol (for four cylinders) at 5700 rpm (the speed at which the engine produces maximum power) equivalent to 141.8 kW and the calculated work done on the four pistons is 84.1 kW. This is an efficiency of 59.3 %. Assuming that the actual engine is burning petrol at the same rate when producing maximum power, 45 kW at the flywheel, this corresponds to an overall efficiency of 31.8%. This is pretty much what would be expected of this type of petrol engine at full power. So the actual engine mep and power output, presumably measured at the flywheel, are consistent with these computed results. It seems likely that the figures obtained from the spread sheet are a reasonable estimate of the work done on the piston.

The 39 kW 'lost' - this is an approximate figure - goes in overcoming friction, particularly at the piston / ring / cylinder interface, the main and big end bearings, camshaft bearings etc. and seals. There are also pumping losses arising from the oil and water pumps.

The computed result in this spreadsheet also overestimates the work done on the piston as it assumes that work continues to be done on the piston by the products of combustion till the piston reaches bdc.

In real engines the exhaust valve opens somewhat before bdc (30 - 50°) which reduces the work done by the piston. Adjusting the spreadsheet for the exhaust valve opening 30° before bdc reduces the mep by just under 2%.

8.6 References
The references contain much more detailed information about modeling engine combustion and associated topics.

'Internal Combustion Engines', C R Ferguson and A T Kirkpatrick, John Wiley and Sons, 2001, ISBN: 9780471356172 43 95.

'Introduction to Internal Combustion Engines', R Stone, 1999, 3rd Ed. Macmillan Press.

Appendix 8.

Heading cells slidercrank2kseries

Rows 10 – 370 are angular positions of the crank measured from bdc.

B3: Crank Throw
B4: Connecting rod length
B5: RPM
B7: P1
B8: Piston Mass

D3: Compression Ratio
D4: R = 290 J/kg deg K

F3: Gamma, 1.4
F8: Stoichiometric Air: fuel ratio, 14.7

H3: Start of ignition (after BDC)
H4: Ignition duration (degrees of crankshaft rotation)
H5: Air density –
H7: Assumed Vol efficiency – for fuel calc

J3: T1 deg K, 310
J4: fuel energy, 46000000 J/kg

L3: Air Cv, 714 J/kg deg K

N3: Air Cp, 1000 J/kg per deg K

P3: $\quad \text{Otto\_eta} = 1 - e^{((1 - \$F\$3) \cdot LN(\$D\$3))}$

R3: $\quad \text{Power\_in} = \dfrac{\text{Total\_energy} \cdot \text{Omega}}{4 \cdot 3.14159}$

N4: $\quad \text{Total\_energy} = \text{Fuel\_mass} \cdot \$J\$4$

P4: $\quad \text{Otto\_imp} = \dfrac{\text{Total\_energy} \cdot \text{Otto\_eta} \cdot \$D\$3}{\text{Vol\_1} \cdot (\$D\$3 - 1)}$

D5: $\quad \text{Omega} = \dfrac{\$B\$5 \cdot 2 \cdot 3.14159}{60}$

F5:
$$dt = \frac{3.14159}{Omega \cdot 180}$$

J5: ign_end = H4 + H3

F6:
$$Piston\_area = \frac{3.14159 \cdot \$D6 \cdot \$D6}{4}$$

H6: Cyl_swep_vol = Piston_area $\cdot$ 2 $\cdot$ B3

D7:
$$Volume\_1 = \frac{\$D\$3 \cdot \$H\$6}{\$D\$3 - 1}$$

F7: Vol_2 = Vol_1 - Cyl_swep_vol

D8: Air_mass_V1 = Volume_1 $\cdot$ H5

H8:
$$Fuel\_mass = \frac{\$H\$5 \cdot \$H\$6 \cdot \$H\$7}{\$F\$8}$$

R3:
$$Power\_in = \frac{\$N\$4 \cdot Engine\_omega}{4 \cdot 3.14159}$$

X374:
$$Power\_in = \frac{\$N\$4 \cdot Engine\_omega}{4 \cdot 3.14159}$$

B12:
$$Crank\_rotation\_rad = \frac{A12 \cdot 3.14159}{180}$$

C12: h_value = B3 $\cdot$ SIN(Crank_rotation_rad)

D12:
$$Sin\_phi = \frac{h\_value}{\$B\$4}$$

E12: Phi_rad = ASIN(Sin_phi)

F12:
$$Phi\_degrees = \frac{180 \cdot Phi\_rad}{3.14159}$$

G12:
$$Cos\_phi = \sqrt{1 - \frac{h\_value \cdot h\_value}{\$B\$4 \cdot \$B\$4}}$$

H12:
$$x\_Piston\_disp = \$B\$3 \cdot (1 - COS(Crank\_rotation\_rad)) - \$B\$4 \cdot (1 - Cos\_phi)$$

I12:
$$Vel\_5\_point\_MA = \frac{H10 - 8 \cdot H11 + 8 \cdot H13 - H14}{12 \cdot \$F\$5}$$

J12:
$$Acc\_5\_point\_MA = \frac{I10 - 8 \cdot I11 + 8 \cdot I13 - I14}{12 \cdot \$F\$5}$$

K12:
$$Volume = K11 - \$F\$6 \cdot (x\_Piston\_disp - H11)$$

L12:
$$Pressure\_Ugamma = L11 - \frac{\$F\$3 \cdot L11 \cdot (Volume - K11)}{K11}$$

M12:
$$Pressure\_from\_base = \$B\$7 \cdot e^{\left[\$F\$3 \cdot LN\left[\frac{Volume\_1}{Volume}\right]\right]}$$

M191:
$$Press\_Ignition\_Inst = \frac{\$D\$8 \cdot \$D\$4 \cdot \$N\$191}{K191}$$

M192:
$$Press\_after\_inst\_ign = \frac{Press\_Ignition\_Inst}{e^{\left[\$F\$3 \cdot LN\left[\frac{K192}{\$F\$7}\right]\right]}}$$

N12:
$$Temp\_deg\_K = \$J\$3 \cdot e^{\left[(\$F\$3 - 1) \cdot LN\left[\frac{\$K\$10}{Volume}\right]\right]}$$

N191:
$$Temp\_inst\_heat\_in = \$N\$190 + \frac{\$N\$4}{\$D\$8 \cdot \$L\$3}$$

N192:
$$Temp\_after\_inst\_input = Temp\_inst\_heat\_in \cdot e^{\left[(\$F\$3 - 1) \cdot LN\left[\frac{\$F\$7}{K192}\right]\right]}$$

O12:
$$Temp\_deg\_C = Temp\_deg\_K - 273$$

P12:
$$Prop\_heat\_released = ? \; IF\left[A12 < \$H\$3 , 0 , \left[1 - e^{\left[-5 \cdot e^{\left[3 \cdot LN\left[\frac{A12 - \$H\$3}{\$H\$4}\right]\right]}\right]}\right]\right]$$

Q12: $\text{Energy\_added\_J} = \$N\$4 \cdot \text{Prop\_heat\_released}$

R12: $\text{Energy\_increment\_added\_J} = \text{Energy\_added\_J} - Q11$

S12: $\text{Temp\_incremrnt\_deg\_K} = \dfrac{\text{Energy\_increment\_added\_J}}{\$D\$8 \cdot 714}$

T12: $\text{Calc\_R} = \dfrac{\text{Pressure\_from\_base} \cdot \text{Volume}}{\text{Temp\_deg\_K} \cdot \$D\$8}$

U12: $\text{Recalc\_T\_deg\_K} = U11 + \text{Temp\_deg\_K} - N11 + \text{Temp\_incremrnt\_deg\_K}$

V12: $\text{Query\_Recalc\_P} = \dfrac{\$D\$8 \cdot \$D\$4 \cdot \text{Recalc\_T\_deg\_K}}{\text{Volume}}$

W12: $\text{Recalc\_P\_Use} = W11 + \dfrac{\$D\$8 \cdot \$D\$4 \cdot S11 - W11 \cdot (\text{Volume} - K11)}{\text{Volume}}$

X12: $\text{PdV\_not\_for\_work} = \text{Recalc\_P\_Use} \cdot (\text{Volume} - K11)$

Y12: $\text{Temp\_incxfactor} = \dfrac{\text{Temp\_incremrnt\_deg\_K}}{1.0756}$

Z12: $\text{Temp\_incl\_factor} = U11 + \text{Temp\_deg\_K} - N11 + Y11$

AA12:
$$\text{Recalc\_dP} = \dfrac{-\$F\$3 \cdot AB11 \cdot (\text{Volume} - K11)}{K11} + \dfrac{(\$F\$3 - 1) \cdot \text{Energy\_increment\_added\_J} \cdot 1.0756}{\text{Volume}}$$

AB12: $\text{Recalc\_P} = AB11 + \text{Recalc\_dP}$

\$AB\$373: $\text{MEP} = \dfrac{\Sigma(AB10 : AB370)}{361}$

\$AB\$374: $\text{Power} = \dfrac{\text{MEP} \cdot 0.5 \cdot \$D\$6 \cdot \$D\$6 \cdot 2 \cdot \$B\$3 \cdot \text{Engine\_omega}}{8}$

AC12: $\text{Work\_done\_by\_piston} = (H11 - \text{x\_Piston\_disp}) \cdot (\text{Recalc\_P} - \$B\$7) \cdot \$F\$6$

28th June 2008.

9. Materials Selection

9.0 Chapter Contents

9.1 Introduction

Materials can conveniently be classified as:

- Metals
- Ceramics
- Polymers
- Composites

There are about 70 metals but only about 20 of these are of interest to engineers. They are not normally used when 'pure' but alloyed with other metals to give the required properties. There are many hundreds of alloys which are in use in various branches of engineering.

Organic materials, based on carbon, are very widespread - over a million organic compounds are known, some of them naturally occurring. However only a small proportion of organic materials are of interest from an engineering viewpoint. This still leaves a lot of plastics, but with a some knowledge many possibilities can quickly be eliminated.

A lot of recent developments in the materials field have concerned composite materials. Here two or more materials are combined to give quite specific properties, for example in fibre reinforced plastics where the reinforcement may be highly directional to provide high strength in a particular direction.

Because of the need to provide a reliable product, a great deal of material selection is based on past experience - a designer feels confident with a material that has been tried and tested in a previous or similar design. This approach risks products becoming out of date because new advances in materials are not incorporated - hence there is a need for an engineering designer to have a good understanding of a broad range of existing materials as well as being aware of developments in new materials.

As both the detail design and the manufacturing processes are dependent upon the choice of material, it is important that these three areas are considered at the same time - and this is one of the features of 'simultaneous' or 'concurrent' engineering. Some preliminary selection of material type may be made at the concept stage, or early on in the design, but most detail decisions, including processing, will need to be decided while the design is being detailed.

9.2 Material Requirements.

Some of the main materials properties that are of interest to engineers are shown in the table below.

Mechanical Properties	Thermal Properties	Resistance to Hostile Environments
Strength, UTS, Yield	Coefficient of thermal expansion	Moisture
Hardness	Thermal conductivity	Temperature extremes
Young's Modulus	Thermal shock resistance	Acids / alkalis
Ductility	Specific heat	Salt solution
Fatigue Strength		hydrogen attack
Fracture Toughness		Nuclear particles

As well as the properties listed above, there are a number of factors which will influence the choice of material:

1. Availability - sizes, minimum quantities.

2. Ease of manufacture - machinability, weldability.

3. Compatibility - electrochemical compatibility with other parts of the system.

4. Reliability - how consistent are the material properties. Measurements of fundamental properties such as Young's modulus and the UTS of metals will vary by + or - 3%. Other properties, such as yield strength and fatigue endurance strength will have greater variation, up to about + or - 8%. However coeficient of friction and wear rate experiments often have much wider variation + or - 30% not being uncommon! For plastics, time dependent issues are involved with many mechanical properties, which further adds to the spread of results. Giving answers to calculations involving material properties to several significant figures demonstrates a lack of understanding, not careful precision calculations! Two significant figures are probably all that is warranted.

5. Cost - although 5th in this list, this factor may well be used first to eliminate a large number of possible options.

6. Recycleability - increasing environmental concern (and resulting legislation) worldwide is driving manufacturers to use materials that can be recycled with minimum difficulty.

9.3 Optimisation - Minimising Mass - Performance Indices
An important objective in almost all mechanical engineering design is to minimise the mass of the component(s) and system(s) as this offers many advantages:

- minimises raw material costs, purchase and delivery
- minimises distribution costs
- helps to reduce the energy required to operate any moving component(s)

Selecting the optimum material is a a vital early step in most design work and a simple example is given below.
Engineering elements perform a physical function which can be defined, they have to satisfy a functional requirement. In the example below, a structural element, length L, is required to carry a tensile load, P, which will not cause the stress to exceed:

material failure stress / specified factor of safety.

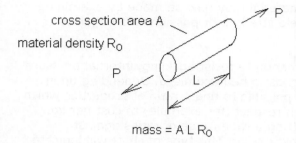

cross section area A

material density R_O

P

P

L

mass $= A \, L \, R_O$

A minimum mass is required.

There are three aspects to this design:

- The functional requirement, F - carrying the specified load P
- The geometry, G - the length of the strut
- The properties of the material, M

Then the performance index, p, is a function of F, G and M.
$$p = f \, (F, G, M)$$

F, G and M are normally independent and separable so the optimum material properties, M, are independent of F and G. The optimum choice of M is therefore the optimum for any value of F and G.

Looking at the example where a minimum mass is required, the maximum allowable working stress is given by:

$P/A = \mathrm{Sigma}_{failure}$ / factor of safety

$A = \mathrm{FoS} \; P \; / \; \mathrm{Sigma}_{failure}$

mass, $m = \mathrm{FoS} \; P \; L \; R_o \; / \; \mathrm{Sigma}_{failure}$

rearranging: $m = (\mathrm{FoS} \; P)(L)(R_o \; / \; \mathrm{Sigma}_{failure})$

(functional requirement - the load that can be carried safely)(specified geometry - length)(material properties)

The highest performance index, p, is given by minimum mass which is given by maximum of the ratio:

$$\text{Sigma}_{\text{failure}} / R_o$$

A preliminary choice of material may now be made by examining plots of failure stress (yield strength or possibly UTS) against density.

Other functional requirements, to resist buckling, internal pressure etc., result in different ratios to be maximised. Depending upon these requirements, it is possible to find a ratio of properties which should be maximised with respect (for example) to cost per kg. Charts are published plotting a wide range of ratios against characteristics such as cost per kg. This type of chart will indicate types of materials which may meet the requirments. In many cases the groups cover quite a wide range of properties and it will be necessary to carry out detailed assessment of some specific materials in groups of materials to enable an optimum (or near optimum) selection to be made.

Further information about this approach can be found in ASM Handbook, Vol 20 - Materials Selection and Design, 1997.

Once a designer has an idea of the required ranges of some of the material properties that are required, a literature or www search can be carried out, using, for example, Matweb (http://www.matweb.com)

9.4 Detailed Evaluation of Materials.
Like all aspects of design, materials selection involves making compromises. It is desirable that materials selection is based on some sort of quantitive assessment. Once the range of possible materials has been narrowed down, the final decision can be made with the aid of an evaluation matrix, where the relative importance of conflicting requirements can be quantified.

While the material choice is being decided, the production process must be considered - this should include details of finishing and any inspection procedures or statistical process control to be applied.

For safety critical items, the inspection methodology, techniques and frequency of inspection of completed parts, and also for parts during their lifetimes, will need to be specified.

Often some significant requirement will dominate the choice of material type and limit the viable options to a narrow range. For example if one wished to manufacture very large numbers of car body shells at low cost in the immediate future, then the only feasible option is fine grain low carbon steel sheet. The exact grade, sheet thickness and processing will depend upon the strength required and how important weight saving is considered to be.

9.5 Ferrous Metals

9.5.1 Introduction
In the early days of the automobile irons and steels, along with timber, were extensively used in vehicles. Although alternative materials, such as plastics and lighter metals are being increasingly used in automotive manufacturing and timber is now only rarely used, ferrous metals continue to be widely used within the automotive industry and in engineering more generally. The versatility of ferrous materials means that they are likely to continue in wide use in many industrial sectors for the forseeable future.

The versatility of steels can be seen from the fact that the Ultimate Tensile Strength (UTS) of steel products can vary from about 250MPa (for 'mild steel' - unalloyed with no heat treatment or work hardening) to over 2000MPa for highly alloyed and heat treated steels.
The lower strength steels are very ductile, particularly when manufactured to give fine grain size which makes them suitable for pressing and deep drawing for vehicle bodyshells and casings and enclosures for all types of equipment.

The additions of a variety of alloying elements, see Appendix 9.1, can significantly alter the properties steels. As an example low alloy steel starts to lose strength at temperatures above about 200°C, but when tungsten or molybdenum, carbon and some other elements are present, high strength can be maintained to temperatures in excess of 500°C. These types of steels are referred to as tool steels and further information can be found in Appendix 9.2.

Another important property of steels is the fact that certain materials can be diffused into the surface of steel at elevated temperatures, often forming a complex compound. The most important material is carbon, which when present in appropriate quantities and cooled at an appropriate rate, provides a very hard carbide structure. Nitrogen can also be diffused into the surface of steels at elevated temperatures and produces nitrides and / or carbonitrides, which as well as providing hardness also provide improved wear resistance and increased fatigue strength. Information about such processes is given in Appendix 9.3.

9.5.2 Plain Carbon Steels

Plain carbon steels are relatively cheap, but have a number of property limitations. These include:

(i) Cannot be strengthened above about 690 MN/m^2 without loss of ductility and impact resistance.
(ii) Not very hardenable i.e. the depth of hardening is limited.
(iii) Low corrosion and oxidation resistance.
(iv) Must be quenched very rapidly to obtain a fully martensitic structure, leading to the possibility of quench distortion and cracking.
(v) Have poor impact resistance at low temperatures.

Alloy steels containing a number of alloying elements have been developed to overcome these deficiencies, albeit at extra cost.

Plain carbon steels contain only iron and carbon and less than 0.5% Mn and less than 0.5% Si.

Low carbon steels contain less than 0.25% carbon, medium carbon between 0.25% and 0.6% carbon.

High carbon steels between 0.6% to 1.4% carbon.

Small additions of other alloying elements give high strength low alloy (HSLA) steels and some tool steels, while higher additions produce tool steels, heat resisting steels and stainless steels.

The principal alloying elements used are: manganese (Mn), nickel (Ni), chromium (Cr), molybdenum (Mo), tungsten (W), vanadium (V), cobalt (Co), silicon (Si), boron (B), copper (Cu), aluminium (Al), titanium (Ti) and niobium (Nb).

9.5.3 General Effects of Alloying Elements - for further details see Appendix 9.1

i) Increase hardness in solid solution (in ferrite) without decreasing the ductility as much as carbon does.
ii) Reduce the critical cooling velocity (except Co) by making the transformation to the equilibrium phase slower. Alloy steels may therefore be hardened by an oil or even air quench, reducing the risk of cracking or distortion that can result from a rapid water quench. Most elements also lower the M_s and M_f temperatures to below room temperature, leading to some 'retained austenite' in the quenched structure.

Carbon content %	Alloy content %	Critical cooling velocity Deg C per sec
0.42	0.55 Mn	550
0.40	1.60 Mn	50
0.42	1.12 Ni	450
0.40	4.80 Ni	85
0.38	2.64 Cr	10

iii) Either increase or decrease the alpha to gamma transition temperature. Elements are either ferrite stabilising e.g. Cr (BCC), W (BCC), V (BCC), Mo (BCC), Al (FCC), Si (diamond cubic) or austenite stabilising e.g. Ni (FCC), Mn (diamond cubic), Co (HCP/FCC>690K), Cu (FCC) and also carbon.

iv) Some form hard, stable carbides. E.g. Cr, W, V, Mo, Ti, Nb, and others such as Mn help stabilise carbides. The carbides may be of the type Cr_7C_3, W_2C, Mo_2C and VC or more complex like Fe_4W_2C etc.

v) Some cause graphitisation of iron carbide (cementite) e.g. silicon, Ni, Co, Al. For this reason these elements are not added to high carbon steels unless counteracted by a strong carbide former.

vi) They confer the characteristic property of the alloying element on the steel. E.g. chromium confers corrosion resistance when more than about 12% is added to a steel, rendering it a stainless steel.

vii) They affect the rate of grain growth at high temperature. Cr speeds up grain growth rate, so it is important not to overheat high chromium steels as coarse grains can give brittle properties. Elements like V, Ti, Nb, Al and Ni slow down grain growth rates and so are used in case hardening steels.

viii) They alter the eutectoid composition and temperature.

ix) They improve mechanical properties such as tensile strength. Hardness is improved due to carbides present. Strength is increased by elements dissolved in ferrite and toughness improved by finer grain structures.

9.5.4 Types of Steels:
Alloy steels are generally classified as low-alloy steels or high-alloy steels. Low-alloy steels have similar microstructures and heat treatment requirements to plain carbon steels and contain up to 3

or 4 % of alloying additions in order to increase strength, toughness or hardenability. High-alloy steels have structures and heat treatments that differ considerably from plain carbon steels. A summary of a some selected types steels is given below.

i) **Low alloy constructional steels:** As well as carbon, these contain additions of Mn, Ni, Cr, Mo etc. Nickel strengthens ferrite in solution but also causes graphitisation of carbides. For this reason it is usually accompanied by strong carbide stabilisers such as chromium, which also strengthens ferrite and increases hardenability. The Ni is usually in the majority, with maximum amounts 4.25% Ni and 1.25%Cr, often resulting in air hardenable steels. Tempering in the range 250°C - 400°C can result in 'temper brittleness', but this can be minimised by additions of 0.3% Mo giving 'nickel-chrome-moly' steels, used in axles, shafts, gears, con-rods etc. Some Mn can be substituted for more expensive Ni. (See Appendix 9.1 for more details).

Low alloy steels can be further subdivided as shown below:

> **a) Low-carbon steels or mild steels.**
> These are used for lightly stressed components in general engineering, often in sheet form where processing includes: welding, bending and forming. For sheet metal components formed by drawing, bending and stretching, fine grain size assists in maintaining a good surface. Some of the popular specifications are 040A10, 045Mb, 070M20, 080A15 and 080M15. Yield strengths are typically in the region of 200 MPa.
>
> **b)Low-carbon free cutting steels.**
> These are the most popular type of steel for the production of turned components where machineability and surface finish are important. Applications include automotive and general engineering. A commonly used specification is 230M07.
>
> **c)Carbon and carbon-manganese case hardening steels.**
> These steels are suitable for components that require a wear resisting surface and a tough core. Specifications include 045A10, 045Mb, 080M15, 210M15, 214M15.
>
> **d) Medium-carbon and carbon-manganese steels.**
> These offer greater strength than mild steels and respond to heat treatment. Tensile strengths in the range 700-1000 MPa can be attained. Applications include gears, racks, pinions, shafts, gudgeon pins, rollers, bolts and nuts. Specifications include 080M30, 080M40, 080A42, 080M50, 070M55, 150M36.

e) Alloy case-hardening steels.

These are used when a high load carrying capacity combined with a hard wear resisting surface is required. The alloying elements provides superior mechanical properties in comparison with carbon and carbon-manganese case hardening steels. Typical applications include gears, cams, rolled and transmission components. Types include 635M15, 655M13, 665M17, 805M20 and 832M13.

f) Alloy direct hardening steels.

These steels include alloying elements such as Ni, Cr, Mo and V and are used for applications where high strength and shock resistance are important. Types include 605M36, 708M40, 709M40, 817M40 and 826M40.

g) Spring steels.

These usually contain 0.6-0.9 % carbon together with similar quantities of manganese to provide appropriate hardenability (US specs. 1065, 1085). About 0.35% silicon is also included to resist 'sag'. About 1% Vanadium is also included in some specifications and small additions of chromium and /or molybdenum may also be made. (US specs. 6150, 8660, 9260).

h) High Strength Low Alloy (HSLA) or microalloyed steels.

A wide range of these steels is available offering yield strengths between 200 and 1000 MPa, according to alloy content and processing. These steels contain less than 0.1% each of elements such as niobium, vanadium and titanium to promote grain refinement or precipitation hardening. Increasingly used in automotive, offshore, pressure vessels and pipeline applications, typically with a tensile strength of about 500 MPa.

ii) Alloy tool and die steels, (B5970 and B54659)

These acquire hardness and wear resistance by incorporating carbides that are harder than cementite, while retaining strength and some toughness. They also have high hardenability and the ability to resist the tempering effects of use in hot working dies and from frictional heating in high speed machining operations. Alloying additions include Cr, W, Mo and V, which are strong carbide formers and also stabilise ferrite and martensite.

A typical composition is 18%W, 4%Cr, 1%V, 0.8%C. Quenching from high temperatures (1300^0C) is necessary, in order to dissolve as much W and C in austenite, for maximum hardness and heat resistance, followed by heating to 300^0C - 400^0C to transform any retained austenite to martensite then to 550^0C to relieve internal stresses and produce carbide particles in a toughened martensite matrix. This martensite is then temper resistant up to 700^{0}C.

9.5.5 Stainless steels:
The addition of more than about 12% Cr renders a steel 'stainless' or corrosion resistant because of a passive layer of chromium oxide Cr_2O_3 on the surface. Steels containing large amounts of Cr are ferritic, as Cr is a ferrite stabiliser. Stainless steels can be classified into three main types.

i) Ferritic stainless steels:
These contain 12% to 25% Cr and less than 0.1% carbon. They are ferritic up to the melting point, i.e. austenite never forms, and therefore cannot be quench hardened to give martensite. They can be work hardened but are oniy ductile above the ductile- brittle transition temperature found in BCC metals.
Applications include domestic and automotive trim, catering equipment and exhaust systems.
Specifications include 403S17 and 430S17.

ii) Martensitic stainless steels:
These contain 12% to 25% Cr and 0.1% to 1.5%C. The higher carbon content restores the alpha to gamma transition temperature by making the gamma loop larger. This means that the steel can be heated into the austenite region and quenched to give a martensitic structure, giving tensile strengths in the range 550-1000 MN/m^2. Hardenability is generally high enough that hardening can be achieved by air-cooling. Uses include knives, cutting tools, dies etc. Specifications include 410S21, 420S29, 420S45, 431S29,416S21, 416S41, 416S37 and 441S49.

iii) Austenitic stainless steels:
These contain both Cr and Ni, and since Ni has a greater effect on the alpha to gamma transition temperature this can be reduced to below room temperature, and the austenitic FCC phase is retained. This gives a stainless non-magnetic steel that, being FCC, is more ductile and can be worked to produce deep shapes used in chemical plant, kitchenware and architectural work. Nickel assists the ductility by resisting the grain growth promoted by Cr, although severe cold work can produce martensite from the austenite. Fast cooling depresses the alpha to gamma transition temperature, giving austenite for as low as 7% Ni, while fast heating raises it, (thermal hysteresis).
The 300 series stainless steels offer the highest resistance to corrosion. While these steels can not be hardened by heat treatment, they do undergo considerable work hardening.

A common alloy is 18% Cr, 8% Ni. Depending on the presence of other ferrite stabilising and austenite stabilising elements and cooling rates, a variety of microstructures can result.
Applications include the food, chemical, gas and oil industries as well as medical equipment and domestic appliances. Specifications include 302S31, 304S15, 316S1 I, 316S31, 320S31, 321S31, 303531, 325S31, 303S42 and 326S36.

Welding Stainless Steels
Welding can lead to the problem of 'weld decay' unless the steel is 'stabilised' by additions of about 1% Nb or Ti. In the heat affected zone (HAZ), where the steel is subjected to temperatures in the range 550°C to 850°C, the carbon present can react with the Cr to form chrome carbide $Cr_{36}C_6$ precipitates on the grain boundaries. This depletes the chromium oxide Cr_2O_3 on the surface and in corrosive conditions the area around the grain boundaries become anodic and corrodes. This problem can be alleviated in one of three ways:

- (i) Resolutionise the precipitates by heating above 930°C and cool quickly through the critical range 550°C to 850°C to allow insufficient time for the transformation to the carbide to start.
- (ii) Only use very low carbon stainless steel (e.g. 304L, 316L), since the time to transformation is much longer, or
- (iii) Use stabilised steels containing 1% to 2% Nb or Ti, both of which are stronger carbide formers than Cr, thus leaving the Cr in solution and as Cr_2O_3 on the surface.

Steels for Exhaust Systems
For many years vehicle exhaust systems were made from low carbon steel that was easy to form and weld which was finished by some coating to assist corrosion resistance, often aluminium paint. However customers are increasingly requiring better quality and longer life vehicles and specially developed stainless steels with good corrosion and creep resistance are now being used. Ferritic 11% Cr alloys are used in cool end components and 17 - 20% Cr ferritic alloys and austenitic Cr - Ni alloys are used in hot end components.

9.5.6 Marageing Steels: These are iron-nickel alloys, a typical example being 18%Ni, 8%Co, 4%Mo and up to 0.8%Ti, with less than 0.05% carbon. Heat treatment involves solution treatment at 800°C - 850°C followed by quenching of the austenite to give a BCC martensitic structure. This is less brittle than the BCC martensite found in plain carbon steels because of the low carbon. Ageing at 450°C - 500°C for 2 hours produces finely dispersed precipitates of complex intermetallics such as $TiNi_3$ resulting in tensile strengths around 2000 MN/m^2. Alter solutionising, they are soft enough to machine easily, before ageing, which can compensate for higher materials cost. They are relatively tough, with good corrosion resistance and good weldability since they do not air harden so rapidly as some steels. Uses include aircraft undercarriage components, dies, tools, engine parts etc.

9.5.7 Hadfields manganese steel: This is a high alloy steel that contains 12%-14% Mn and 1% C. It is austenitic at all temperatures and therefore non-magnetic. It has a unique property in that when the surface is abraded or deformed, it greatly increases surface hardness while retaining a tough core. For this reason it is used in pneumatic drill bits, excavator bucket teeth, rock crusher jaws, ball mill linIngs and railway points and switches. Water quenched from 1050°C to retain carbon in solution, the soft core has a strength of 850 MN/m^2, ductility of 40% and a Brinell hardness of 200, but after abrasion this rises to 550 BHN. The reason for the rapid rise in surface hardening is uncertain, though martensite formation or, more likely, work hardening have been proposed.

9.5.8 Steels for Cryogenic Service
For vessels operating from from room temperature down to the temperature of liquid nitrogen (-195°C) a 9% nickel alloy steel has been developed. ASTM specifies a minimum yield strength of 515 MPa, a minimum tensile strength of 690 to 825 MPa and a minimum Charpy impact value of 20.3 J at -195°C.

For service down to lower temperatures austenitic stainless steels must be used.

9.5.9 Classification of Steels
These notes provide a brief introduction to UK and US specifications for ferrous metals, their properties and applications.

Most steels used in engineering have very similar Young's modulus, 210 GPa; density, 7800 kg per cubic metre; and Poisson's ratio, 0.28. The shear modulus is about 80 GPa, but there is some variation in this figure. Stainless steels and tool steels have slightly different values.

UK and US specifications are both used in the UK and are outlined below.

The coding system used for steels in the UK is given in British Standard 970. Originally 'EN' numbers were used, and can still be found in some older books, but the current standard, developed in the 1970s and 1980s, uses a six-digit designation, for example

070M20. The first three digits of the designation denote the family of steels to which the alloy belongs:

000-199 Carbon and carbon-manganese steels. The first three figures indicate 100 times the mean manganese content.

200-240 Free cutting steels where the second and third digits represent 100 times the minimum or mean sulphur content.

250 Silicon-manganese spring steels.

300-399 Stainless, heat resisting and valve steels.

500-999 Alloy steels in groups according to alloy type.

The fourth digit of the designation is a letter (A, H or M) denoting that the steel will be supplied to meet the following requirements:

A: The steel will be supplied to close limits of chemical composition (no mechanical or hardenability properties specified).

H: A combination of hardenability and chemical analysis.

M: A combination of mechanical properties and chemical analysis.

Where the fourth letter is 'S', it denotes a stainless steel specification.

The fifth and sixth digit represent 100 times the mean carbon content of the steel (this does **not** apply to stainless steel specifications). For example 080A40 denotes a carbon-manganese steel, supplied to close limits of chemical composition, containing 0.7-0.9 per cent manganese and 0.4 per cent carbon.

It should be noted that the specifications 251A60 and 251H60 differ in the chemical composition tolerance bands which are narrower in 251A60 than in 251H60. This is the typical difference between A and H series steels.

9.5.10 Below is a Comparison of some old and new BS steel specifications.

BS 970 designation	UTS(MN/m^2)	Yield stress(MN/m^2)	Old BS EN number	Approx. Eqiv. AISI US 4 fig Spec.
230M07	475		1A	
080M15	450a	330a	32C	
070M20	560a	440a	3B	
210M15	490		32M	
215M15	720		202	
080M30	620a	480a	6	1030
080M40	660a	530a	8	1040
635M15	770 min		351	
655M13	1000 min		36	
665M17	770 min		34	4620
605M36, 1.5%Mn 0.25%Mo	700-850 a	540 a	16	
709M40, 1%Cr 0.3%Mo	700-1200 a	550 - 950 a	19	4140
817M40, 1.2%Cr 0.3%Mo	850 - 1000 a	700 a	24	4340
410S21	700 - 850a	a	56A	
431S29	850 - 1000	a	57	
403S17	400 min	280		
430S17, 17% Cr	400 min	280		
304S15, 10%Ni 18%Cr	500a	250a	58E	
316S11, 11Ni 17Cr 3Mo +Ti	500a			
303S31	500a		58M	

Note 'a' - varies according to processing / heat treatment.

Reference: British Standards Institute, BS 970, various dates.

9.5.11 US Specifications

In the USA a number of 4 digit code systems (mainly identical) were developed by interested organisations: SAE (Society of Automotive Engineers), AISI (American Iron and Steel Institute). These have been brought together in a Unified Numbering System for Metals and Alloys (UNS) by the ASTM (American Society for Testing Materials).

The UNS uses a letter prefix to designate the material, eg: G for carbon and alloy steels, A for aluminium alloys, C for copper-base alloys and S for stainless or corrosion-resistant steels.

For the steels, the first two numbers following the letter prefix indicate the composition, excluding the carbon content.

The second number pair refers to the approximate carbon content. Thus, G10400 is a plain carbon steel with a carbon content of 0.37 to 0.44 percent. The fifth number following the prefix is used for special situations. For example, the old designation AISI 52100 represents a chromium alloy with about 100 points of carbon. The UNS designation is G52986.

The old 4 - digit AISI type specifications (omitting the initial 'G' and the final digit) are still in use.

The UNS designations for stainless steels, prefix S, utilize the older AISI designations for the first three numbers following the prefix. The next two numbers are reserved for special purposes. The first number of the group indicates the approximate composition. Thus 2 is a chromium-nickel-manganese steel, 3 is a chromium-nickel steel, and 4 is a chromium alloy steel. Sometimes stainless steels are referred to by their alloy content. Thus S30200 is often called an 18-8 stainless steel, meaning 18 percent chromium and 8 percent nickel.

Some of the main groups of steels and their SAE - AISI specifications are given in the table below:

Spec.	Alloying elements	Spec.	Alloying elements
10xx	Plain carbon, non sulphurised and non phosphorised	46xx	Nickel molybdenum: 1.75% Ni, 0.25% Mo

11xx	Free cutting carbon steel, re-sulphurised	48xx	Nickel molybdenum: 3.5% Ni, 0.25 Mo
13xx	Manganese steels: 1.75% Mn	51xx	Medium chromium: 0.8 - 1.0% Cr
23xx	Nickel steels: 3.5%	52xx	Chromium, high carbon: 1.45% Cr, 1.00% C min.
25xx	Nickel steels: 5%	61xx	Chromium vanadium steels: 0.8%Cr, 0.1%V
31xx	1.25% Ni, 0.6% Cr	86xx	Chromium nickel molybdenum steels: 0.55% Ni, 0.5% Cr, 0.2% Mo
32xx	1.75% Ni, 1% Cr	87xx	Chromium nickel molybdenum steels: 0.55% Ni, 0.5% Cr, 0.25% Mo
33xx	3.5% Ni, 1.5% Cr	92xx	Manganese silicon: 0.8% Mn, 2.0% Si
40xx	Molybdenum: 0.2% & 0.25%	93xx	Nickel chromium molybdenum: 3.25% Ni, 1.2% Cr, 0.12 Mo
41xx	Chromium molybdenum	94xx	Manganese nickel chromium molybdenum: 0.95 - 1.35% Mn, 0.45% Ni, 0.4% Cr, 0.12% Mo
43xx	Nickel chromium molybdenum: 1.82% Ni, 0.5 and 0.8% Cr, 0.25% Mo	97xx	Nickel chromium molybdenum: 0.55% Ni, 0.2% Cr, 0.2% Mo
XXBXX.B	Boron steels	98xx	Nickel chromium molybdenum: 1.00% Ni, 0.8% Cr, 0.25% Mo

Commonly used classes are 23xx, 25xx, 31xx, 32xx, 33xx, 41xx, 43xx, 46xx and 48xx.

The 4140 and 4340 are two classes that have been developed for use at high strength levels, UTS values of up to 2000 MPa can be achieved by appropriate heat treatment.

9.5.12 Cast Steels
Steel castings are made in sizes from 1 N to over 2000000 N. Steel is not as fluid as other casting metals and care must be taken to have adequate thickness to ensure mould filling. Normally the minimum wall thickness is 6 mm, but with special processing thinner walls are acceptable and in investment castings section thicknesses of 1.5 mm tapering down to 0.75 mm are common.

Cast steels can be classified as low C (C less than 0.2 %), medium carbon (C between 0.2 and 0.5 %), high carbon (C greater than 0.5 %), low alloy (total alloy less than 8 %) and high alloy (total alloy greater than 8 %).

cast steels do not exhibit the directional properties of wrought and forged steels and as most engineering properties of cast steels are similar to the averaged properties of wrought and forged steels, it may be advantageous to use cast steel components to withstand multi-directional loading rather than a wrought or forged component.

9.5.13 Cast Irons
9.5.13.1 Introduction
Casting of metals is a very long established manufacturing method and many variations have been developed over the years to cater for new materials and products.

The term cast iron covers a wide range of iron-carbon-silicon alloys containing from 2 - 4% carbon and from 0.5 to 3% silicon. Alloys frequently also contain varying percentages of sulphur and phosphorus and alloying elements such as manganese, chromium, molybdenum, copper and titanium. Depending upon the type and grade the content of these elements will be tightly controlled. To achieve the desired properties it is also necessary to control the processing of the molten metal and its cooling rate.

Cast iron is classified into five types according to the graphite morphology:

☐ Grey iron
☐ Ductile iron
☐ Malleable iron
☐ Compacted graphite iron

☐ White iron

9.5.13.2 Grey Iron, also known as flake iron
Grey iron castings have been produced for more than 2000 years. When the composition and cooling rate are appropriate, the carbon precipitates in the form of graphite flakes that are interconnected. Grey iron fractures primarily along the graphite and the fracture appears grey, hence the name 'grey iron'.
The cooling rate during solidification plays a major role in the size and shape of the graphite flakes. The tensile strength of a single piece of gray iron can vary by as much as 70 MPa, thinner sections, which cool quicker, being stronger than thicker sections.

The graphite flakes impart some very useful properties: excellent wear resistance, machinability and damping capacity. On the negative side the material gray iron has almost zero ductility and very low impact strength.

Material	Relative damping capacity
Grey iron, coarse flake	100-500
Grey iron, fine flake	20-100
Ductile iron	5-20
Pure iron	5
Eutectoid steel	4
Aluminium	0.4

The tensile strength of grey iron is normally between 150 and 450 MPa.

The ease of casting, excellent machinability and wear resistance were the characteristics which made grey iron very popular in the early and middle 1900s for use as cylinder heads, cylinder blocks, differential and gearbox casings.

9.5.13.3 Ductile iron, also known as spheroidal graphite (sg) iron, nodular iron
Ductile iron was invented in the late 1940s and patented by the International Nickel Company. By adding magnesium to the molten metal under controlled conditions, the graphite structure becomes spheroidal or nodular. This form of graphite results in significantly better mechanical properties than those of grey iron, however the thermal conductivity and the machinability of ductile iron is lower than the values for grey iron.

The tensile strengths of of ductile irons varies from 400 to over 800MPa according to grade, while the elongation reduces from 18% for the lowest strength grade to 2.0% for the highest stength grade.

Austempered Ductile Iron (ADI)
Austempering as a treatment for alloy steels was discovered in the 1930s. The main advantages are that although the structure formed (bainite - acicular ferrite with carbide needles) is not as hard as martensite (about 50 Rc compared to about 60 Rc) which forms during a conventional quenching process, the structure is much tougher and because the cooling is interrupted, there is less distortion. In irons the high silicon content suppresses the precipitation of the carbide phase and a lamellar structure of acicular ferrite and high carbon austenite is formed.

With unalloyed irons, very rapid quenching from the autenitising temperature - even of small section thicknesses - is necessary to to avoid the precipitation of ferrite or pearlite. By incorporating alloying elements that lengthen the ferrite and pearlite transformation times, slower cooling rates, such as can be obtained by molten salt bath quenching or forced air cooling, can be used. The most effective alloying addition is molybdenum, but additionally copper and / or nickel may also be added as may limited ammounts of manganese. The material retains the nodular graphite distribution of ductile iron, but the matrix is acicular ferrite in a high carbon austenite. The lower strength grades have UTS values of 800MPa with elongation 10%, much superior to the grey irons and the conventional ductile irons. Higher strength grades have UTS values up to 1400MPa
The fatigue endurance strength of austempered low alloy irons is about 0.35 times the UTS for UTS values below 800 MPa, for higher UTS values the rate of increase of fatigue strength is less.
A lot of detailed information can be found in reference C3.

The advantageous mechanical properties combined with the ability to cast parts means that these irons are replacing plain carbon and low alloy steels for many components.

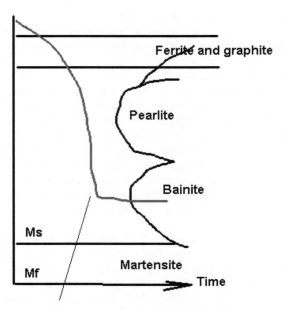

Ms

Mf

Ferrite and graphite

Pearlite

Bainite

Martensite

Time

**Representation of austempering
on hypothetical CCT diag.**

9.5.13.4 Malleable Iron

Whiteheart malleable iron was invented in Europe at the beginning of the 19th century, blackheart malleable iron was invented in the USA. As cast the material has no free graphite, but when subjected to a prolonged annealing process the graphite is present as irregularly shaped nodules called temper carbon. The properties are similar to ductile iron and as the cost of the prolonged annealing process (up to 30 hours) means these irons are expensive, their use is now very limited.

9.5.13.5 Compacted graphite iron (CGI)

CGI was developed in the 1970's - it has a structure intermediate between those of grey flake iron and nodular ductile iron. CGI can be made consistently by the Bruhl Oxycast route or the SinterCast method. This material was developed to provide an iron that did not need extensive alloying but would be stronger than grey iron while being easier to machine than nodular iron. CGI's typically have a 35% greater stiffness and 75% higher tensile strength than grey iron and a higher fatigue strength than aluminium at automobile engine operating temperatures. Tensile strengths between 250 and 450 MPa, ref. C2, are available (yield strengths 175 to 315 MPa). The first significant automotive application, in 2003, for this material was for the cylinder blocks of the diesel engine being developed by PSA (Peugeot Citroen Group) and Ford to power their luxury cars. Using this material means that wall thicknesses need only be half those needed when using with flake cast iron. The block has a weight of only 60 kg, but is stronger and stiffer.

Much development work has concentrated on machining (high power is needed and clamping must be done carefully to avoid distortion while machining) and this can now be done satisfactorily.

9.5.14. Cast Irons for Crankshafts

Crankshafts suffer cyclic loading so the fatigue endurance strength of the material is critical to their performance. The highest quality crakshafts are forged in alloy steel and heat treated, however this is expensive, both from material and processing aspects especially for large scale production. For large scale production casting offers cost savings and for many years cast irons have been used for some automombile petrol engine crankshafts. The significant improvements in the properties of cast irons now available means that use of cast irons is increasing.

For cast irons a key factor determining the fatigue performance is the distribution of the graphite in the structure. In grey or flake irons, the graphite is distributed as long thin flakes, many of which will be exposed on any machined surface. These provide large numbers of in-built surface defects from which fatigue cracks can grow. Hence the fatigue endurance strength of such irons is quite low. The presence of these flakes also means that such irons are relatively insensitive to notches.

Fatigue testing of ferrous materials indicates a stress level below which no failure occurs, however many load cycles are applied, this is called the fatigue endurance strength or endurance limit. Normally the number of cycles to reach this limit is between 10^6 and 10^7 and if a test piece lasts this long it is assumed that it will last indefinitely. However some failures of cast iron have occurred after more than 10^7 load cycles and onsequently fatigue testing carried out by BCIRA is done on the basis of 2×10^7 cycles (ref. C1).

The ratio of fatigue endurance strength/UTS for cast iron in reversed bending is between 0.33 and 0.47 (ref. C1). Alloying additions and heat treatment which raise the UTS will normally not improve this ratio. Fillet rolling / surface rolling does normally improve the fatigue performance.

For many applications nodular irons are superior to other types of iron and can be processed to have mechanical properties similar to those of low and medium carbon steels (UTS: 370 - 800 MPa, 0.2% proof stress: 230 - 460 MPa, ref. C1). This has resulted in considerable increase in the production and use of nodular irons for items such as crank shafts for car engines where reasonable strength combined with the capability for economical large scale production is more important than obtaining the maximum possible strength.

9.6 Aluminium Alloys
9.6.1 Introduction
Aluminium in sheet form is cold rolled to a thickness between 0.2 and 6 mm, though plate is available in thicknesses up to 150mm. The low strength of pure aluminium means that it is used mainly for coatings and decorative purposes.

Most aluminium alloys used in engineering have very similar Young's modulus: about 70 GPa and density: 2700 - 2800 kg per cubic metre, about one third that of steel. Aluminium is often considered as a substitute for steel, however the lower E value means that structure stiffness will need to be checked as well as strength and manufacturing processes.
The potential savings in weight when compared to steels mean that aluminium alloys are increasingly being used in automotive and rail carriage applications

Similar specifications are in use in the UK and US for wrought alloys, based on 4 digits. Casting alloys in the US use 1XX.X etc coding system whereas in the UK LM numbers are used.

9.6.2 Guide to Wrought Alloys
The wide range of alloys available can broadly split into two groups, the work hardening alloys and the heat treatable alloys.
In the notes below some indication is given of 0.2% proof stress and UTS, for rolled plate, but these are dependent upon processing/temper.

9.6.3 Work Hardening Alloys
Alloys in this group harden and increase in strength as they are cold-rolled (or worked). Any one alloy, therefore, can have different strength and ductility properties depending upon how much cold-working has been imposed. The degree of cold-working is denoted in the alloy designation by a suffix letter (H) and a digit from 1 to 8 indicating increasing strength.

Maximum ductility, often desirable for subsequent forming operations, is obtained by annealing - a process in which the metal is heated to a temperature of around 360^0C to remove the effects of any cold-working. Annealed metal is denoted by the suffix '0' in the alloy designation.

1XXX: Commercially pure Aluminium, 99% pure and greater.

1050, 1080, 1200: These are easily formed and joined, but have the lowest strength charactenstics of all the alloys. Highly resistant to weathering and to chemical attack, these alloys are ideal for chemical processing plant applications where strength is not critical; pressings requiring high ductility, foil and many paneling applications.

3XXX: Manganese alloys

3103, 3105. 3103 is a popular alloy that offers higher strength than commercial purity metal but which retains excellent ductility, good corrosion resistance and joining properties. The alloy is widely used in the building and transport industries. 3003 aluminium foil 0.04, 0.06 or 0.08 mm thick is converted into honeycomb and used with outer skins of aluminium or plastic for lightweight panelling in avaition and other transport applications. 3105 can be considered to be a "Green Alloy," being manufactured mainly from recycled material. The finished sheet and strip has consistent mechanical properties and forming characteristics. This alloy is particularly suitable for painting, making it popular in the sign making and building products industries. Anodising is not recommended.

5XXX: Magnesium containing alloys.

5005: Used for decorative and architectural uses where good anodising quality is required.

5251, 5083: These two are another step up in strength. They respond well to MIG and TIG welding and have particularly good corrosion resistance to salt water Of the two, 5083 is the stronger and is ideal for high strength welded applications such as marine components, rail and road transport, cryogenic structures and a variety of pressure vessels.

9.6.4 Heat-Treatable Alloys
The strongest of the aluminium alloys are those that gain strength by special heat-treatment processes. The alloys are identified by the suffix 'T' plus the addition of digits denoting variation of heat treatment.

2XXX: Copper containing alloys.

2014A: One of the most widely used heat treatable alloys, it offers a high strength with excellent machinability. It is widely used in highly stressed aircraft applications where strength to weight ratio is critical. The alloy has only fair corrosion resistance and corrosion

is a problem in aircraft. For other applications it is often specified with a pure aluminium cladding. It does not respond well to MIG and TIG welding.
0.2% Proof stress: 430 MPa, UTS: 480 MPa.

6XXX: Magnesium - silicon containing alloys.

6082: This medium/high strength alloy is the most popular of the heat treatable alloys. Normally supplied in the fully heat treated condition. Can also be fully annealed to allow cold working to be carried out. This alloy is readily anodised, machined and welded thus providing a good multi-purpose, durable and heat resistant alloy.

7XXX: Al-Zn-Mg-Cu containing alloy.

7075: This is a high strength **Al-Zn-Mg-Cu** alloy. The tensile strength is typically 565 MPa thus offering an outstanding strength to weight ratio for critical applications.
0.2% Proof stress: 420 - 480 MPa, UTS: 500 - 550 MPa.

9.6.5 Aluminium Casting Alloys
These typically contain up to about 12% silicon, copper and / or magnesium and manganese are also included in most specifications. The two most useful UK specification alloys are LM6 and LM25 (equivalent to Aluminium Association alloy: 356.0).

Alloy	Si %	Cu %	Mg %	Mn %	Others - max. limits %
LM6	11.5	less than 0.1	less than 0.1	less than 0.5	0.6 Fe; 0.1 Ni; 0.1 Zn
LM25	7.0	less than 0.1	0.4	less than 0.3	0.5 Fe; 0.1 Ni; 0.1 Zn

LM25 offers marginally better mechanical properties and is a natural choice for a part that subsequently requires machining. Alloy LM6 is suitable for leak tight fittings as well as castings that require later welding. Its ductility, moreover, may allow components to be cast straight then bent to shape later. LM25 is available in four conditions of heat treatment and retains the good weldability of LM6.
Sand casting techniques can achieve a tolerance of +/- 0.4mm and a wall thickness down to 3mm.
Strict adherence to working procedures and quality control is needed to ensure optimum properties are obtained. It is particularly important to ensure that the casting process does not lead to

entrapment of air or to particles of sand being washed off the mould walls. This is best achieved, not by the conventional method of pouring a stream of the molten metal into the mould from the top, but by pumping up the molten aluminium in through the bottom of the mould.

9.6.6 Aluminium Forgings
Aluminium forgings for structural applications are usually formed by closed die forging. Mechanical properties are better than those of castings and applications include wheels and aircraft frames.

9.6.7 Aluminium 'Superforming' or 'Superplastic' alloys
In some very fine grain alloys, Al-Li and Al-Cu-Zr, high temperature (typically 470° C to 520° C) deformation may take place by extensive grain boundary sliding and diffusion or by mass diffusion. As long as strain rates are kept within limits, deforming forces can be very low. Such 'superplastic' behaviour can result in elongations of 1000's of percent. Aluminium alloys that can undergo 'superplastic' deformation include 2004, 5083 and 7475. This process is used for producing sheet metal components for transport and architectural applications. Some specialist car manufacturers (Aston Martin and Morgan) use superplastic forming for some body panels.

9.6.8 Aluminium Metal Matrix Silicon Carbide Composite
Although aluminium alloys have the advantage of low density compared to steels, they have a significant disadvantage in that they have only about 1/3 the stiffness of steels and they lose strength more rapidly than steels as the temperature rises. This is a particular disadvantage for applications such as brake calipers in high performance vehicles where saving weight is critical (most brakes are mounted outboard and are part of the unsprung mass) and the brakes may suffer hard use. An important way to improve the stiffness and high temperature properties of aluminium is to mix in a suitable particulate solid, silicon carbide (SiC) is the normally chosen material. Mixtures containing up to about 30 % (SiC) can be fairly easily made and kept uniform, above this content it is difficult to get a reasonable mix. However the disadvantage of this composite is that that the SiC is very hard and very abrasive. This means cutting tools for machining can have very short lives, grinding is preferable but is limited.

Applications include brake calipers, often available as a premium price option on high performance cars.

9.7 Magnesium and Magnesium Alloys

9.7.1 Introduction:

Un-alloyed magnesium has too low a strength for any engineering use. Although magnesium alloys have a lower strength (160 to 365 MPa) than aluminium alloys, their low density (magnesium is the least dense of any structural metal) about 1750 kg/m^3, means they have as high a strength to density ratio. The Young's modulus is 45 GPa.

The fatigue endurance strength of magnesium alloys is about 70 to 100 MPa for smooth specimens, but the presence of notches or small radii will greatly reduce it.

Magnesium and its alloys have comparatively high damping capacities compared to other metals, up to about 3 times that of cast iron and up to about 30 times that of aluminium.

9.7.2 Types of Alloys:

Three main groups of magnesium alloys are in common use:

- i) Magnesium-manganese alloys - used mainly for sheet metal fabrications, they are readily weldable.
- ii) Magnesium-aluminium-zinc alloys - used mainly for gravity die and for sand casting as well as extrusions and forgings. Can be heat treated by solution treatment and precipitation hardening.
- iii) Magnesium with rare earths including zirconium (which imparts a fine grain structure for improved mechanical properties) are used in both cast and wrought form.

9.7.3 Codes Used to Specify Magnesium Alloys:

The British Standard uses the letter 'MAG' followed by a number. The ASTM uses two letters and numbers, firstly two letters indicate the major alloying elements (A - aluminium, B - bismuth, C - Copper, D - cadmium, E - rare earth, F - iron, H - thorium, K - zirconium, M - manganese, Z - zinc, etc.) which are followed by two numbers indicating the nominal percentage contents of these two elements. Where an alloy is hear treated, the letters and numbers are followed by a dash and a letter (and possibly a number indicating the temper).
In the Unified Numbering System (UNS) the numbers M10001 to M19999 have been reserved for magnesium and magnesium alloys.

9.7.4 Typical Applications:

Components for textile and printing machinery, vehicles (engine covers and sumps, seat frames, steering wheels), aircraft, hand held power tools, camera and mobile phone bodies, cases for portable computers.

Uses in automotive engine and driveline systems is limited by the tendency of many alloys to creep and lose clamping force at temperatures above about 100°C. A lot of research is curently going into developing new alloys more resistant to creep.

9.7.5 Potential Hazard

In large sections magnesium is difficult to ignite (high thermal conductivity reduces this danger) however dust and fine chips are easy to ignite and suitable precautions should be taken.

9.7.6 Processing

Magnesium alloys are weldable by any of the processes that can be used on aluminium, eg: MIG, TIG, Laser Beam.
The machinability of magnesium and it alloys is excellent.
Magnesium alloys can not be cold worked, they work harden very rapidly at room temperatures.

9.7.7 Corrosion Resistance

Magnesium and magnesium alloys are vulnerable to corrosion. To minimise this impurity levels, e.g. iron, need to be kept to very low levels. Because some of the traditionally used corrosion protection coatings were unfriendly to the environment, more acceptable coatings and sealers are being developed.

9.8 Titanium and its Alloys

9.8.1 Introduction: Although when 'pure' (99% - 99.5%) Titanium does not have a particularly high strength (UTS at room temperature: 330 - 650 MPa), when alloyed (with aluminium, copper, manganese, molybdenum, tin, vanadium, or zirconium) it's strength increases considerably (UTS at room temperature 800 - 1450 MPa). The elevated temperature strength properties of titanium and its alloys are also good.

Young's modulus for titanium and most of it's alloys is about 110 GPa (125 GPa for Ti-6Al-4V) and the shear modulus is about 45 GPa. The fatigue endurance strength at 10^7 cycles of 'pure' titanium is 0.5 times the UTS and for the alloys is 0.4 to 0.65 times the UTS.

When these mechanical properties are considered with it's very good corrosion resistance and a density of 4500 kg/m^3 (slightly over half that of steel) it means that despite its high cost, it is used in a range of specialist areas.

Un-alloyed titanium is used for its corrosion resistance in chemical plant.

Applications for high strength alloys include components for aerospace - air frame and turbine parts - connecting rods in high performance engines, bolts, etc.

9.8.2 Classification of Titanium Alloys:
Alloys can be classified according to the phases present. They are often referred to just by the nominal compositions. In the US there are ASTM and ASM specifications. In the UK the IMI Ltd. codes for the alloys are frequently used.

9.8.3 Typical Properties of some Alloys

Alloy type, properties and use	Composition. ASTM Grade	IMI code	UTS, MPa	0.2% Yield Strength, MPa	Elong. %	Fracture Toughness, MPa(m)$^{0.5}$
Unalloyed. Non-heat treatable. Used for parts requiring high corrosion resistance.	commercially pure, >99% Ti ASTM: 1, 2, 3, 4	110, 115, 125, 130, 155, 160	330 - 650	220 - 550	20 - 30	70 +
Small addition of palladium increases the corrosion resistance	commercially pure, 0.05% - 0.2% Pd ASTM: 7, 11	260, 262	480	350	28	
Alpha and near alpha: Good high temperature strength	Ti-2.5Cu	230				
Alpha and near alpha: these alloys have high strength and good creep resistance and are used in aircraft	Ti-2.25Al-11Sn-1Mo-5Zr-0.2Si, Ti-6Al-5Zr-0.5Mo-0.25Si	679, 685	1000	900		50 - 60

frames and jet engine components.						
Retains toughness and ductility at low temperature, hence extensively used in cryogenic applications.	Ti-5Al-2.5Sn-Extra low interstitial		>690	>620		
Alpha-Beta: Heat treatable (solution treated, quenched and aged) good hot forming qualities. Creep strength not as good as most Alpha alloys.	Ti-6Al-V4, Ti-4Al-4Mo-2Sn-0.5Si	318, 550	900 - 1100	800 - 1000	14 - 17	40 - 60
Beta: Can be cold worked in solution and quenched condition (unlike alpha alloys) and then aged to give very high strengths.	Ti-11.5Mo-6Zr-4.5Sn, Ti-3Al-8V-6Cr-4Mo-4Zr		1400	1300	11	50

9.8.4 Applications of Titanium Alloys

Because of the high cost of titanium and its alloys applications in the automotive industry are restricted to performance vehicles and include connecting rods and suspension components.

As the metal is inert to body fluids it is used for surgical implants. The excellent chemical resistance also makes it suitable for applications in chemical plant and for power station condenser tubes. The high strength to weight ratio, combined with chemical resistance makes it suitable for airframe and many aero engine components.

9.9 Copper and its Alloys - Brasses and Bronzes

The main use of virtually pure copper is for electrical wiring. Brasses are alloys of copper and zinc and have a range of useful properties. Some brasses are very easy to machine (nominal: 58% copper, 4% lead and 38% zinc) and can offer overall part cost savings despite a higher raw material cost than steel, where significant or complex machining is needed. Cartridge brass (nominal: 70% copper, 30% zinc) has excellent ductility and is suitable for deep drawn components and those requiring severe cold forming. Most grades have better corrosion resistance than non-stainless steels.

Originally car radiators were made entirely from brass, however as copper became more expensive aluminium became more competitive and most vehicle radiators are now either entirely made from aluminium or else have an aluminium matrix with plastic 'header and footer'. About the only remaining use for brass in vehicles in electrical components, particularly for terminals.

Bronzes are alloys of copper and tin. They are not normally found in vehicles but some grades have excellent corrosion resistance to sea water and these grades are often used for marine applications.

9.10 Superalloys

Superalloys are designed to be used at temperatures of 540°C and higher , typically up to 0.7 x their absolute melting temperature, which may be up to around 1000°C. At 760°C most superalloys have a yield strength in excess of 500MPa.
They are also corrosion resistant. About three quarters of superalloys are used in aerospace, typically about one half of the weight of a modern jet engine is made up of superalloys.

There are 3 types:

Iron Nickel based - these are an extension of stainless steel technology and are frequently wrought. Typically contain 20-40% Ni, 15-20% Cr, 30-50% Fe, plus Mo, Al, Ti.

Nickel based - may be wrought or cast. Typically more than 40% Ni, 10-20% Cr, up to 10% Al and Ti, 5-10% Co and small amounts of B, Zr and C. Mo, W and Nb are also commonly added.

Cobalt based - may be wrought or cast. Typically contain 35-60% Co, 20-30% Cr, up to 35% Ni with some W and Mo.

Appropriate compositions of all types can be forged, rolled or formed. The more highly alloyed compositions are normally processed as castings. Fabricated structures may be built up by welding and brazing, but highly alloyed compositions containing a large amount of hardening phase are difficult to weld.

As well as jet engines, these alloys are also used for fixtures and jigs to be used in furnaces.

Most superalloys are propriertary, the following shows the main types and trade names:

Nickel chromium alloys, 'Inconel', International Nickel Co.
Nickel iron alloys, 'Ni-Resist', International Nickel Co.
Nickel based and Cobalt based, 'Hastelloy', Haynes International.

9.11 Material For Engine Valves

About the only potential application for super alloys in vehicles is for engine exhaust valves, parts of which operate at temperatures above 700°C. Alloys used are 21-4-N and 21-4-NS.

Some of the alloys that have been used for exhaust valves are shown in the table below:

Specification	Features	Composition
EN53	Good creep resistance up to 700°C	C 0.55-0.65, Si 1.4-1.7, Mn 0.3-0.6, Ni 0.5 max., Cr 5.75-6.75, S & P 0.05 max.
EN 59 (XB Steel)	Can be hardened	C 0.74-0.84, Si 1.75-2.25, Mn 0.2-0.6, Ni

		1.15-1.65, Cr 19-20.5, S & P 0.03 max.
EN 54	Good resistance to corrosion, good strength at high temp. Needs hard face on stem tip	C 0.35-0.5, Si 1-2.5, Mn 1.5 max., Ni 10 max., Cr 12-16, W 2-4, S & P 0.045 max.
EN 54A	Good resistance to corrosion. Needs hard face on stem tip and seating (usually a 'Stellite')	C 0.37-0.47, Si 1-2, Mn 0.5-0.8, Ni 13-15, Cr 13-15, W 2.2-3, Nb 0.16-0.22, S & P 0.045 max., (Mo 0.4-0.6 if specified)
EN 55	Slightly better resistance to scaling than En 54	C 0.18-0.45, Si 1-2.5, Ni 6-12, Cr 17 min., W 2-4, S & P 0.045 max.
Jessop G32	High creep and fatigue strength at 750-800°C	C 0.3,m Si 0.5, Mn 0.8, Ni 12.5, Cr 19, Co 45, V 2.8, Nb 1.3, M0 2
Nimonic 80	Very high resistance to corrosion. High strength at high temp.	C 0-0.1, Si 1max., Co 0-2, Cr 18-21, Mn 1max. Fe 0-5, Al 0.5-1.8, Ti 1.8-2.7, Ni remainder

The old BS number specifications: BS EN 51, 52, 53, 54, 54A, 55 and 59, were often referred to as 'Valve Steels'

9.12 Bearing Materials
9.12.1 Introduction
Bearing materials need to have a combination of the following properties:

☐ Resistance to welding of the shaft to the bush. It is normal to use different materials for the shaft and bush as if the the same materials are used the shaft and bush will be mutually soluble, facilitating welding and adhesive wear.
☐ Sufficient strength and hardness to support the load.
☐ Must allow small impurities and debris to embed in the surface to minimise damage to the shaft and bush.

☐ Should have good thermal conductivity to assist with heat dissipation, either when components are sliding in contact or when hydrodynamic lubrication is present

Where loads and speeds are not particularly high a simple bearing may be suitable. For example at low loads and speeds a steel shaft can run satisfactorily in a brass or bronze bush lubricated with grease. Bushes made from sintered metal powder (which may have a density of upwards of 65% that of solid) can retain oil and grease for long periods of time and are used in domestic appliances and office machinery.
At low speeds plastics may be used, depending upon pressure. PTFE, one of the most inert plastics known is widely used for bridge expansion bearings. Although the pressures are quite high, the speeds are very low.
Graphs showing acceptable limits of sliding speed x projected area of bearing are published, see ref. G14.

For high speed high load bearings, such as main engine bearings, a complex multi layer material is normally used as the bush, which is only relied upon when starting up and stopping. During normal operation the load is carried by an oil film formed by the hydrodynamic action caused by the viscosity of the oil and the relative motion of the shaft and bush which prevents metal to metal contact, see Chapter 12.

The key features of the main classes of bearing materials are summarised below:

9.12.2 Grey Iron
The graphite flakes in grey iron provide lubricity which is useful for speeds of up to 40m/s and pressures of up to 1MPa. However cast iron has poor conformability (the ability to deform plastically to compensate for slight mis-alignment in assembly) which means freedom from dirt and good alignment are essential.

9.12.3 Babbitt Metal
Babbitt metal is a general term used for soft lead and tin base alloys which were originally cast as bearing surfaces on cast iron, steel or bronze shells.
In the 1950s the Vandervell Company developed a continuous process for manufacturing babbitt 'thinwall' bearings which coated a steel backing strip about 3mm thick with a thin layer of babbitt. The coated strip was cut to length and bent into the appropriate diameter semi-circle ready for fitting to engines. This process reduced costs and improved bearing quality and this type of bearing construction, often with additional thin layers applied, is still very widely used.

Babbitts display excellent conformability and embedability (the ability to embed particles in itself).

Increasing the lead content in a tin based babbitt provides higher hardness, greater ease of casting but lower strength. A key feature of babbitt metals is that their strength at 100°C is about half whatever their strength at 20°C is.

ASTM B23 grades 1 and 15 are used in ICE, but alloy 15, containing a small amount of arsenic, has better high temperature strength and performance.

Alloy B is used in diesel engine bearings.

ASTM B23 grade	Sn	Sb	Pb	Cu	As	Compressive UTS at 20°C, MPa
1	91.0	4.5	0.35	4.5	-	88.6
3	84.0	8.0	0.35	8.0	-	121
15	1.0	16.0	82.5	0.5	1.1	108
B	0.8	12.5	83.3	0.1	1.1	-

9.12.4 Silver Lined Bearings

These are a similar construction to babbitt bearings with an electro-deposited layer of of silver on a steel backing, with an overlay of 0.025 - 0.125mm of lead. A flash coat of indium on top of the lead may be used to increase the corrosion resistance of the bearing. These bearings perform well in heavy duty applications in diesels and aero-engines.

9.12.5 Aluminium and Zinc Alloys

These may be supplied in the form of strip bonded to a steel backing shell or as cast or a continuously cast hollow bar.

Applications are mainly for those involving high load and low speed.

9.12.6 Copper Base Bearing alloys

The following three types of copper alloys are used in cast form for applications as bearings and also to provide wear resistance:

- Phosphor bronzes, Cu-Sn, Cu-Sn-Pb alloys contain small amounts of phosphorus, 0.1 - 1 % and hardness increases with P content.
  High lead Cu-Sn-Pb alloys are well suited to applications where lubrication may be deficient.
- The manganese, aluminium and silicon bronzes have high hardness, tensile strengths and good resistance to shock.

Copper - lead alloys are cast onto steel backing strip in thin layers (0.5 mm) which are then cut and bent into semi-circles to make bearing shells.

Porous Bearings are made by pressing mixtures of powder, mainly copper and tin, in the case of sintered bronze bushes.

Typically these contain 85 - 90 % copper, 10 % tin, 0.1 - 1.75 % graphite, 1 % max. iron and between zero and 4 % of lead. More specific details are provided in ASTM Standard B438-83.

Iron based bushes are also made which contain up to about 20 % copper.

Porosity may be up to 35 % of the total volume (which is available for impregnation with lubricants) depending upon processing.

These types of sintered bearings are widely used where lubrication has to last for the life of the equipment, such as vacuum cleaners, small motors in domestic and office appliances, fans, etc.

9.12.7 Other Bearing Materials
A range of other materials are in use for special applications, such as rubber for bearings running in water, carbon-graphite is used where contamination by oil or grease is not acceptable. A number of plastics can be used unlubricated: PTFE ('Teflon'), nylon, polycarbonate ('Lexan'), acetal ('Delrin'). The latter two can easily be injection moulded, facilitating economic manufacture.

9.13 Hard Surfacing Materials
A number of hard coatings can be applied to metals, usually steels, by either welding or a thermal process such as flame spraying. A variety of proprietery processes and materials are available offering usually offering some combination of wear and erosion resistance. Cobalt based materials, 'Stellite' have been widely used for valve seat inserts in aluminium cylinder heads to prevent recession of a seat cut directly into the comparatively soft aluminium.
Stellite alloys can usually be supplied in cast form or applied as weld overlays. Small components of a simple shape required in large numbers can be produced economically by powder metallurgy. Up to 1 % boron is added to facilitate sintering. This process is used for valve seat inserts.
Stellite grades 1 (UNS No: R3001), 4, 6, 12 and 190 are Co-Cr-W alloys containing 26 - 30 % Cr, 4.5 - 14 % W, up to 1.5 % Mo, 0.4 - 3.3 % C, 1.5 - 3 Ni, 0.7 - 2 Si, 0.5 - 2.5 % Mn, balance - about 50 - 60 % Co.

9.14 Plastics
9.14.1 Introduction
Plastics are composed of long chain like molecules (which may also have branches or links across between chains) called polymers. Carbon is the common element of all polymers, but other elements such as hydrogen, oxygen, nitrogen, sulphur, silicon and halogens can also be present in varying proportions depending upon the type. Polymers may be divided into two classes: thermoplastic and thermosetting. Thermoplastic polymers melt on heating to form viscous liquids and reversibly solidify on cooling. Thermoplastics may be used 'neat' or with reinforcement.

Thermosetting polymers (often abbreviated to: thermosets) on heating will degrade before they melt. They are cured by chain a linking chemical reaction usually initiated at elevated temperatures and pressures, but there are types which cure at room temperature through the use of catalysts. Thermosets are usually reinforced.

While there are are large numbers of polymers and new formulations and variations are developed almost daily, most may be described as 'commodity plastics'. While the quantities of plastics used in vehicles has increased rapidly in recent years, the main applications are for interior fittings and trim, bumpers, housings and some body panels. A number of applications are 'under bonnet', where the operating conditions are much more severe, but still comparatively few applications are directly engine related, which requires superior properties necessitating the use of engineering or high performance plastics. These types are considerably more expensive than commodity plastics.

One common under bonnet applications of plastics is for inlet manifolds. Complicated shapes can easily be moulded and a smooth interior surface, desirable for good airflow, is standard for such mouldings. Aluminium alloy castings have a much rougher surface which could not be improved to the level of the plastic without incurring considerable costs.

A general comparison with metals is given in the table below:

Electrical and Thermal Insulation	Most combinations of plastic resin and filler are good electrical and thermal insulators when compared to metals
Chemical Resistance	Some plastics offer extreme resistance to chemical reagents and solvents. PTFE in one of the most inert and also has better thermal

	resistance than most other plastics.
Magnetic Properties	Most plastics do not respond to an electromagnetic field
Density	Most polymers have a SG between 1.1 and 1,7. Some combinations of resin and reinforcement offer good strength to weight and stiffness to weight ratios
Transparency	Some plastics offer transparency, sometimes good optical clarity
Colourability	Most plastics can be coloured to some extent, many can take an unlimited range of colours and display high visual quality
Toughness	Many plastics offer toughness
High Temperature Strength	The strength of most plastics falls away rapidly at higher temperatures. It is common to use an inert filler to increase the elevated temperature strength of plastics such as 'Nylons'.

References

Meaning of reference numbers prefix letters:

- A - automotive primarily
- C - casting primarily
- G - general metals or materials

References
A1: 'An Introduction to Modern Vehicle Design', Ed. J Happian-Smith, Butterworth-Heinemann, 2001.
A2: 'Light Metals for the Automotive Industry', SAE SP-1683, 2002.
A3: 'Designing and Achieving Lightweight Vehicles', SAE SP-1684, 2002.
A4: 'First and Second International Symposia on Superplasticity and Superplastic Forming Technology', Ed. D G Sanders and D C Dunard, ASM, 2003, ISBN: 0-87170-758-6.
A5: 'Resistance Welding', by H Zhang and J Senkara, CRC, Taylor and Francis, 2006, ISBN: 0-8493-2346-0.
C1: 'Cast Iron, Physical and Engineering Properties' by H T Angus, Butterworths, 2nd ed. 1976.
C2: 'Marks' Standard Handbook for Mechanical Engineers', 10th Ed.,

McGraw-Hill, 1996.

C3: 'High Strength Austempered Ductile Cast Iron', by E Dorazil, Ellis Horwood, 1991.

C4: 'Casting Solutions for the Automotive Industry', SP-1504, SAE, 2000.

G1: 'Properties and Selection of Irons, Steels and High Performance Alloys', ASM Metals Handbook, 10th Ed. 1990.

G2: 'Metals Handbook', ASM, 2nd, Desk ed., 1998.

G3: 'Innovations in Sheet Steel and Bar Products', SP-1764, SAE 2003.

G4: 'Microalloyed Steels 2002', ASM 2002, ISBN: 0-87170-773-X.

G5: 'Introduction to Engineering Materials', John, V. B., Macmillan.

G6: 'Properties of Engineering Materials', Higgins, R.A, Hodder and Stoughton.

G7: 'Engineering Metallurgy Vol.1', Higgins, R.A, Hodder and Stoughton.

G8: 'Foundations of Materials Science and Engineering', Smith, W. F., McGraw-Hill.

G9: 'Selection and Use of Engineering Materials', J A Charles, F A A Crane and J A G Furness, Butterworth Heinemann, 1997.

G10: 'The Alloy Tree - A Guide to Low Alloy Steels, Stainless Steels and Nickel-base Alloys', J C M Farrar, CRC, Woodhead Publishing Ltd., 2004, ISBN 1 85573 766 3.

G11: 'Carbon and Alloy Steels', ASM Speciality Handbook, 1995, ISBN: 0-87170-557-5.

G12: 'Stainless Steels', ASM Speciality Handbook, 1994, 0-87170-503-6.

G13: 'Microalloyed Steels 2002', ASM, 2002, ISBN: 0-87170-773-X.

G14: 'Tribology Handbook', Ed. M J Neale, Butterworth.

G15: 'Engineered Materials Handbook', ASM, 1995, ISBN: 0-87170-283-5.

Appendix 9.1 Effects of Alloying Additions to Steel

Element	Influence	Uses
Carbon	Most important alloying element. Is essential to the formation of cementite and other carbides, bainite and iron-carbon martensite. Within limits increasing the carbon content increases the strength and hardness of a steel while reducing its toughness and ductility.	Added to construction steels to increase strength, hardness and hardenability.
Nickel	Stabilises gamma phase by raising A_4 and lowering A_3. Refines grains in steels and some non-ferrous alloys. Strengthens ferrite by solid solution. Unfortunatly is a powerful graphitiser.	Used up to help refine grain size. Used in large amounts in stainless and heat-resisting steels.
Manganese	Deoxidises the melt. Greatly increases the hadenability of steels. Stabilises gamma phase. Forms stable carbides.	High manganese (Hadfield) steel contains 12.5% Mn and is austenitic but hardens on abrasion.
Silicon	De-oxidises melt. Helps casting fluidity. Improves oxidation resistance at higher temperatures.	Up to 0.3% in steels for sandcasting, up to 1% in heat resisting steels.
Chromium	Stabilises alpha phase by raising A_3 and depressing A_4. Forms hard stable carbides. Strengthens ferrite by solid solution. In amounts above 13% it imparts stainless properties. Unfortunately increases grain growth.	Small amounts in constructional and tool steels. About 1.5% in ball and roller bearings. Larger amounts in Stainless and heat-resisting steels.
Molybdenum	Strong carbide-stabilising influence. Raises high temperature creep strength of some alloys. Slows tempering response.	Reduces 'temper brittleness' in nickel-chromium steels. Increases red-hardness of tool steels. Now used to

		replace some tungsten in high-speed steels.
Vanadium	Strong carbide forming tendency. Stabilises martensite and increases hardenability. Restrains grain growth. Improves resistance to softening at elevated temperatures after hardening.	Used to retain high temperature hardness, eg in dies for hot-forging and die casting dies. Increasingly used in high speed steels.
Tungsten	Stabilises alpha phase and forms very hard carbides. renders transformations very sluggish, hence hardened steels resist tempering influences.	Used mainly in high-speed steels and other tool and die steels, particularly those for use at high temperatures.
Cobalt	Slows the transformation of martensite, hence increases 'red hardness'.	Used in super high speed steels and maraging steels, permanent magnet steels and alloys.

Appendix 9.2 Classes of Alloy, Tool and Die Steels.

Type	Spec. US UK	Comp. (%)	Heat treatment, °C and hardness Rc	Uses
Tungsten high-speed steel	T1, BS4659: BT1	0.75 C 4.25 Cr 18 W 1.2 V	Double pre-heat: 600 and 850 Austenitise: 1290 - 1320 Quench into molten salt, oil, or air blast Double or triple secondary harden / temper at about 565 for about 1 hour Rc: 60 - 65	Cutting tools, particularly those likely to face shock load, ie: interrupted cutting
Molybdenum high-speed steel	M2, BS4659: BM2	0.83 C 4.25 Cr 6.5 W 1.9 V 5 Mo	Double pre-heat: 600 and 850 Austenitise: 1250 Quench into molten salt, oil, or air blast Double or triple secondary harden / temper at about 565 for about 1 hour Rc: 60 - 65	Tougher than equivalent 18-4-1 tungsten HSS steel. Cutting tools, drills, punches, cold forging dies.
Cobalt high-speed steel	T6, BS4659: BT6	0.8 C 4.75 Cr 20 W 1.5 V 0.5	Double pre-heat: 600 and 850 Austenitise: 1300 - 1320 Quench into	Has good red hardness and toughness. Tools for severe machining duties, eg on high tensile

		Mo 12 Co	molten salt, oil, or air blast Double or triple secondary harden / temper at about 565 for about 1 hour Rc: 60 - 65	steels and cast irons.
Chromium hot-work steel	H12, BS4659: BH12	0.35 C 5 Cr 1.35 W 0.4 V 1.5 Mo 1 Si	Preheat: 800 Austenitise: 1300 - 1320 Quench into molten salt, oil, or air blast Double secondary harden / temper at about 500 to 600 for about 1 hour Rc: 38 - 55	Suitable for hot die work. Low carbon content means tools can be water cooled without cracking. Extrusion dies, mandrels, hot forming and hot pressing tools
High-carbon, high- chromium, cold-work steel	D3, BS4659: BD3	2.1 C 12.5 Cr 0.3 Mn 1 max W 1 max V	Preheat: 815 Austenitise: 925 - 980 Quench into molten salt, oil, or air blast (thin sections only) Double secondary harden / temper at about 150 to 400 for about 1 hour Rc: 54 - 61	Dies for blanking, forming, thread rolling. Rolls, slitter knives. Dies for moulding abrasive powders, eg ceramics.
Oil-hardening, cold-work steel	O1	0.9 C 0.5 Cr 0.3 V max 1.2	Preheat: 815 Austenitise: 925 - 980 Quench into molten salt,	Dies for blanking, forming, thread rolling. Rolls, slitter knives. Dies for moulding

		Mn	oil, or air blast	abrasive powders,
		0.5 W	(thin sections	eg ceramics.
		1 max	only)	
		V	Double	
			secondary	
			harden /	
			temper at	
			about 150 to	
			400 for about	
			1 hour	
			Rc: 54 - 61	

Appendix 9.3 Surface Heat Treatments

1. Thermal Hardening
In thermal hardening a hard layer is formed at the surface of plain carbon and low alloy steels of medium carbon content (0.3 - 0.6%) by heating the steel till it reaches the austenistising temperature (about 850°C, depending upon carbon content) then rapidly quenching it to form a martensitic structure.

The depth of hardening can be controlled by the rate of heating, rapid heating for a 5 - 20 seconds with an induction coil will limit the hardened zone to material adjacent to the surface. The more rapid the cooling the greater will be the depth of hardening (up to the limit of the austenitised zone) - the thinner the section the easier it is to cool rapidly. However the faster the quench the greater the danger of distortion or cracking. Increasing alloying content also gives greater depth of hardening and will allow a less severe quench to be used.

The depth of hardening is normally in the range of 1 - 5 mm.

2. Carburising
Carburising is a process in which carbon (up to 0.8 - 0.9%) is diffused into the surface of a steel component which is subsequently hardened by quenching (and then often tempered).

The process is carried out in a controlled gaseous atmosphere, or a molten salt bath in the temperature range of 850 - 950°C. The process is applicable to a wider range of steels than thermal hardening, so a wider range of properties of the surface and of the core can be obtained. Again increased alloying content permits the use of a less severe quench, reducing the danger of distortion and cracking. Some distortion normally occurs and must either be allowed for (not always possible) or a grinding allowance provided.

Although case depths can be up to several mm, most applications use less than 2 mm.

3. Carbonitriding
Carbonitriding is a variation on carburising in which nitrogen is diffused into the steel along with carbon. In the days of cyanide based molten salt carburising baths, this could readily be achieved by lowering the temperature of the bath to about 750°C. Appropriate mixtures of gases tend to be used currently.

Advantages of this process include improved wear and fatigue resistance of processed components.

4. Nitriding and Nitrocarburising

In nitriding, nitrogen is diffused into the surface of steel components by heating them to about 520°C in an atmosphere of ammonia or exposing them to a low pressure nitrogen + hydrogen atmosphere while they are subjected to a glow discharge. To obtain a high surface hardness (above 750 HV) elements that form hard nitrides, eg Al, Cr, Mo, V, must be present in the steel.

Due to the lower temperature than that used for carburising, the process times are much longer (20 + hours) and this factor combined with the fact that there is no quench means that danger of distortion is greatly reduced.

Nitrocarburising is a variation on nitriding, normally carried out between 570 and 585°C in either a molten salt bath or gaseous atmosphere. A treatment time of 90 - 120 minutes gives a shallow layer, about 20 micro m, and although this is not particularly hard, it provides excellent wear and fatigue resistance.

There are a number of proprietary processes: Tufftride, Tennifer, Nitrotec. In some variations sulphides are added to the salt bath, giving even better wear resistance. Two processes are Sulfinuz and Sursulf.

Sulf BT

Sulf BT is low temperature (200°C) salt bath process that adds only sulphur to the surfaces of ferrous components, this provides excellent wear resistance.

5. Boriding (boronising)

In this process boron is diffused into the surface of a plain carbon or low alloy steel at approximately 950°C to form a layer of iron borides about 100 micro m thick with a hardness in the range 1800 - 2100 Hv. The process can also be used on some other alloys eg cobalt, nickel and titanium alloys. Processing time is a few hours and is carried out with the components packed in granules.

6. Metalliding

The most important process in this category is probably the one developed by Toyota, Japan, known as the Toyota Diffusion (or TD) process in which carbide forming elements such as vanadium and niobium are diffused into steels from a salt bath at about 1000°C. Carbide layers 5 - 12 micro m of very high hardness, about 3000 Hv, are produced.

The term metalliding is also used to describe processes in which coatings are electroplated from molten salt baths.

10 Mechanisms: Converting Piston (Linear) Motion to Crank Rotation and Rotary Motion to Linear Motion - Using Cams. Springs

10.1 Introduction

When the first steam engines where built, in the early 19th century, they were massively constructed and operated at slow speeds, beam engines typically only performing a few cycles per minute. Consequently dynamic loads were small and gravity loads dominated. Developments in engines have resulted in small, lightweight construction designed to operate at high speeds, gravity loads and stresses are very small compared to the dynamic loads and the stresses that these generate.

This section will examine the dynamic loads and stresses in some engine components. In IC engines with pistons the slider crank mechanism is used to transform the reciprocating motion of the piston to a rotary motion of the crankshaft needed to ultimately drive the wheels.

From the layout of the chosen mechanism it is necessary to determine the velocities and accelerations in order to determine the forces and torques acting on the components and consequently the stresses. Before the days of digital computers mechanism velocity and accelerations were determined by graphical techniques, drawing out scale velocity and acceleration diagrams for every position that needed investigation. This was very time consuming! Nowadays most mechanism analysis is normally done with a motion analysis package.

10.2 The Scotch Yoke

One method of converting reciprocating motion to rotary motion is to use a 'Scotch Yoke' mechanism, see diagram below:

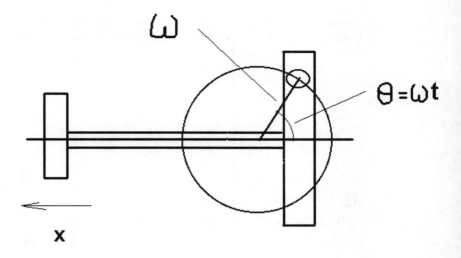

If the crank, radius r, is rotating counter clockwise (ccw) at a constant angular velocity, ω the piston will execute simple harmonic motion (shm):

$$x = r \cos(\omega t)$$

differentiating gives the velocity $= - r \omega \sin(\omega t)$

Differentiating again gives the acceleration $= - r (\omega)^2 \cos(\omega t)$

However there are some problems with the detail of this mechanism. To avoid impact loading of the yoke when the piston changes direction requires complicated design which would involve duplication of bearings and some type of pre-loading. This would make the mechanism heavy and complex and the author does not know of any engineering applications.

10.3 The Slider Crank

The universal solution adopted currently is the slider crank, satisfactory bearing arrangements are much simpler than in the case of the Scotch yoke. For a constant crank angular velocity the velocity of the piston is not shm.

A simple analysis is possible if it is assumed that the connecting rod is at least 3 times the crank throw and this is shown below.

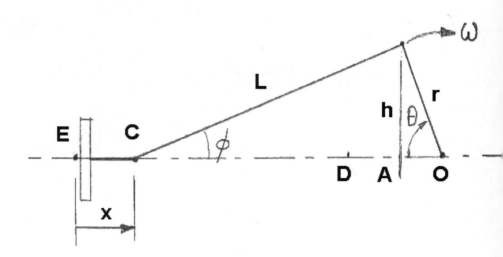

The crank, radius r, is assumed to be rotating clockwise about point O at a constant angular velocity ω

x is the displacement of the gudgeon pin (currently at point C) from its position (point E) when the piston is at tdc.

$$x = OD + DE - AC - OA$$

$$x = r + L - r \cos(\theta) - L \cos(\phi) \ \ldots\ldots\ (10.1)$$

Now $\sin(\phi) = h/L$ and $\sin(\theta) = h/r$

$$\cos(\phi) = (1 - \sin^2\phi)^{0.5}$$

$$\cos(\phi) = (1 - h^2/L^2)^{0.5}$$

$$\cos(\phi) = (1 - (r^2\sin^2\theta/L^2)^{0.5}$$

Letting n = L/r = Connecting rod length/crank radius

$$\cos(\phi) = [1 - (\sin^2\theta)/n^2]^{0.5}$$

If n is considerably greater than 1, then by the binomial expansion:

$$\cos(\phi) = 1 - 0.5(\sin^2\theta/n^2)$$

hence: $x = r + L - r\cos(\theta) - L(1 - 0.5\sin^2\theta/n^2)$

but $\cos(2\theta) = 1 - 2\sin^2(\theta)$

so $x = r(1 - \cos\theta) + L[1 - 1 + 0.25(1 - \cos(2\theta)/n^2)]$

Hence piston displacement is:

$$x = r(1 - \cos\theta) + L[1 - \cos(2\theta)/(4n^2)]$$

$$x = r(1 - \cos\theta) + r^2[1 - \cos(2\theta)]/(4L)$$

Now piston velocity, $v = dx/dt = (dx/d\theta).d\theta/dt = \omega.dx/d\theta$

$$v = \omega r[\sin\theta + (r/4L)2\sin(2\theta)]$$

Acceleration

$$a = r\,\omega^2[\cos\theta + (r/L)\cos(2\theta)]$$

However modern engines have connecting rods that are typically only about 2 - 3 times the crank throw and less in some cases. It should be noted that while using a shorter connecting rod has the benefit of reducing the engine height somewhat, it has the disadvantage of increasing the angle if inclination of the connecting rod to the cylinder axis which increases the side forces between the piston and cylinder walls which increases the friction, wear and friction losses at the piston - cylinder wall interface. In these configurations the motion of the piston will be significantly different to shm.

It is reasonably straightforward to develop a spread sheet to do motion analysis of a slider crank and an example of this is given in Appendix 8.
The spread sheet starts at bdc and goes through 360° in steps of 1° (unlike equation 10.1, above which has the angle zero at tdc) to compute the piston displacement. The displacement values are then numerically differentiated twice, using a 5 point scheme which provides some smoothing with little loss of accuracy. The piston (and gudgeon pin) displacement, velocity and acceleration are shown in columns H, I and J, respectively. Once the acceleration

has been calculated, and assuming the gas pressure variation during the combustion stroke has been computed, the variation in the forces acting in the connecting rod and bearings, can be determined, this was explained in Chapter 8, the possible effects of these forces on the connecting rod are considered in Chapter 11 section 5.

10.4 The Valve Train of an Internal Combustion Engine
10.4.1 Introduction
To allow the maximum amount of mixture (or air for a diesel) to be drawn into the cylinders it is desirable that the inlet valve(s) open as quickly as possible, with as high a lift as possible and remain open for as long as possible followed by rapid closing. To achieve these aims the components in the valve train are subjected to high accelerations (and hence forces) as the inertia of the components has to be overcome.
During the valve opening phase the cam provides the necessary force and during the closing phase the valve spring(s) provides the forces (except in an engine with desmodromic valve operation - where a second cam provides the closing forces. Currently only Ducati motorcycles use this system).
At the time of writing, June 2008, Honda is developing a racing motorcycle engine with pneumatically operated valves enabling the engine to reach high rpm.
To simplify the analysis it will be assumed that the cam profile is symmetrical, ie, where the closing phase is the 'mirror image' of the opening phase. In practice this may not be the case.

10.4.2 Practical Details
Although high accelerations are needed to give rapid opening and closing, too rapid a change in acceleration - the 'jerk' or 'jerk rate' - will give rough operation due to the sudden changes in forces. For this reason cam profiles are designed not to give very rapid changes in accelerations.
As higher forces can more easily be provided by the cam than by the valve springs, it is common to use higher accelerations when starting the opening of the valves and when slowing their closing at the end of the closing phase. These aspects are controlled by the cam, whereas the slowing of the valve at the end of the opening phase and the acceleration of the valve at the start of the closing phase are controlled by the valve springs.

10.4.3 Analysis - Acceleration of Cam Follower
The analysis of anything other than a simple configuration can be quite complex, the analysis will depend upon the type of follower and the detailed geometry. The two common cam follower systems

used are: (i) rollers and (ii) flat foot or 'mushroom' followers, which are names for tappets.

In this section we will make some simplifying assumptions: that a knife edge follower is being used and the axis of motion of the follower passes through the axis of rotation of the cam. This will not be very accurate or representative, but will give some idea of values.

i) The most simple assumption for analysis is to assume that the opening and closing is simple harmonic motion (SHM). Assume that the engine speed is 4000 revs/minute, this gives a cam shaft rotation speed of 2000 revs/minute (in a 4 stroke engine the cam turns at half the crankshaft speed) so the time taken for 1 revolution of the cam shaft is 0.03 seconds
Also assume that the cam is opening and closing the valve for 120° of its rotation.
Hence the complete valve cycle is completed in 1/3 camshaft revolution, or 0.01 seconds.
The equation describing SHM is: displacement = amplitude x cos(omega x t)

> where t = time and
> omega is the 'angular velocity' of the system in rad/s, and is equal to (2 x 3.14159)/(the time for 1 cycle)

So the omega value here is 2 x 3.14159/0.01 = 628.3 rad/sec.

Differentiating the expression for displacement gives:

> velocity = - omega x amplitude x sin(omega t), then differentiating again:

> acceleration = - (omega)^2 x amplitude x cos(omega t)

> The maximum acceleration occurs when the term cos(omega t) has the maximum value of 1, this occurs at the extremes of the motion.

If the cam has a lift of 20 mm, the amplitude of the motion is 10 mm, and the maximum acceleration is given by:
> acceleration$_{max}$ = (628.3)^2 x 0.01 = 3948 m/s^2

ii) An alternative assumption is to assume that that the peak of the cam is finished with specific constant radius with a centre at a distance 'e' from the centre of the cam. The term 'e' may be called the eccentricity. The peak radius is often blended to the the base circle by a large radius curve.

In this case the acceleration of a 'mushroom' - flat foot - follower in the vicinity of the maximum cam lift is given by: (cam shaft angular velocity)^2 x eccentricity. If the cam base circle is blended to the nose radius by a large radius, the maximum acceleration occurs when the follower is on this larger radius and is equal to the large blend radius x (cam shaft angular velocity)^2

10.4.4 Analysis - Valve Train Forces.
If the cam shaft is a direct acting overhead unit then all the components in the (short) valve train will undergo the same acceleration. The exception to this is the spring, for which an allowance may be made by using 1/3 of its mass as an effective mass, see section 10.5 6.

Maximum force will then be:

> F = max. acceleration x (masses of tappet + retainer + colletts + valve + 1/3 of spring)

At least this much force must be generated by the valve spring at its maximum compression.

The analysis becomes more complex when the engine does not have an overhead cam shaft, or when there is an overhead cam shaft that operates the valves by rockers. When this is the case the intertia of the rocker needs to be considered and the 'lever effect' of the rocker needs to be considered - as the two side arms of the rocker are frequently unequal.

As an example consider the layout shown below:

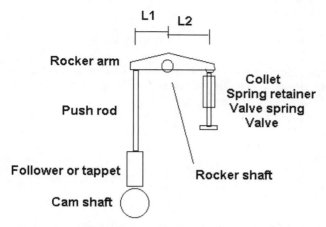

**General arrangement of valve gear in an engine
with the cam in the side of the cylinder block**

Let us assume the following values and dimensions:

- 1) tappet 200 gm
- 2) push rod 250 gm
- 3) valve, collet, retainer and 1/3 spring, total 300gm
- 4) rocker arm 200 gm
- 5) L1 20 mm
- 6) L2 40 mm

The easiest way to carry out the calculations is to determine the equivalent mass of the valve train at the valve side, then use:

$$F_{valve\ side} = m_{total\ equiv.\ on\ valve\ side} \times x''_{valve\ side.}$$

Components in group (3) above, are the items on the valve side with a mass of 300 gm.

The rocker now needs to be represented as an equivalent mass at the valve side.
First the moment of inertia needs to be estimated. Depending upon the design of the rocker it may be possible to perform a 'compound pendulum' experiment to determine this. If this is not possible then an estimate of the radius of gyration of the rocker about the rocker shaft (k_p) can be made. The radius of gyration is the radius at which the mass would have to be concentrated to give the same moment of inertia. For a uniform slender rod, length, L, pivoted about its centre, this is: $k_p = L/(12)^{0.5}$

For this rocker it will be assumed that the radius of gyration about the rocker shaft is 10mm, hence the moment of inertia about the rocker shaft is mass x $(k_p)^2$

This gives $I_{rocker} = 0.2$ x $(0.01)^2$ kg m^2 = 0.000020 kg m^2

To determine the equivalent mass at the distance of the valve axis from the rocker shaft pivot, L2, start with the free body diagram below:

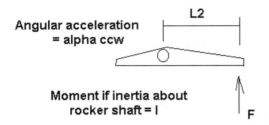

Torque = Moment of inertia x alpha

F L2 = I x alpha

Let the linear acceleration (upwards) of the point on the rocker where F is acting be x"

Then writing x"/L2 = alpha into the equation above gives (NB I is upper case i, NOT 1):

F L2 = I x"/L2 and re-arranging gives:

$F = I x"/(L2)^2$

So the equivalent mass of the rocker on the valve side is: $I/(L2)^2$ kg

In the analysis below F on the valve side will be referred to as $F_{valve\ side}$. From equilibrium of the rocker, take moments about the rocker shaft, so $F_{valve\ side}$ L2 = $F_{cam\ side}$ L1.

Let the mass of the components on the cam side (1 + 2 from list above) be $m_{cam\ side}$ and let the force required to give this mass a (downward) acceleration x"$_{cam\ side}$ be $F_{cam\ side}$ so:

$F_{cam\ side} = m_{cam\ side}$ x"$_{cam\ side}$

Both sides of the rocker arm have the same angular acceleration, alpha:

$$\text{alpha} = x''_{\text{cam side}}/L1 = x''_{\text{valve side}}/L2$$

The force on the valve side to accelerate the cam side at $x''_{\text{cam side}}$ is given by

$$F_{\text{valve side}}\ L2/L1 = m_{\text{cam side}}\ x''_{\text{cam side}}$$

and the force on the valve side to give the mass on the cam side an acceleration of $x''_{\text{valve side}}$ is given by:

$$F_{\text{valve side}}\ L2/L1 = m_{\text{cam side}}\ x''_{\text{valve side}}\ L1/L2 \text{ or}$$

$$F_{\text{valve side}} = m_{\text{cam side}}\ x''_{\text{valve side}}\ (L1/L2)^2$$

So the equivalent mass of the cam side at the valve side = $m_{\text{cam side}}$ $(L1/L2)^2$

For the example above:

Equivalent mass at valve side = mass of valve + retainer + collet + 1/3 of spring + $I_{\text{rocker}}\ /(L2)^2$ + (mass tappet + mass push rod)$(L1/L2)^2$

Putting in values:

$$m_{\text{eq valve side}} = 0.3 + 0.000020/(0.04)^2 + 0.450(20/40)^2$$

$$m_{\text{eq valve side}} = 0.425 \text{ kg}$$

If the maximum acceleration required by the valve when being driven by the spring is 3000 m/s^2, then the spring force needed is 3000 x 0.425 = 1275 N.

10.4.5 Materials for Cam Shafts
Over head cam shafts in automotive engines are usually lubricated by oil spray and splash and as the nominal line contact between cam and follower does not promote the maintenance of an oil film, it is important to use a cam shaft material which has some ability to run against the follower under conditions of boundary lubrication. Cam shafts are frequently cast iron, often an iron alloyed with some combination of nickel, chromium and molybdenum. A 'chill casting' process is often used, this involves inserting suitably shaped iron 'chills' into the mould. This results in rapid cooling of the adjacent surfaces which leads to the formation of a high proportion of combined carbon, which is a very hard carbide of iron as distinct from the free graphite form. The surfaces that have been selectively hardened in this way are ground to the required profile in the normal way. If gears integral with the shaft are required the gear

blank areas can be 'chilled' and the blank ground to finished dimensions. Such gears share the same good wear resistance as the 'chilled' cam profiles.

10.5 Springs
10.5.1 Introduction
Springs are widely used in mechanisms to exert a force. In many critical applications, vehicle suspension springs and engine valve springs, they are subjected to rapid changes in length and their mass must be kept to a minimum to reduce undesirable dynamic effects. This inevitably means that such springs are working at high stress levels which has implications concerning the choice of materials and manufacturing processes. This section will concentrate on coil springs working in compression, dealing with design, stress analysis, choice of materials and manufacturing processes.

10.5.2 Forces Acting
The equations below assume that the spring coil is loaded centrally along the spring axis, which remains straight and the ends are free to rotate about the spring axis relative to one another. In practice these conditions are often not met, end fixings commonly do not distribute the load centrally and in some car suspension systems the coil axis assumes a curved shape that varies depending upon the deflection. The design factor used must take account of any departures from the ideal assumptions.

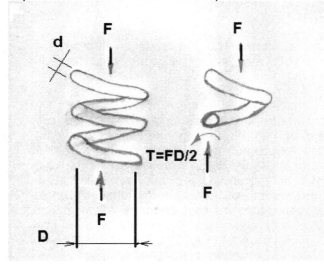

The loads in the wire can be deduced from the layout diagram on the left and the FBD on the right of a part of the coil and are:

A force F parallel to the spring axis acting nearly transverse to the wire axis and through its centre and
A torque T = FD/2 about the axis of the wire.

Both of these generate shear stresses in the wire.

$$S_s = \pm \, FDd/4J + F/A \text{ where}$$

J is the polar moment of area of the wire cross section, D is the mean diameter of the coil and d the wire diameter.

The first term is due to torsion and the second term is due to the transverse shear force and this expression ignores the curvature of the wire in the spring.

$$\text{As } J = 3.14159 \, d^4/32 \text{ ..and.. } A = 3.14159 \, d^2/4$$

The equation for shear stress can be written as:

$$S_s = [8 \, F \, D/d^3 + 4 \, F/d^2]/3.14159$$

The spring index C is defined as D/d and for many springs is in the range 6-12. The two terms in the previous expression for shear stress can be combined by introducing a shear stress correction factor:

$$K_s = (2 \, C + 1)/2C \text{ ... which gives}$$

$$S_s = K_s 8 \, F \, D/3.14159d^3$$

10.5.3 Curvature Effect
As the wire is coiled, the rotation of the wire on the inner side of the coil occurs over a shorter distance than rotation on the outer side of the coil. This means that the shear stress on the inner side of the coil must be greater than that at the outside of the coil. This also means that the centre of rotation of the wire must be displaced away from the wire axis towards the centre of the coil, although the actual displacement is quite small.

Two factors have been proposed to include the effects of both the curvature and the transverse shear:

$$K_w = \frac{4C-1}{4c-4} + \frac{0.615}{C} \qquad\qquad K_B = \frac{4C+2}{4C-3}$$

K_w, the Wahl factor ..and.. K_B, the Bergstrasser factor.
The results from these two methods usually differ by less than 1%.

The curvature correction factor can be determined by cancelling the effect of transverse shear, done below for the Bergstrasser factor:

$$K_c = \frac{K_B}{K_s} = \frac{2c(4c+2)}{(4c-3)(2c+1)}$$

When fatigue is likely to be a factor (or the spring material must be considered to be brittle) K_c is used as a stress concentration factor. Normally in fatigue calculations the stress concentration factor would be corrected to K_f because of notch sensitivity, but for high strength steels the notch sensitivity is close to 1, so the full value of K_c (or K_B or K_W in some procedures) is used.

10.5.4 Equations Used in Design

The relationship between load and deflection is given by:

F = G d^4 ð/8 D^3 N_a ... where
G is the shear modulus, for spring steel a value of 80 GPa can be used.
ð is the deflection and
N_a is the number of active turns, in determining this account must be taken of the ways that the ends of the coil are finished and appropriate corrections made.

The linear spring rate is then:

R = F / ð = G d^4/8 D^3 N_a

The basic stress is given by: S_s = 8 D F/3.14159 d^3 .. and the corrected stress:

S_{sc} = 8 D F K_W/3.14159 d^3

Design methods used to be based on nomograms, however spreadsheets are now used. The Society of Automotive Engineers (SAE) publish a 'Spring design Manual' that contains information about design, appropriate design methodology, reliability and materials.

Normally a design will involve some constraints about the space available, (governing D) required spring rate, limits of motion, availability of wire diameter, material, maximum allowable stress when the spring is solid. Some iterations will probably be needed to reach the best solution. Fatigue testing is commonly carried out on new designs of springs destined for critical applications.

10.5.5 Materials and Manufacture
'Music wire', AISI 1085 steel is used in diameters up to 3 mm for the highest quality springs.

For diameters up to 12 mm, AISI 1065 may be used in the hardened and tempered condition or cold drawn.

For larger wire diameter, or for highly stressed applications, low alloy steels containing chrome - vanadium, chrome - silicon and silicon - manganese, hot rolled, hardened and tempered (to 50 - 53 Rc hardness, equivalent to about 1600 to 1700 MPa UTS) are used.

For most spring materials increasing the wire diameter reduces the UTS, and if the UTS is plotted against the wire diameter on semi - log graph paper, the line is often nearly straight for many of the metals used for springs.

Research suggests that the yield shear stress of most metals lies in the range of 0.35 to 0.55 times the UTS, in the absence of specific information, a value of 0.5 time the UTS can be used for hardened and tempered carbon and low alloy steels.

The fatigue strength of springs can be increased by cold setting and particularly by shot peening, which can increase the fatigue endurance strength by as much as 50%. Both processes are routinely carried out on highly loaded automotive suspension springs.

10.5.6 The Effective Mass of a Spring
Springs are normally used to provide a force in a dynamic system, this frequently means that one end of the spring will be moving and the other end will either be stationary or moving at a different velocity. This section looks at the derivation of the effective mass of a spring with one end fixed and the other moving at a velocity V_e, see diagram below:

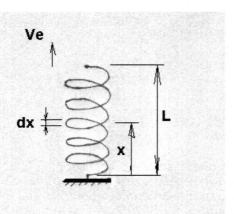

It is assumed that the spring is uniform along its length, L and that the total mass of the spring is m_s, so the mass of a small element of the spring of length dx at x from the fixed end is given by:

$dm = m_s dx/L$

The velocity of the element x from the fixed end is given by:

$v_x = v_e x/L$

The kinetic energy of the element, mass(velocity)^2/2, is given by:

$[m_s dx/L][v_e x/L]^2/2$

Rearranging and integrating gives:

$$KE = \frac{m_s v_e^2}{2L^3} x^2 dx$$

$$= \frac{m_s v_e^2}{2L^3} \int_0^L x^2 dx$$

$$= \frac{m_s v_e^2}{2L^3} \cdot \frac{x^3}{3} \Big]_0^L$$

$$= \frac{m_s v_e^2}{2 \times 3}$$

The KE of the spring is one third that of a mass equal to that of the spring moving at a velocity of v_e showing that the equivalent mass to be used in such circumstances is 1/3 of the mass of the spring. The effective mass being equal to 1/3 of the actual mass of the spring is valid whether the spring is a conventional coil or a uniform bar, an example is given in chapter 14.

10.5.7 Surge in Springs

If one end of a helical spring is held fixed and the other end suddenly compressed and then held fixed, a compression wave is formed that travels along the spring, is reflected from fixed ends (now both ends) and the motion continues until it is damped out. This phenomena is referred to as 'surge' and the natural frequencies of this wave are important in spring design as it is undesirable that the frequency of a disturbance coincides with any of the spring's natural frequencies.

The wave equation for the longitudinal vibration of rods is modified so it can be applied to springs. The derivation of this is given in ref. 10.1 and the result of this is:

$omega_n = 3.14159 \ n \ (k/m_s)^{0.5}$ rad/s.
or

$f_n = (n/2)(k \ g/W_s)^{0.5}$ Hz .. where n = 1, 2, 3 ...

where k is the spring stiffness, W_s is the total weight of the spring.

Example using data from chapter 14 section 7:
k = 6000 N/m, total mass of spring = 0.0255 kg.

$omega_n = 3.14159 \ (6000/0.025)^{0.5}$ rad/s.

$omega_n = 1524$ rad /s (for n = 1 as it is normally the lowest natural frequency that is of most interest).

Typically a car engine at maximum rpm of 6000 has the camshaft rotating at 3000 rpm and a complete opening and closing cycle for a valve would occupy 1/3 of the time for 1 camshaft rotation giving an equivalent of 9000 rpm or 942 rad/s for the valve cycle. This is well below the lowest natural frequency of the spring of 1524 rad/s.

10.6 Reference

10.1 'Vibration of Mechanical and Structural Systems', M L James, G M Smith, J C Wolford, P W Whaley, Harper and Row, 1989, ISBN: 0-06-043261-6

11 Engine Block, Crankshaft, Gudgeon Pins, Connecting Rods

11.1 Introduction
This chapter deals with some of the key components in the lower part of the engine.

11.2 Cylinder Block
11.2.1 Introduction
The engine (or cylinder) block, below left, is the main structural component of the engine. The bottom face of the block is normally on the centre line of the crankshaft and for many years individual main bearing shell housings were used which bolted into the bottom of the cylinder block. However to improve the rigidity of the engine block it is now common for all the lower half of the main bearings to be held in a ladder frame, below right, which bolts to the bottom of the cylinder block.

Although early four cylinder engines often had only two or three main bearings, modern engines with 'in line' cylinders have a main bearing between each cylinder and the five main bearings, with thin wall shells in position (the middle three each having a central groove) can be seen in the picture above left. The frame on the right has 4 of the shells in place, all are continuous without a central groove. The maximum load on the main bearings will be on the lower halves during the combustion stroke, the shells without the central groove have higher load carrying capacity than those with the groove.

There are dowels on one side of the end bearings of the frame which provide accurate location when the frame is being bolted to the bottom of the block.

It is just about possible to see part of the annular flat thrust bearing on the side face of the middle main bearing in the block. The finely ground part of the crankshaft on which this runs can be seen in section 11.3.

The lower ends of the wet cast iron liners can just be seen in the two cylinders near the bottom of the picture, the liners have been removed from the two cylinders at the top.

The block and frame in the picture above is for a Rover 'K Series' engine in an aluminium alloy casting. This engine has the unusual feature of using 10 long bolts, about 450 mm in length, which run essentially the full height of the engine and hold all the main components together.

The top of the block commonly coincides with the top of the piston crown at tdc. At the front of the block there are normally housings for the oil pump and the cooling water pump often with an adjacent thermostat. Passages from the water pump lead water around the cylinders and into the cylinder head. Passages from the oil pump take oil to the crankshaft main bearings where passages drilled in the crankshaft take oil to the big end bearings. Oil is also supplied, via the cylinder head, to the overhead cam shaft and drain holes lead back through the head and block to the sump.

The picture below shows a partially cut away section of the middle part of an engine cylinder block from a Ford engine. This is a cast iron block and there are no separate cylinder liners. (The cylinder head is an aluminium alloy casting). To the right of the centre the cooling water passage between the two middle two cylinders can be seen near the top of the picture. The lower part of this web has been cut away to reveal the middle main crankshaft bearing, the hole in the lower bearing cap in front of this bearing is to fix the cap to the lower part of the (cut away) web.

The three conical dimples each side of the bearing are in the crankshaft counterweights and are drilled to balance the crankshaft.

The other visible counterweight at the left does not have any
dimples drilled in it. Part of the connecting rod from the left hand
piston to the crankshaft big end bearing can just be seen.
The circular section 'tube' at the bottom of the picture seals the
joint between the cylinder block and the engine sump. Such seals
are normally made from a synthetic rubber.

11.2.2 Cylinder Block Materials and Manufacture

Originally grey cast iron was the material used for engine blocks, it was relatively easy to cast and machine and the flakes provided an element of lubricity. It also had good damping properties. The popular grades were B.S.1452: 14 and 17, corresponding to UTS values (test bar diameter 22 mm) of 215 MPa and 275 MPa respectively. However in the latter half of the 20th Century, as the interest in reducing weight increased, aluminium alloys were introduced and are now used for almost all cylinder blocks in automobile engines. Typical casting alloys contain from 7 - 12 % silicon, see section 9.6.5.

BMW's latest 3.0 liter in-line six-cylinder engine is the first production engine with a cylinder block made from a magnesium outer and an aluminum core. This offers the lightest cylinder block practical, and is ideal for high performance cars. BMW state that this combination is 24% lighter than an all aluminium alloy block. There is a separate ladder frame made from magnesium which contains the main bearing caps with steel inserts to reinforce the caps.

One recent exception to using aluminium for automotive diesel cylinder blocks is the V6 engine block developed by Citroen, Peugeot and Ford which uses a compacted graphite iron (CGI).

Virtually all pistons in small petrol and diesel engines are aluminium alloys, this helps to keep the reciprocating mass down. However if aluminium is run against aluminium, rapid wear will occur. Two ways of preventing aluminium running on aluminium are used in engines:

> a) Use a cast iron cylinder liner. These may be 'dry', where an accurately machined thin wall cast iron liner, with a retaining lip at the top is dropped into the accurately bored cylinder block or alternatively a 'wet' cast iron liner is used. Cast iron liners may be fitted as inserts during the casting of the aluminium cylinder block.

> b) A special alloy coating, such as 'Nikasil' is applied to the cylinder walls.

The advantage with (a) is that damage to cylinder bores can be overcome by re-boring and fitting larger pistons, however with (b) repairs are often not possible with the coated aluminium bores.

Compression rings are normally a cast iron and in some cases are chromium plated.

11.3 Crankshafts

The picture above shows the crankshaft and flywheel, with teeth round its rim for the starter motor pinion to engage with, form a Rover 1.1 litre 'K' Series engine.

High quality crank shafts are forged from Ni-Cr-Mo, Cr-Mo, or similar steels, with a total alloy content of up to about 2.5 % with additionally about 0.3 - 0.4 % carbon. Following forging the cranks are normally heat treated to give a combination of strength and toughness and then the critical dimensions ground to finished size. Crank shafts for mass market engines are made from less costly materials steels, possibly medium carbon and sometimes nodular cast iron.

Crank shafts for high performance engines are often processed prior to final grinding to size, by a process to increase their fatigue strength. Processes used include nitriding, using a molten salt bath, such as 'Tufftride' or in a gas atmosphere. Alternatively the fillets at the ends of the bearings may fillet rolled, this imparts a residual compressive stress which improves the fatigue endurance strength in these areas.
Before being built into engines crank shafts are often balanced statically and dynamically.

11.4 Gudgeon Pins - Also known as piston pins
11.4.1. Introduction
The gudgeon pin (which connects the piston to the connecting rod in a conventional internal combustion engine, ICE) is subjected to a combination of shearing and bending loads. However the length to diameter ratio is short and simple beam theory only gives accurate

results for beams with large length:depth ratios (greater than about 10:1) so conventional beam analysis will not be accurate. There will inevitably be some deformation of the bushes that hold the gudgeon pin in both the piston and the connecting rod. The matter is complicated further by the fact that the piston is an aluminium alloy and the gudgeon pin and connecting rods are steel. It is therefore likely that a simple analysis assuming pure shear will also not be accurate. It should also be noted that a simple calculation assuming a uniform shear stress is not accurate as even when a component is in pure shear due to transverse loading, the shear stress distribution is not uniform - consideration of complimentary shear stresses indicates that the shear stress must be zero at the top and bottom surfaces and a maximum half way up the section.

Although simple calculations of the types described above will give order of magnitude values for stresses, for this type of configuration it is necessary to carry out FEA to obtain more accurate results. How this may be done is described below.

11.4.2 Finite Element Analysis
To obtain reasonable results it is necessary not just to model the gudgeon pin, but also to use a simplistic model of the piston and connecting rod and include the effects of the contact between them. If appropriate contact zones are not specified, the FEA package will 'weld' the parts together giving incorrect results. This means the parts need to be individually modelled and then brought together into an assembly for analysis. This has been done using the student edition of PTC Pro/Engineer and Mechanica.

Because of symmetry it was only necessary to model one quarter of the piston / connecting rod / gudgeon pin (the connecting rod was orientated as it would be at tdc or bdc). The gudgeon pin dimensions and the width of the bushes in the piston and connecting rod are taken from a Nissan engine:

- half length of gudgeon pin: 35 mm
- pin OD: 20.6 mm
- pin IDs: 11.61 mm and (mainly) 12.68 mm
- piston boss width: 21.2 mm
- half connecting rod boss width 12.15 mm
- force upwards on bottom of connecting rod 1250 N.
- half of connecting rod breadth: 15 mm
- the piston: aluminium, connecting rod and gudgeon pin: steel
- theoretical mean compressive stress in con.rod: 6.9 MPa.

The appropriate constraints were placed on the symmetry planes and the top of the 'piston' was restrained from moving in the 'Y' direction.

Contact surfaces were specified between the gudgeon pin and the piston and between the gudgeon pin and the connecting rod. Setting up FEA involving contacts requires care, particularly if the the users experience of the software is limited. The results displayed below should be considered to be indicative rather than accurate.

11.4.3 Results
The sketch below shows the zones where the von Mises stresses were greatest:

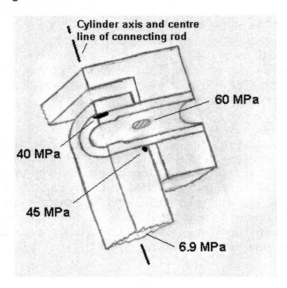

There is bending of the gudgeon pin in the centre. However the largest von Mises stress is half way up, or at the mid level, in the gudgeon pin.
Dividing the shearing force into the csa of the gudgeon pin gives an average stress of 12.1 MPa. Allowing for the fact that the shear stress distribution is not uniform and assuming the maximum is twice the mean value, gives a maximum shear stress of just over 24 MPa at the mid level of the pin. The bending stresses would be expected to be zero at the mid level of the pin so the only contribution to the 60 MPa von Mises stress value from the FEA must be the shear stress. Clearly with such a large difference between hand calculations and FEA results suggests that this configuration is more complex than appears and demonstrates the importance of using FEA for such a configuration.

The load on the complete connecting rod would be 5000 N and as can be seen from the calculations in section 11.5, the maximum force on the piston can be 3 - 4 times greater (the diameter of the piston in this calculation is 80 mm, whereas in 11.5 it is 75 mm). In this case it may be assumed that the maximum von Mises stress in the gudgeon pin is about 250 MPa at the point in the combustion cycle when the pressure is greatest. As the load is cyclic, it is clear why the pin has to be heat treated (and lubrication is needed) as this approximate analysis indicates that the minimum needed fatigue endurance strength is in excess of 250 MPa meaning the UTS will need to be in excess of 500 MPa.

11.4.4 Material for Gudgeon Pins
Because gudgeon pins only oscillate (as opposed to rotating continuously) they do not form a stable oil film which makes them vulnerable to wear. Commonly a medium carbon steel is used which is heat treated prior to the pin being ground to final size. In some engines the pins are held in the little end by an interference fit. In this case they rely for lubrication on oil splashing around in the crank case, or more efficiently, on oil being sprayed onto the underside of the pistons. This assists piston cooling as well as lubricating the gudgeon pin / piston interface. In some engines where the gudgeon pin is not an interference fit in the small end the connecting rods little ends are fitted with a brass or bronze bush and the rods are drilled from the big end to the little end and some of the oil supplied to the big end from the crank shaft main bearings goes up the connecting rod to the little end and lubricates the gudgeon pin.

11.5 Connecting Rods
11.5.1 Introduction
The loads on connecting rods are are at various parts of the engine cycle: compressive, tensile and bending. For parts of the cycle, particularly when the mixture burning, there will be compressive forces acting and compressive stresses in the rods. However at the end of the exhaust stroke, when the piston starts to accelerate downwards, drawing in fresh mixture, there will be tensile stresses in the connecting rod. Around mid stroke, when the lateral acceleration of the connecting rod is maximum, it will also be undergoing angular acceleration and these will give rise to bending stresses.

11.5.2 Effects of Vertical Accelerations - Tension and Compression
As can be seen from Chapter 10, the piston accelerations do not follow simple harmonic motion, due to the finite length of the connecting rods. This results in the acceleration in the region of TDC being significantly greater in magnitude than the acceleration at

BDC, the angle of crank rotation is measured from BDC in the graph below:

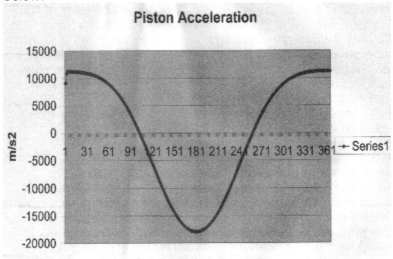

Although the signs are positive and negative, both at TDC and BDC the connecting rod is first slowing either the upward or downward motion of the piston, then accelerating it in the opposite direction and (in the absence of any gas pressure acting on the piston) this will cause tensile forces in the connecting rod.

The data in this example is from a 1.1 litre Rover 'K' Series engine with a bore of 75mm and a stroke of 63mm (described as 'over square') and a connecting rod length of 138.5 mm between centres. The piston mass is assumed to be 0.3 kg and the connecting rod mass 0.375 kg.

The engine is assumed to be running at 6500 rpm (probably slightly beyond the limits of the standard engine). The csa of the connecting rod is assumed to be as shown in section 11.6.5.

From the chart above (taken from the spread sheet) the maximum acceleration at TDC is 17900 m/s^2, with a total mass of 0.675 kg to accelerate, this requires a force of 0.675 x 17900 = 12080 N. Assuming the connecting rod has a cross section area of 300 mm, the stress will be 12080/300 = 40.3 MPa. Even if there is a stress concentration factor present and a surface roughness factor to be considered, this should be below the fatigue endurance strength of most steels that would be considered for manufacture of connecting rods.

When the piston is at TDC and ignition has just taken place, gas pressure is acting down on the piston and has to accelerate the piston before compressive forces are transmitted to the connecting rod to generate torque in the crankshaft. Assuming a maximum

combustion pressure of 5 MPa is acting over the crown of the piston, this is a force of $5 \times 3.14159 \times (75)^2/4 = 22089$ N.
The downward acceleration of the 0.3 kg piston is 17900 m/s^2 which requires a force of $0.3 \times 17900 = 5370$ N, leaving 16719 N to generate a compressive stress in the connecting rod. The compressive stress is $16719/300 = 55.7$ MPa.
Fatigue cracks normally only grow during tensile stress cycles, so from a fatigue or simple compressive stress failure, 55.7 MPa is unlikely to be a problem. However compressive stresses can give rise to instability failures in slender components and thin plates. So the connecting rod will be assessed against possible buckling failure in the section 11.6.

11.5.3 Effects of Lateral Acceleration
An approximate calculation of the maximum bending stresses due to lateral acceleration of the big end of the connecting rod can be made by assuming the connecting rod has a uniformly distributed mass, the little end in the piston has zero lateral acceleration and the big end on the crankshaft will have a maximum lateral acceleration when the big end carrying it is at 90° to the stroke direction. The acceleration of the big end perpendicular to the stroke direction will then be given by: $r(omega)^2$,
where r is the radius of the crank throw, half the stroke, and omega is the engine angular velocity in radians per second. At this instant the connecting rod will be subjected to a lateral acceleration that varies from zero at the little end to the above maximum at the big end. Using the weight per unit length of the connecting rod this acceleration distribution will give a linearly varying distributed load per unit length.

With the crank throw mid way between BDC and TDC, the fact that the connecting rod is not vertical is ignored in the calculation below.

Substituting the numbers form the previous section:

Big end acceleration = $0.0315[2 \times 3.14159 \times 6500/60]^2 = 14600$ m/s^2

At the mid length, the assumed location of the centre of mass, the lateral acceleration of the connecting rod will be half of the above value, ie 7300 m/s^2.

The lateral force needed to provide this acceleration to the centre of mass is:

$0.375 \times 7300 = 2737$ N
The equivalent load is shown schematically below:

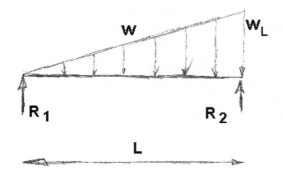

$R_2 = 2 R_1$ and $R_2 + R_1 = 2737$ N

From Roark, ref. 11.1: $R_1 = w_L L/6$ and $R_2 = w_L L/3$

So $3w_L L/6 = 2737$ N giving $w_L = 6 \times 2737/(3 \times 0.1385) = 39523$ N

The maximum bending moment is at $x = 0.5773 L$ and has a value:
$M_{max} = 0.0641 w_L L^2$

Substituting values: $M_{max} = 0.0641 \times 39523 \times (0.1385)^2 = 48.6$ Nm

This will give rise to a maximum bending stress given by:

$\text{sigma}_{max\ bending} = M y / I$

Substituting values:

$\text{sigma}_{max\ bending} = 48.6 \times 0.01 / 12.5E\text{-}9 = 38.9$ MPa.

This stress is well below the likely fatigue endurance strength of steels likely to be chosen for connecting rods.

11.5.4 Discussion
It should be noted that the shape chosen for the connecting rod cross section is a simplification and the actual connecting rod has a smaller cross section than used in the example calculations. Also the actual connecting rods are not a uniform cross section area (CSA), the CSA is larger at the big end than at the little end.

The maximum tensile and compressive stresses occur when the pistons are at TDC and BDC, however the maximum bending stresses occur with the piston in mid stroke, so even when the stresses are combined the maximum resultant stress will not be much larger than the individual values.

The above analysis was very approximate and when designing connecting rods for high performance engines it would be advisable to carry out FEA, with preliminary motion analysis to provide the dynamic loadings. Careful modeling would be needed to ensure fillets around the big and little ends are accurately represented as these are the regions were stress concentrations are likely to occur. For highly loaded connecting rods some polishing and inspection of the surfaces would be needed to ensure there were no significant stress raisers due to poor surface finish. Obviously the FEA can not consider such surface effects which can be critical in applications involving fatigue loading.

11.5.6 Materials and Manufacturing Processes for Connecting Rods
High quality connecting rods, made from similar materials and using similar processes to those employed in the manufacture of high quality crank shafts, are forged from Ni-Cr-Mo, Cr-Mo, or similar steels, with a total alloy content of up to about 2.5 % with additionally about 0.3 - 0.4 % carbon. Following forging the rods would be heat treated to give a combination of strength and toughness and then the critical dimensions are ground to finished size.
For high performance engines where cost is a minor consideration, titanium alloys are used.

Connecting rods for mass market engines are made from less costly materials steels, possibly medium carbon and sometimes nodular cast iron.

Some connecting rods are mode via a powder metallurgy pressing and sintering process. This is often combined with a fracture process to give a 'perfect fit' of the big end bearing cap to the bottom of the connecting rod. The rod is formed in one piece and notched at either side of the centre line of the big end at the required location of the join. A suitable impact is used to fracture the big end and the crystalline surfaces provide superb location when the end cap is assembled back onto the rod.

11.6 Buckling of Slender Struts Under Compression
11.6.1 Introduction
A type of failure that is sometimes overlooked for a body subject to compressive loading is that due to instability, called buckling. The longer and more slender the column is, the lower the safe compressive stress that it can withstand. The slenderness of a column is measured by the slenderness ratio, L/k, where L is the length of the column and (lower case) $k = (I/A)^{0.5}$ the radius of gyration of the cross sectional area about the centroidal axis. The minimum radius of gyration is the one to be considered. This

corresponds to the minimum value of I, the second moment of area of the section. A is the cross section area.

11.6.2 Eulers Formula

Euler (1707 - 1783) analysis applies to slender columns, the formula, for the critical axial concentric load that causes the column to be on the point of collapse for frictionless pinned ends (no bending moment at the ends) is given below.
This analysis involves defining the critical axial load.
If a small axial compressive load is applied to a straight slender rod and the system is pulled sideways slightly and released it will spring back to the straight position. If a large axial compressive load is applied, any sideways movement of the system will result in the system collapsing.

The critical axial compressive load represents the boundary between these two conditions. The system is just held in the deflected position by the compressive load. This is the neutral equilibrium configuration.

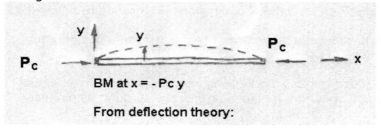

BM at x = - Pc y

From deflection theory:

$$EI \frac{d^2y}{dx^2} = -P_c\, y$$

$$let \quad a^2 = \frac{P_c}{EI}$$

$$\frac{d^2y}{dx^2} + a^2 y = 0$$

The solution of this is given by:

$$y = C_1 sin(ax) + C_2 cos(ax)$$

Boundary conditions:
    i) when x = 0, y = 0, so $C_2 = 0$

    ii) when x = L, y = 0, so $0 = C_1 sin(aL)$

$$\therefore \quad al = n\pi \;, \quad n = \text{any integer}$$

$$\frac{P_c}{EI} = \left(\frac{n\pi}{L}\right)^2$$

$$\text{or} \quad P_c = \frac{EI\,n^2\pi^2}{L^2}$$

$$\text{or for } n = 1: \quad P_c = \frac{EI\pi^2}{L^2}$$

In most engineering it is the lowest value of the critical force that is of interest, so the formula with n = 1 is normally used.

Depending upon the value of n, different modal shapes are produced. In the case of a slowly applied load only the first modal shape is likely to be produced, however in the case of a high speed impact, higher modal shapes may be produced:

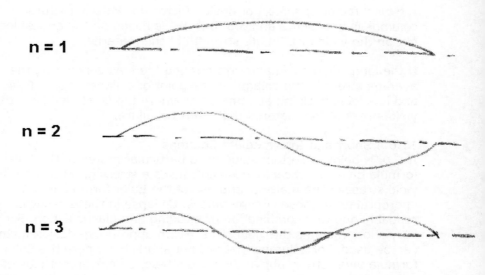

n = 1

n = 2

n = 3

For a particular column cross section and length, the load capacity F_c depends only upon the modulus of elasticity E. Since there is little variation in E among diferent grades of steel, there is no advantage in using an expensive, high strength alloy steel instead of structural steel for columns with L/k greater than about l20.

11.6.3 Effective Length
Eulers equation as written can be applied to a column with ends fixed in any manner if the length is taken as that between sections of zero bending moment. This length is called the effective length, L_e and is equal to KL (upper case) K, where L is the actual length and K is a constant dependent upon the end fixings. Theoretical values for different types of column ends are shown below. It should be noted that design codes issued by some organisations often recommend values that are somewhat different to these theoretical values, see right hand column.

End Fixings	Theoretical K value	Practical K value
pinned frictionless ends:	K=1	K=1
fixed ends:	K=0.5	K=0.65
fixed - pinned and guided:	K=0.7	K=0.8
fixed - free:	K=2	K=2.1

A typical factor of safety, or design factor, for Euler structural columns is between 2 and 3.5, **but** this is based on the **critical load**, not on the yield or ultimate strength of the material.

If the long column remains straight and the load concentric, the average stress in the column at the point of collapse is $s_c = F_c/A$ and it is local buckling at some point where the stress is below the yield stress of the material that leads to failure.

11.6.4 Short and Intermediate Columns
If L_e/k is below a certain value for a particular material, the Euler formula gives a critical load which causes a stress greater than the yield stress of the material and use of the Euler formula is not appropruiate in these circumstances. Collapse in these cases is probably due to a combination of buckling and plastic action. For very short columns the yield stress (with appropriate design factor) can be used. For columns that are not short, but where the Euler formula gives stress above the yield stress, empirical methods of design are used. One popular equation in use since the early 1900s is the Johnson formula which can be used for columns with slenderness ratios below a transition slenderness ratio or column constant, C_c.

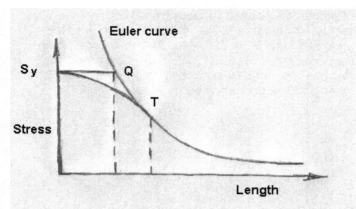

At Q the Euler curve gives too high a load and an alternative formula should be used.
Select point 'T' so $P_c/A = S_y/2$ then:

$$P_c = \frac{A S_y}{2} = \frac{\pi^2 E I}{L^2} = \frac{\pi^2 E A}{\left(\frac{L}{k}\right)^2_c}$$

$$\left(\frac{L}{k}\right)^2_c = \frac{2 \pi^2 E}{S_y}$$

$$C_c = \sqrt{\frac{2 \pi^2 E}{S_y}}$$

When the value of the slenderness ratio, L_e/k, is less than the critical slenderness ratio, C_c, the Johnson formula (or similar) should be used.

The Johnson Formula:

$$F_c = A S_y \left[1 - \frac{S_y (KL/k)^2}{4 \pi^2 E} \right]$$

As a very rough guide, for steel, the Euler buckling formula is only applicable for columns with L_e/k exceeding about 100, depending upon the yield stress.

It should be noted that sheets and plates may suffer buckling. Where a fabricated 'I' section beam has an insufficiently thick web, this can also suffer from buckling. Standard sections are sized so this is unlikely to be a problem.

11.6.5 Example Calculation Applied to Data from section 11.5.2

It is assumed that the connecting rod is made from steel with E = 200 GPa and a yield strength S_y = 250 MPa. As can be seen below, this gives a critical slenderness ratio of 125.7. It is assumed that the connecting rod has a simple 'H' section with an overall depth of 20 mm corresponding to the section sketched below:

$$C_c = \sqrt{\frac{2\pi^2 E}{S_y}}$$

$$C_c = \sqrt{\frac{2\pi^2 \, 200\,E9}{250\,E6}}$$

$$= 125.7$$

$$I = \frac{b\,d^3}{12}$$

$$= \frac{(0.02)^4}{12} - \frac{(0.01)^4}{12}$$

$$= 12.5\,E-9 \; m^4$$

$$k^2 A = I$$

$$k^2 = \frac{12.5\,E-9}{0.0003} = 41.6\,E-6 \; m^2$$

$$k = 0.00645\,m = 6.45\,mm$$

$$l = 138.5\,mm$$

$$\frac{l}{k} = \frac{138.5}{6.45} = 21.47$$

The big end bearing means that the most likely buckling axis is the dashed horizontal line on the sketch. The 'I' value for the buckling calculation is evaluated about this centre line. From the I value the radius of gyration, k, is calculated and used to determine the actual slenderness ratio of 21.47 which is well below the C_c value, indicating that the Johnson formula for short and intermediate columns must be used. This is done below:

$$F_c = A S_y \left[1 - \frac{S_y (K L/k)^2}{4 \pi^2 E} \right]$$

$$= 300 \times 250 \left[1 - \frac{250 \left(\frac{1 \times 0.1385}{0.00645} \right)^2}{4 \pi^2 \; 200 \, E3} \right]$$

$$= 73900 \; N$$

A is the cross section area, in the above using mm^2
S_y is the yield strength, given in MPa, so after multiplying the units outside the bracket are in N.

K is the end fixing factor, 1 for a pin joint, L is the length of the connecting rod between centres (m), k the radius of gyration of the connecting rod (m)

For Young's modulus, E, 200 GPa has been used and divided by 1000000, leaving 200E3 on the bottom line, now E as on an engineering calculator, not Young's modulus.

This gives a load carrying capacity of 98.5 % of that of a short column.

The design factor, or FoS, based on load, is 73900/16719 = 4.4, which is almost certainly adequate.

References
11.1 'Roark's Formulas for Stress and Strain', by W C Young, 7th Ed. McGraw Hill.

12 The Design of Bearings

- how to stop components in that have to move relative to one another wearing.

12.1 Introduction
Most mechanical engineering products and systems involve components that move relative to one another. Ensuring these operate with a minimum of wear, friction (and therefore a minimum of heat generation) is vital to the long term performance of these products and systems.

Bearings minimise the wear and friction between 2 surfaces in relative motion. This can be done in a number of ways:

- i) Provide an intermediate rolling element.
- ii) Provide a fuid film to keep the 2 surfaces apart.
- iii) Provide a material at the interface that minimises friction and / or wear.

    This 'interface material' might be:

    - A grease film
    - A soft metal or plastic layer bonded onto one of the surfaces.
    - A chemical film which has inherent lubricating properties such as graphite, molybdenum disulphide, tungsten disulphide or PTFE

12.2 Rolling Bearings
12.2.1 Introduction

- Use rollers as the intermediate rolling element for very high radial loads.
- Use balls for radial and some axial load.
- Use taper rollers (in pairs of bearings) for high radial and axial loads.
- Use needle rollers for rapidly fluctuating radial loads.

Web sites of the major bearing companies: SKF, Timken, provide detailed information for designers often including interactive calculators.

Features:

- Friction is very low, typically the coefficient of friction is between 0.0015 and 0.002.
- Have to be manufactured to very close tolerances - can be expensive.
- Need to be fitted (carefully) to accurately manufactured housings and shafts.
- Because of very high stresses in small contact zones between the rolling elements and the tracks, bearings are usually made from hardened 52100 chromium steel, which limits the maximum operating temperature to about 180° C. For operation at higher temperatures, more exotic materials must be used, which is likely to be very expensive.
- Some lubrication is essential, if the operating (or storage) environment is corrosive, appropriate seals must be fitted.
- Usually fail by fatigue - hence some short lives can occur.

12.2.2 Rolling Element Bearing Lives

Bearing lives may be determined by the ISO equation for the basic life rating (ISO 281:1990) used in conjunction with manufacturers charts and data for basic load ratings, static or dynamic.

$$L_{10} = (C/P)^p \text{ or } C/P = (L_{10})^{1/p}$$

where L_{10} = basic rating life, millions of revolutions, the life that 90% of a large sample of bearings is expected to equal or exceed.

C = basic dynamic load rating, N

P = equivalent dynamic load, N

p = life equation exponent, 3 for ball bearings, 10/3 for roller bearings.

The above equation can be extended to relate:

desired load: F_D (kN), life L_D (hours) and speed $n_D 60$ (r/min)

to the

catalogue rating: C_{10}, rating life L_R (hours), rating speed $n_R 60$ so:

$$F_D(L_D n_D 60)^{1/p} = C_{10}(L_R n_R 60)^{1/p}$$

To give:

$$C_{10} = F_{10}(L_D n_D 60 / L_R n_R 60)^{1/p}$$

SKF rates its bearings for 1 million revolutions so that the L_{10} life is $60 L_R n_R = 10^6$ revolutions.

As an example: If a life of 8000 hours is required at 1800 r/min with a load of 3000 N with a reliability of 90 %, what rating would be needed from the SKF catalogue?

Substituting values in the equation for C_{10}:

$$C_{10} = 3000[8000(1800)60/1000000]^{1/3} = 28.6 \text{ kN}$$

From the on line SKF catalogue it appears that a 30 mm bore 6306 type deep groove ball bearing may well meet this requirement.

Because of the life equation exponent, 3 or 3.33, a small increase in the equivalent load will cause a large drop in the L_{10}. This means that rolling bearings are not particularly suitable where overloads or shock loading are likely. Consequently rolling bearings are not normally used in main or big end bearings in IC engines as combustion applies a shock load to these bearings. The exception this is for 2 stroke engines using crankcase compression which would result in the lubricating oil for hydrodynamic bearings being diluted with petrol, reducing the viscosity of the resulting liquid rendering it unable to keep the surfaces separate. For these applications rolling element bearings are used as a mixture of about 1 part in 50 of oil in petrol provides adequate lubrication for such bearings. Unfortunately the presence of this oil in the petrol means that the products of combustion are less environmentally acceptable. The problems of emissions and poor fuel consumption have led to far fewer 2 stroke engines being manufactured than was the case 30 years ago.

12.2.3 Materials
While the vast majority of rolling bearings use hardened steel for the rolling elements and tracks, some applications require other materials, such as plastics or ceramics. Euro Bearings manufacture plastic and other specialist rolling element bearings.
One manufacturer has improved the performance of rolling bearings made from steel by the use of very clean steel. The reduced impurity content reduces the sites available for crack initiation and improves fatigue performance.

Bearings for use in gas turbine jet engines need to withstand shaft operating temperatures of up to 230°C. On shutting down jet

engines even higher temperatures are reached as heat 'soaks back' from hotter engine components after the cooling system closes down.
Bearings for these applications are often made from M50 high speed tool steel. Unfortunately the high hardness and low ductility of this material means that these bearings are vulnerable to fracture if debris gets into the lubricating system. This is more of a potential problem in desert operating conditions.

Silicon nitride (Si_3N_4) bearings are in regular use in Formula 1 racing cars. Wheel bearings (angular contact ball bearing type) are usually 'hybrid', silicon nitride rolling elements (balls) and steel races. To give a higher temperature capability than is available from standard 52100 steel, so called high nitrogen steels have been developed. This type of bearing typically gives an increase in life by a factor of 10. However when used in a Formula 1 car the life is about 2000 km.
Hybrid bearings are also used in formula one gear boxes. Costs presently limit wider application - a set of hybrid bearings for a Formula 1 gearbox costs about 5000 Euros - over £3000.
Cerobear GmbH such make ceramic bearings.

12.3 Fluid Film Bearings
12.3.1 Introduction
The coefficient of friction in a lubricated bearing varies depending upon the absolute viscosity, the speed and the pressure per unit projected area, but has the same general form shown in this 'Stribeck' plot. To the right of the dividing line the surfaces are totally separated by hydrodynamic forces which increase linearly with speed whereas in the zone to the left, some surface contact is occurring, which decreases (reducing friction) as the lubrication develops.

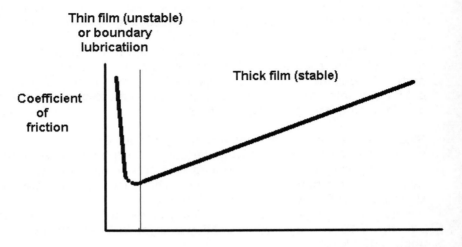

Bearing characteristic: viscosity x speed/load per projected area

(sometimes called the 'Stribeck' curve)

A fluid film dragged (due to its viscosity) into converging gap, can generate extremely high pressures (high enough in some circumstances to cause plastic deformation of a metal). The pressure generated depends upon the fluid viscosity, the taper of the gap and the relative speed of the moving surfaces. A second order effect is the viscosity - temperature characteristic of the fluid. This mechanism is very reliable in continuous (rotational) motion, but for high speed - high load applications an oil cooler may be needed.

These notes will introduce some of the theory and describe the calculation procedure for an fluid lubricated plain journal bearing design.

In a dry bearing, the shaft tends to 'climb' up the bearing, whereas in a lubricated bearing, the lubricant being drawn into the bearing tends to push the shaft away from the bearing on the entry side, see Fig.L1:

Shafts rotating clockwise

Q

Lubricated - lubricant is drawn into
gap, pushing shaft to left

Dry - shaft 'climbs up' right side of bearing
Fig. L1.

12.3.2 Newtons Law of Viscous Flow:
The shear stress in a fluid is proportional to the rate of change of
velocity with respect to 'y', ie:

$$\tau = \frac{F}{A} = \mu \frac{du}{dy}$$

where μ is the dynamic or absolute viscosity

If it is assumed that the shear rate is constant, then: du/dy = U/h
and

$$\tau = \frac{F}{A} = \mu \frac{U}{h}$$ Units of absolute viscosity are Pa.s or
N.s/m^2.

The ASTM method for determining viscosity uses a 'Saybolt
Universal Viscometer' and involves measuring the time taken by a
volume of fluid to descend a specific distance down a tube of a
certain diameter.

12.3.3 Petroff's Law: If a shaft radius, 'r', is rotating in a bearing,
length, 'l', and radial clearance, 'c' at 'N' revs per s, then the surface
velocity is:

$$u = 2\pi r N_{m/s}$$

The shearing stress is the velocity gradient x viscosity:

$$\tau = \mu \frac{u}{h} = \frac{2\pi r \mu N}{c}$$

The torque to shear the film is force x lever arm length:

$$T = (\tau A)r = \left(\frac{2\pi \mu r N}{c}\right)(2\pi r l)r = \frac{4\pi^2 r^3 l \mu N}{c}$$

If a small force, 'w', is applied normal to the shaft axis, the pressure (force/projected area) in N/m^2 is:

p = w/2rl The frictional force is fw, where 'f' is the coefficient of friction, so the frictional torque is:

T = fwr = (f)(2rlp)(r) = $2r^2flp$

Equating the two expressions for T and solving for f gives:

$$f = \frac{2\pi^2 r \mu N}{cp}$$
which is Petroff's Law.

$$\frac{\mu N}{p}, \quad \frac{\tau}{c}$$
are dimensionless groups.

The bearing characteristic or Sommerfeld Number is defined as:

$$S = \left(\frac{r}{c}\right)^2 \left(\frac{\mu N}{p}\right)$$

This is a key quantity in bearing design.

While the above equation is the original form of the Sommerfeld Number, it has since been realised that the performance of a hydrodynamic bearing is not only dependent upon the shaft or journal rotation, but also upon any rotation of the load vector and of the bushing. Hence the value of N which is important for bearing performance is:

$N = N_j + N_b - 2N_w$

where N_j is the journal or shaft speed of rotation
N_b is the bush speed of rotation
N_w is the load vector speed of rotation

Converting this to dimensionless form gives:

$$S' = S(1 + (N_b/N_j) - 2(N_w/N_j))$$

and it is the S' value that is used to enter the Raimondi and Boyd charts along the abscissa.

Fig. L2, below, shows some bearing nomenclature

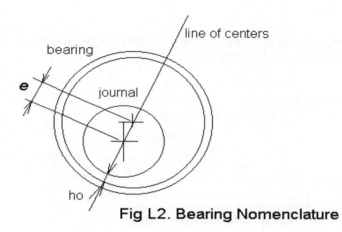

Fig L2. Bearing Nomenclature

12.3.4 Assumptions:

- 1 The lubricant obeys Newton's laws of viscous flow.
- 2 Intertia effects of the lubricant are neglected.
- 3 The lubricant is incompressible.
- 4 The viscosity of the lubricant is constant throughout the film.
- 5 The pressure does not vary in the axial direction.
- 6 The curvature of the bearing can be ignored.
- 7 There is no flow in the axial ('z') direction.
- 8 The film pressure is constant in the 'y' direction, and depends upon 'x'.
- 9 The velocity of a lubricant particle depends on its 'x' and 'y' coordinates.

From the free body diagram of the forces acting on a small cube of lubricant:

$$\frac{dp}{dx} = \frac{d\tau}{dy} \quad , \quad as \quad \tau = \mu \frac{\partial u}{\partial y} \quad : \quad \frac{dp}{dx} = \mu \frac{\partial^2 u}{\partial y^2}$$

Assuming there is no slip at the boundary, with 'x' held constant, integrate twice with respect to 'y' which gives:

$$u = \frac{1}{2\mu} \frac{dp}{dx} (y^2 - hy) - \frac{U}{h} y$$

which is the velocity distribution as a function of 'y' and the pressure gradient, dp/dx, see Fig.L3:

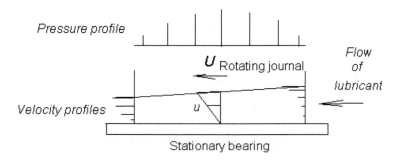

Fig.L3. Velocity profiles in converging lubricant film

The velocity distribution across the film is obtained by superimposing a parabolic distribution (the first term) onto a linear distribution (the second term). When the pressure is a maximum, dp/dx = 0 and the velocity is u = - Uy/h.

If 'Q' is the quantity of fluid flowing in the 'x' direction per unit time:

$Q = \int u \, dy$ In practice these integrations have to be modified to include the effects of end leakage etc. Most automotive main and big end bearings have a L:D ratio quite a lot less than 1 (actually 0.33 for the big end bearings and 0.465 for the big end bearings for the 1.1 litre 'K-Series' engine) this leads to high oil flow which assists engine cooling while helping to minimise the length of the engine. Oil supply is through a hole in the upper half where the bearing pressures are low. Some bearing shells have a central groove, this causes it to function like two separate side by side bearings and this reduces the maximum pressure and the total load carrying capacity.

12.3.5 Detailed Design - Assumptions

A number of parameters may be under the control of the designer, but there are another group which are dependent on the first group and can be used to define operational limits for the bearing. Assumption 4, above, that the viscosity is constant throughout the film, is not very accurate as the oil temperature rises as it passes through the bearing and as the viscosity is strongly dependent upon the temperature, it means that bearing design normally involves some iteration, either using tables (see Appendix 12.1) charts (those by A A Raimondi and J Boyd, 'A Solution for the Finite Journal Bearing and its Application to Analysis and Design: III', Trans. ASLE 1, 1958, 194-209, are widely used) or computer software.

To ensure full hydrodynamic lubrication is maintained in the bearing the 'bearing modulus (mu.N/p) should be equal to or greater than 1.09×10^{-9}

Given or controlled by the designer:

- lubricant viscosity, mu
- load per unit projected area, p
- speed, 'N'
- dimensions: r, c, l and beta (the angle subtended by the load bearing portion of the bearing).

The following are dependent upon the first group:

- coefficient of friction
- temperature rise, 'deltaT'
- oil flow rate, 'Q'
- minimum film thickness, h_o

Many charts use US units for viscosity, ie reyns (usually plotted as micro-reyns). To convert reyns to Pa.s, multiply by 6890.

In the absence of specific information, it may be assumed that mineral lubricating oil has a density of about 850 kg/m^3 and a specific heat of about 1675 J/kg°C.

For hydrodynamic bearings, a length / diameter ratio of about 1 (say 0.8 to 1.3) is believed to be a good compromise. l/d ratios of <1 may be used where a compact design is important, such as in a multicylinder automotive engine. Reducing the l/d ratio increases the proportion of the flow out of the bearing ends (the side flow, Q_s) which aids cooling.

The minimum film thickness acceptable depends upon surface finish and should allow expected particles to pass through without causing damage. For some applications, eg in automotive engines, filtering is provided to remove particles whose size would be likely to exceed the minimum film thickness. The following h_o values have been suggested:

☐ 0.0000025 m for finely bored small bronze bushes.
☐ 0.00002 m for commercial babbitted bearings.
☐ $0.0000025 < h_o < 0.000005$ m for automotive engines with fine surface finish bearings and lubricant filtering.

Maximum oil temperatures should not be allowed to be excessive as oxidation and degradation become rapid. For general purpose machinery, an oil operating temperature of 60°C should give a good long life. Above 100°C the rate of oxidation increases rapidly. Temperatures of 120°C should be avoided in industrial equipment. In automotive engines lubricant temperatures can reach 180°C, but automotive oils are specially formulated (and are now frequently fully 'synthetic') to withstand such conditions.

The list below gives typical maximum values of bearing 'nominal' pressures (load/length x diameter).

Electric motors, steam turbines, gear reducers, centrifugal pumps about 1 MPa

Automotive engines - main bearings: 4 - 5 MPa

crankpin: 10 - 15 MPa
gudgeon pin: 14 - 35 MPa

Diesel engines - main bearing: 6 - 12 MPa

crankpin: 8 - 15 Mpa

Typically the working absolute viscosity of the oil in automotive engine big end and main bearings is 0.007 - 0.008 Pa.s which corresponds to SAE grade 40 oil at 105°C.

12.3.6 Design Procedure

1 Select an l/d ratio, 1 is probably a good starting point.

2 Using the specified load and an appropriate 'nominal' pressure, select the bearing length and diameter.

3 Specify an appropriate radial clearance, 'c', probably based on either a close (H8/f7) or free (H9/d9) running fit.

4 Decide on an initial lubricant viscosity. Because viscosity varies considerably with temperature, it is normally necessary to carry out the calculations below at two values of viscosity, one slightly below and the other slightly above the anticipated final value.

5 Evaluate the 'bearing characteristic number' or Sommerfeld number ('S').

6 From a table or chart plotting the 'minimum film thickness variable' against the 'bearing characteristic number', read off the minimum film thickness number for the calculated bearing characteristic number and the selected l/d ratio.

7 The minimum film thickness can now be calculated - and checked to see if it is reasonable.

8 The eccentricity ratio can be calculated.

9 If required, the angular position of the minimum film thickness (phi) can be found from an appropriate table or chart.

10 From a table or chart plotting the 'coefficient of friction' variable against the 'bearing characteristic number', read off the coefficient of friction' variable for the calculated bearing characteristic number and the selected l/d ratio.

11 Calculate the coefficient of friction. Using this with the radius and load, calculate the torque needed to overcome the friction. Using the coefficient of friction and the shaft speed, calculate the power lost in friction.

12 From a table or chart plotting the 'flow variable' against the 'bearing characteistic number' read the flow variable for the calculated characteristic number and the selected l/d ratio. Calculate the total oil flow.

13 From a table or chart plotting the 'flow ratio' against the 'bearing characteristic number', read off the flow ratio for the calculated bearing characteristic number and the selected l/d ratio. Calculate the side leakage of lubricant.

14 Calculate the rise in temperature of the lubricant - it is common to assume all the heat is carried away by the flowing oil and the the temperature of the side leakage oil is the mean of the inlet and outlet temperatures.

15 On a viscosity - temperature chart, check the viscosity of the the oil after it's temperature has increased by the amount calculated above, and assuming an appropriate inlet temperature.

16 Repeat the above calculations as needed to check the results with a viscosity at the mean of the inlet and outlet lubricant temperatures.

A worked example is given in Appendix 12.2

12.4 Lubricating Oils
The earliest lubricants consisted of animal and vegetable fats and although satisfactory before the advent of steam and other engines, their low resistance to oxidation, combined with chemistry which results in acids being formed during oxidation, leading to corrosion, meant that very soon after mineral oil was discovered, these fats went out of use.

Crude mineral oil consists mainly of varying amounts of paraffins, napthenes and aromatic compounds.
In the early days of mineral oil use, the source of the crude oil was significant, however cracking and refining developments meant that the source of the crude oil ceased to be significant. Until the 1940s all lubricating oils were obtained by cracking mineral oil then refining the appropriate products and incorporating appropriate additives. Now synthetic oils which are not directly derived from refined mineral oils are increasingly being used for arduous applications in automotive engines.

At low speeds the lubricating film is likely to break down and the surfaces come into contact. This must be allowed for in reciprocating motion (piston - cylinder liner) and also when normally continuous motion is starting or stopping. To accommodate intermittent motion, a thin soft layer (plastic or metal alloy depending upon the load) may be fixed or plated to one of the surfaces. When the two surfaces come into contact, the softer material tends to smear rather than wear. Any hard particles at the interface should be pushed into the softer material before causing too much damage.

For applications involving high local contact stresses and high sliding speeds, where the geometry does not favour the maintenance of full fluid film lubrication (hypoid gears) extreme pressure additives (sulphur and chlorine compounds) are added to the oil, then when metal to metal contact occurs, high local temperatures are generated, giving a local chemical reaction forming solid film lubricant in situ on the surface where required.

The list below summarises the main types of additives used in automotive engine lubricants.

Antiwear Agents
These form a protective film over the metal surface, reducing scuffing and wear especially on valve gear, cams and followers. Zinc dialkyldithiophosphate (ZDDP) was very widely used as an anti-wear additive to protect contacting metal surfaces with zinc and other compounds when metal to metal contact occurred, however the quantity of zinc dialkyldithiophosphate is now limited to minimize the adverse effect it can have on catalytic converters.

Friction Modifiers
Enhance vehicle fuel economy by reducing the metal to metal friction,
Examples include PTFE particles, electrostatically charged particles. Some of these additives also function as anti-wear agents and vice - versa.
It should be noted that one supplier of PTFE has been strongly opposed to adding it to engine oils, however a number of tests seem to indicate that it is beneficial.

Viscosity Modifiers
A major problem with mineral oils, and to a lesser extent with synthetic oils, is that they undergo a rapid change in viscosity with temperature. The viscosity of a mineral oil may well be halved for every 20°C rise in temperature.
Certain polymers improve the viscosity characteristics of the lubricant by reducing the change in viscosity with change in temperature. Many of these compounds are long chain molecules and these eventually become damaged with prolonged use.
Oils containing such viscosity improvers are termed 'multi-grade' oils.

Pour Point Depressants
These are added to lower the pour point or low-temperature fluidity characteristics of the lubricant.

Dispersants
Help suspend solid contaminants in the oil, inhibit and disperse sludge, soot and other insolubles and reduce the formation of varnish deposits.

Detergents
Minimise deposits on components such as pistons.

Antifoam Agents
These are used to change the surface tension between air and oil, so bubbles break-up rapidly and prevent foam formation.

Antioxidants
Hot oil oxidizes in the presence of air, causing it to become acidic and producing sludge. Antioxidants interfere with this chemical mechanism, reducing the rate of oil deterioration and extending the life of the oil.

Antirust Additives
Prevents the formation of rust by forming a surface film to protect the metal

Corrosion Inhibitors
Corrosion inhibitors protect lubricated metal surfaces from chemical attack by water or other contaminants.

12.5 Greases

For applications involving slow, occasional or intermittent motion where the loads are not very high, greases may be used. A grease is a solid or semi - fluid lubricant consisting of a dispersion of a thickening agent in a lubricating fluid. The thickening agent may consist of a clay or a soap, the lubricating fluid is usually a mineral oil, a diester or a silicone. A mineral oil will run out of a bearing over a short period of time, a grease should remain in the bearing for a very long time.

12.6 Solid Lubrcants

Certain solid chemicals, mainly graphite, molybdenum disulphide, tungsten disulphide and PTFE can be applied to surfaces and because of their lamellar structure (or in the case of PTFE, their chemical inertness) they prevent metal to metal contact reducing friction and greatly reducing wear.
Important applications of these are lubricating joints that have to function in space as neither conventional oils nor grease work in space. Graphite only offers these benefits in the presence of small

amounts of moisture, it functions satisfactorily in ambient conditions on earth, but will not function in space.

PTFE is very widely used as a coating on tools such as wood saws. All these solid coatings suffer wear during operation and when the coating has worn through the joints will fail, possibly by seizure. Determining the appropriate coating application method and thickness is an important part of designing mechanisms to operate in space.

12.7 Simple Plain Bearings

Where slow speed - low load components rub together, possibly lubricated by grease, one of the surfaces will often be a non - metal, frequently a plastic.

Porous bushes, frequently made from sintered brass and impregnated with oil, are often used in domestic appliances and office eqipment where the loads are not excessive and where no maintenance is expected.

12.8 The Lubrication of the Piston Cylinder Interface in ICEs

As the piston stops and reverses direction at the end of each stroke, it is difficult to maintain an oil film at all times. The matter is complicated by the need to use a scraper ring to remove excess oil from the cylinder walls. Early research, summarised in ref. 12.2, has shown that the following:

- The surfaces of the piston ring and cylinder were never totally separated by a continuous film of lubricant throughout the entire cycle.
- With oil of higher viscosity there was considerably more hydrodynamic lubrication.
- At higher engine speeds there is more hydrodynamic lubrication than at low engine speeds.
- At higher piston ring loads there is greater breakdown of the hydrodynamic film.
- On starting up the engine, during the first revolution the lubrication was almost completely non - hydrodynamic, after 9 revolutions the oil film had built up and provided considerable hydrodynamic lubrication.

Over the years development work has resulted in a standard finish for cylinder bores of fine honing in a criss - cross pattern at a specific angle.

12.9 Seals

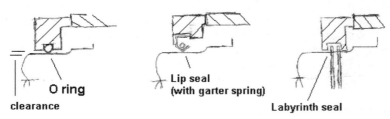

O ring

clearance

Lip seal
(with garter spring)

Labyrinth seal

To ensure the satisfactory operation of almost any bearing system it is essential to keep out any contamination or dirt. In many applications it is equally important to prevent any lubricant escaping, because it is bad for the environment, it may contaminate product and depletion of the lubricant will adversely effect the bearing operation and lead to premature failure.

Three types of seals are shown in the sketch above, for the types on the left and in the middle, a good fine surface finish on the shaft is essential.

- On the left is an 'O' ring seal. This uses a rubber ring slightly compressed by its housing, pressing it against the shaft. The degree of compression should be just sufficient to seal the operating pressure (with appropriate factor of safety). Excessive compression of the seal leads to excessive friction and wear. Too soft a rubber or too big a clearance will lead to the rubber seal being extruded out of the clearance. This type of seal can be used for rotation or reciprocating motion. These seals are widely used in general engineering.
- In the middle is a lip seal. This consists of a rubber lip pressed against the rotating shaft by a garter spring. High fluid pressure on the spring side - the right hand side in the sketch - increases the radial force pressing the lip against the shaft. High pressure on the opposite side of the seal to the spring will tend to lift the seal. This seal should therefore be used to seal fluid on the spring side and it is not suited to reciprocating motion. This type of seal is widely used in automotive engineering to seal wheel bearings and shafts in engines, particularly crank shafts.
- On the right is a labyrinth seal which is a non contacting 'seal' and rather than prevent leakage it reduces leakage by only offering a long, slender, meandering pathway for the fluid to escape along. These bearings are usually used in high temperatures applications where any contact would result in seizure and very rapid wear. As there is no contact, the surface finish of the shaft is not critical. Gas turbines and jet

engines use labyrinth seals at the ends of blades and on hot areas of shafting. The components are usually made from a stainless steel.

References

* 12.1: 'Mechanical Engineering Design', J E Shigley and C R Mischke, McGraw-Hill, 6th Ed., 2001, ISBN: 0-07-356939-8.

12.2: Friction and Lubrication of Solids', Part 1, F P Bowden and D Tabor, Oxford at the Clarendon Press, 1953.

A12.1: 'K' Series Engine Overhaul Manual, Publication Part no. AKM 6497, Rover Group Limited, 1990.

A12.2: Fuel Economy of the Gasoline Engine, by Blackmore, D. R and Thomas, A., Macmillan, London, 1977.

Appendix 12.1 Tabulated data based on Raimondi and Boyd for Hydrodynamic Bearing Design

(l/d)	h_o/c	S	phi	(r/c)f	(Q/rcN_sl)	Q_s/Q	p/p_{max}
inf	1.0	inf	70.9	inf	3.14159	0	
	0.9	0.240	69.1	4.8	3.03	0	0.826
	0.8	0.123	67.2	2.57	2.83	0	0.814
	0.6	0.0626	61.9	1.52	2.26	0	0.764
	0.4	0.0389	54.3	1.20	1.56	0	0.667
	0.2	0.021	42.2	0.961	0.760	0	0.495
	0.1	0.0115	31.6	0.756	0.411	0	0.358
1	1.0	inf	85	inf	3.14149	0	
	0.9	1.33	79.5	26.4	3.37	0.15	0.540
	0.8	0.631	74	12.8	3.59	0.28	0.529
	0.6	0.264	63.1	5.79	3.99	0.497	0.484
	0.4	0.121	50.58	3.22	4.33	0.68	0.415
	0.2	0.0446	36.2	1.70	4.62	0.84	0.313
	0.1	0.0188	26.45	1.05	4.74	0.919	0.247
	0.03	0.00474	15.47	0.514	4.82	0.973	0.152
0.5	1.0	inf	88.5	inf	3.14149	0	
	0.9	4.31	81.6	85.6	3.43	0.173	0.523
	0.8	2.03	74.9	40.9	3.72	0.318	0.506
	0.6	0.779	61.45	17.0	4.29	0.552	0.441
	0.4	0.319	48.14	8.10	4.85	0.730	0.365
	0.2	0.0923	33.3	3.26	5.41	0.874	0.267
	0.1	0.0313	23.66	1.60	5.69	0.939	0.206
	0.03	0.00609	13.75	0.610	5.88	0.980	0.126
0.25	1.0	inf	77	inf	3.14149	0	
	0.9	12	79	210	3.5	0.25	0.51
	0.8	7.6	74.5	150	3.7	0.32	0.485
	0.6	2.9	60	67	4.3	0.55	0.41
	0.4	1	46	23.5	4.94	0.75	0.325
	0.2	0.27	31.5	8.4	5.6	0.88	0.24
	0.1	0.08	22	3.6	5.9	0.945	0.18
	0.03	0.013	12.6	1.8	6.2	0.975	0.145

Appendix 12.2 Example - Lubrication Calculation - Hydrodynamic Bearing Design

1. Introduction

The standard assumptions are made in this calculation, see above. The design procedure used in this example makes use of dimensionless groups in tables or plotted against the Sommerfeld number on a series of charts (A A Raimondi and J Boyd, "A Solution for the Finite Journal Bearing and its Application to Analysis and Design", parts I, II and III, Trans. ASLE, vol 1, no. 1, 159-209) to determine other values for the bearing. These charts are reproduced in many texts on Mechanical Engineering Design, see ref. 12.1.

A plain bearing with hydrodynamic lubrication is to be designed to carry a load of 2500 Newtons at a shaft speed of 30 revs per second, = N.

Initial assumptions

SAE grade 40 oil will be used and the mean oil temperature in the bearing is 68.3°C (which corresponds to 155°F). At this temperature the oil has an absolute viscosity of 4 micro reyn (i.e. 27.5 mPa.s or 0.0275 Pa.s). The density is assumed to be 850 kg/m^3 and the specific heat 1800 J/kg °C

As a starting point it will be assumed that the: length / diameter ratio = 1 and for a first calculation length = diameter = 2 radius = 40 mm will be used. l = d = 2 r = 40mm

It is also assumed that the bearing / shaft is between a 'free running fit' - H9/d9 and a 'close running fit' - H8/f7 with a radial clearance of 0.04 mm.

2. Calculation

First check that the 'unit load' (load / projected area of bearing) is acceptable:

The unit load = load / (length x diameter) = 2500 / (0.04 x 0.04) = 1.56 MPa. This is perhaps on the high side for machinery (but low for IC engines) but this value is accepted for this example.

Bearing designs are commonly based on tables or charts using the 'Bearing Characteristic Number' or Sommerfeld Number, this is defined (in a non - dimensional way) as:

$$S = (r / c)^2(mu \ N/P)$$

where: r is radius, c is the radial clearance, mu is the absolute viscosity, N is shaft speed in revs/s and P is the unit load.

As there is no information given about rotation of the bush or load vector, it is assumed that these are not rotating and that S = S'. So:

Substituting values: S = (0.02 / 0.00004)^2(0.0275 x 30 / 1563000) = 0.132

i)

Determine the minimum film thickness variable h_o/c where h_o is the minimum film thickness for the specified of l/d ratio: $h_o/c = 0.41$ so the minimum film thickness

$$h_o = 0.41 \times 0.00004 = 0.0000164 \text{ m}$$

It is important that the minimum film thickness be significantly greater than the maximum surface roughness. Keep in mind the fact that surface roughness is usually given as an average roughness amplitude (Ra) and the extreme peak to valley depths may well be 3 - 6 times greater than the Ra.

The minimum film thickness = radial clearance - eccentricity

$h_o = r - e$, divide both sides by c

$h_o/c = 1 -$ epsilon where 'epsilon' is the eccentricity ratio.

The eccentricity of this design is $e = c - h_o$

$$e = 0.00004 - 0.0000164 = 0.0000236 \text{ m}$$

ii)

Determine the friction variable $f \, r/c$ where f is the coefficient of friction, the value of $f \, r/c$ is 3.3 so

$$f = 3.3 \times 0.00004 / 0.02 = 0.0066$$

The torque to overcome the friction = coefficient of friction x load x radius, substituting values

$$T = 0.0066 \times 2500 \times 0.02 = 0.33 \text{ Nm.}$$

The power lost is: torque x angular velocity, substituting values

$$\text{Power lost} = 0.33 \times 2 \times 3.14159 \times 30 = 62.2 \text{ watts.}$$

iii)

Determine the flow variable, $Q/(r \, c \, N \, l)$: $= 4.3$, substituting values:

The total flow, $Q = 4.3 \times 0.02 \times 0.00004 \times 30 \times 0.04 = 4.128$ E-6 m^3/s

iv)

Determine the (side) flow ratio (leakage ratio): $Q_s/Q = 0.66$, substituting values

The side leakage, $Q_s = 0.66 \times 4.128$ E-6 $= 2.724$ E-6 m^3/s

Rise in Oil Temperature.

It is assumed that the oil that is retained in the bearing rises in temperature by deltaT and the oil that leaks out of the side of the bearing rises in temperature by deltaT/2. First the volume flow rates need to be converted to kg/s.

Total oil mass flow rate = 4.128 E-6 x 850 = 0.003509 kg/s

Side leakage mass flow rate = 0.66 x 0.003509 = 0.002316 kg/s

Mass flow rate remaining in bearing = 0.34 x 0.003509 = 0.001193 kg/s

Carrying out an energy balance assuming that all the energy put into the oil raises only the oil temperature:

62.2 = 1800 (0.002316 deltaT/2 + 0.001193 deltaT)

The rise in oil temperature: deltaT = 14.7° C, assume 15° C.

Oil cooling.

As it was assumed at the outset that the mean oil temperature was 68.3° C, this means that the inlet oil temperature would be 68.3 - 7.5 = 60.8° C and the outlet temperature 75.8° C. Provided there is sufficient cooling available to ensure the oil from the bearing outlet is cooled to 60° C or less, then this design may well be acceptable. As the viscosity of most oils changes very rapidly (typically halving for a 20° C temperature rise) it is important to check operation will still be satisfactory outside these limits - for example when starting from cold and during short periods of overloading.

As well as the above charts there are also charts to provide additional information such as the maximum film pressure, the angular position where the oil film thickness is a minimum and where it terminates.

Appendix 12.3 Example - Lubrication Calculation - Approximate Energy losses in Main and Big End Bearings

In this example an approximate calculation is made to estimate the losses in the engine main bearings and big end bearings, using dimensions for a Rover K series engine - from ref A12.1

- Main journal diameter = 48mm
- Main journal width = 16mm
- Big end journal diameter = 43mm
- Big end journal width = 20mm
- Clearance in bearings 0.021 - 0.049 mm

It is assumed that:

- The average radial clearance is 0.035 / 2 =0.0175mm
- The engine speed is 3000RPM = 50revs/second
- The minimum oil film thickness under load is 0.003mm and that this extends for 1/3 of the journal periphery
- Of the 5 main bearings and the 4 big end bearings it is assumed that at any one time there are 2 main bearings and 1 big end bearing under load with minimum oil film thickness. The other bearings are assumed to be essentially unloaded and the journals central in the bearings. These is very approximate assumptions!

- The oil used is assumed while in the bearing to have a viscosity of 0.007 Pa.s

Main bearing sliding velocity = 50 x 3.14159 x 0.048 = 7.54 m/s

Big end bearing sliding average sliding velocity = 50 x 3.14159 x 0.043 = 6.754 m/s, this will fluctuate somewhat with the oscillation of the connecting rod.

Shear stress in the oil film = viscosity x sliding speed / film thickness

For the main bearings than are not loaded:

Shear stress in film = 0.007 x 7.54 / 0.0000175 = 2980 Pa

Multiply by area to give the force to shear the film: 2980 x 3.14159 x 0.048 x 0.016 = 7.19 N

Multiply by the sliding speed to give the power required: 7.19 x 7.54 = 54.2 watts.

For the big end bearings than are not loaded:

Shear stress in film = 0.007 x 6.754 / 0.0000175 = 2616Pa

Multiply by area to give the force to shear the film: 2616 x 3.14159 x 0.043 x 0.020 = 7.07N

Multiply by the sliding speed to give the power required: 7.07 x 6.754 = 47.7 watts.

Assuming there are 3 unloaded main bearings and 3 unloaded big end bearings, the total power lost from these 8 unloaded bearings is 3 x (54.2 + 47.7)

For the loaded main bearings:

Shear stress in film = 0.007 x 7.54 / 0.000003 = 17593 Pa

Multiply by area to give the force to shear the film: 17593 x 3.14159 x 0.048 x 0.016 / 3 = 14.15 N

Multiply by the sliding speed to give the power required: 14.15 x 7.54 = 106.7 watts.

For the loaded big end bearing:
Shear stress in film = 0.007 x 6.754 / 0.000003 = 15759 Pa

Multiply by area to give the force to shear the film: 15759 x 3.14159 x 0.043 x 0.020 / 3 = 14.19 N

Multiply by the sliding speed to give the power required: 14.19 x 6.754 = 95.86 watts.

Total for all the 9 bearings:

= 95.86 + 2 x (106.7) + 3 x (54.2 + 47.7) = 615 watts

The engine output (1100cc) is nominally 45 kW at 5700rpm so at 3000rpm the power will probably be about 26 kW, mechanical (friction) losses will probably be similar. Publications (ref. A12.2) suggest big end, main bearing bearing and seal friction represents about 10% of the total losses.

The figure above is clearly below that proportion. No account was taken for thrust bearings or seals in the above calculation.

13 Bolted, Welded, Brazed and Adhesive Joints

13.1 Introduction - Choice of Joining Process

The key feature of bolted joints is that they can be dismantled comparatively easily. However they are costly in that additional parts are needed (washer, nut) compared to riveted or welded joints and they require more skill / effort to assemble. For these reasons they should only be used where there is a strong possibility that the parts will at some stage require to be separated. For other joints it is usually preferable to use some other method of connection such as welding, brazing or adhesives.

To form a fusion welded joint the two metals to be joined are heated to their their melting point and a small pool of molten metal forms at the start of the joint. The weld can be carried out by moving the heating source (usually an oxy-acetylen flame or an electric arc) along the joint with the welding pool solidifying behind the heat source joining the components together. Usually a filler rod is added to the weld. In some processes the filler as a rod is dipped manually into the pool every 1 to 2 seconds, in other continuous processes, a wire is fed through the torch transmitting the electric arc as well as providing a stream of molten metal to add to the weld. This is a feature of the metal inert gas (MIG) process which is very widely used, particularly for welding applications which benefit from automation.

To weld two metals together successfully they must have some mutual solubility and reasonably similar melting points. In practice most fusion welds involve joining two identical or only slightly different grades of steel together, or two similar grades of aluminium together.

The main disadvantage of fusion welding is the high temperature that the metals must be heated to locally, this has the following disadvantages:

- Mechanical properties may be adversely affected, commonly loss of UTS.
- The metal in the vicinity of the joint may distort.
- There may be residual stresses in the vicinity of the weld, in extreme cases this can lead to cracking.
- Only very similar metals can be joined.

Where the restrictions above can not be met, then a brazing process may be suitable. Brazing involves heating the components to a temperature below their melting points but above that of a filler metal which wets the metal of each component.

The availability of high quality adhesives has meant that increasing use of these is being made in all areas of engineering, particularly for alloy automobile bodies where there high temperature operation is not an issue.

13.2 Bolted Joints
13.2.1 Introduction
There are several considerations when designing a bolted joint. Firstly the required clamping force (and hence size) of each bolt and secondly the distribution of the fasteners when more than one is needed (which will normally be the case). Some other points that are important when specifying bolts / or designing a joint are given below:

1. Tightening the the bolt to the appropriate torque to give the needed clamping force is critical. This is difficult to do for short bolts (accidental under or over tightening can easily occur) but becomes increasingly easier the longer the bolt clamping length is made. For this reason the use of short bolts for critical applications involving high clamping forces should be avoided.

2. The torque required to develop a specific tension is very dependent upon the friction in the threads - and the coefficient of friction can vary widely according to the lubricant used. Special 'torque oils' are available for use with fasteners in critical situations which give reasonably consistent friction.

3. The thread form of many bolts gives rise to a stress concentration factor of 2+ to 3+. A similar magnitude of stress concentration may be present in screws where the thread runs the full length to the head.

4. As a rule of thumb, where a joint is to include a gasket for sealing purposes, the maximum bolt centre distance should be no more than 6 x bolt diameter. To allow for wrench access, the minimum bolt spacing should not be less than 3 x bolt diameter.

5. Bolts must be tightened so that whatever loading is applied, they are always in tension. However normally the shear stresses caused by any shear loads should be calculated. In the case of joints subjected to cyclic loading, using a high preload will usually give a longer fatigue life than using a lower preload. For bolts used in very highly loaded fatigue applications, eg engine cylinder heads, it is

common practice to tighten them till they are plastically deformed. Obviously this means they should not normally be re-used (some car engine manufacturers allow one re-use).

6. Threads in aluminium parts that have to carry high loads should be fitted with stainless steel 'helicoils'.

7. When a bolt is screwed into a block of metal, the stiffness of the threads on the bolt will probably be very different from the stiffness of the threads in the block into which the bolt is screwed. This means that almost the entire load will probably be carried by the first one or two turns of the engaged thread. Increasing the length of engaged thread will not change this. To mitigate this problem, the cross section of the boss into which the bolt is screwed should have a carefully calculated cross section that tapers. If this is done correctly the load will be carried over several turns.

8. Three widely available grades of metric bolts for engineering applications are:

Grade	Min. UTS, MPa	Stress at permanent set limit R 0.2% MPa	Stress at proof load, MPa	Min. elongation after fracture %	Material	Notes
8.8	800	640	580	12	med. carbon, Q & T	general purpose
10.9	1040	940	830	9	may be alloy steel, med. carbon steel, Q & T, or med. C steel with additives Q & T	highest strength grade that should be used in a marine environment
12.9	1220	1100	970	8	alloy steel, Q & T	highest strength, also used for socket head caps.

Some of the above values vary slightly in BS 6104, depending upon the bolt diameter, conservative values are used in the above table.

Strictly a 'screw' is the name for a fastener with a full length thread, this is often undesirable as where the thread meets the bolt head there will be a high stress concentration. Bolts are only threaded part of their length, leaving full diameter to take bearing loads and to facilitate a smooth blend or fillet with the bolt head.

The vast majority of bolts and screws have their threads rolled nowadays, the grain flow and the compressive residual stresses in the root of the threads means that these threads have superior fatigue performance to cut threads.

Metric bolts have their grade number marked on their heads.

US SAE specification bolts have no head markings for the lower strength grades, 1 (410 MPa UTS) and 2 (min. UTS 480 MPa for diameter between 1/4 and 3/4 inch, min. UTS 410 MPa for diameter between 7/8 - 1.5 inch) the higher strength grades have different arrangements of 3, 5 or 6 radial lines marked on their heads and sometimes an ASTM designation number.

The sketch on the left shows a UNC bolt head with three radial grade lines indicating a UTS for diameter between 1/4 to 1 inch of 825 MPa corresponding to SAE grade 5. (For diameters between 1.125 and 1.5 inch, min. UTS is 720 MPa).

The sketch in the middle is a metric item with 8.8 grade marked.

On the right is a sketch of a metric socket head cap in A2-70 stainless steel (a type 304 stainless steel with a minimum UTS of 700 MPa).

Another grade of stainless steel is A4-80 which is 316 grade with a UTS of 800 MPa.

Most stainless steel bolts are supplied in grade 8.8, A2-70 or A4-80.

13.2.2 Effect of Initial Bolt Pre - Load

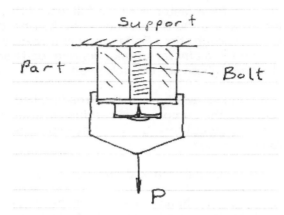

In the diagram above assume that the one end of the bolt and part are welded to the support and the nut is just put on 'finger tight' to remove any play.

The deflection of a bar (bolt) under axial load:

$$\text{delta} = P\,L\,/\,A\,E$$

where P = load, L = length, A = cross section area and E = Young's modulus.

Stiffness = k = load/ delta, N/m, rearranging the above and with subscript p meaning part and b meaning bolt:

$$k_b = A_b\,E_b\,/\,L_b \text{ and } k_p = A_p\,E_p\,/\,L_p$$

P_b = part of load P carried in bolt and P_p = part of load carried in part.

$$P = P_b + P_p$$

The deflection of the bolt = $P_b\,/\,k_b$ and of the part = $P_p\,/\,k_p$ and these must be equal.

$$P_b\,/\,k_b = P_p\,/\,k_p$$

$$P_b = k_b(P - P_b)\,/\,k_p$$

$$P_b\,k_p = P\,k_b - P_b\,k_b$$

$$P_b\,(k_b + k_p) = P\,k_b$$

$$P_b = P\,k_b\,/\,(k_b + k_p) \text{ and similarly: } P_p = P\,k_p\,/\,(k_b + k_p)$$

Suppose that the nut is tightened so additional tensile load, F_o is placed in the bolt, then the force in the bolt:

$$F_b = P\, k_b\, /\, (k_p + k_b) + F_o$$

This causes an equal and opposite compressive force in the part, so

$$F_p = P\, k_p\, /\, (k_p + k_b) - F_o$$

In practice F_o is applied on assembly, before the load P is applied. The initial force F_o must always be made large enough to keep the part in compression, ie F_p must be negative. This is needed to maintain a gasket seal or merely to reduce the effects of cyclic loading on the bolt.

A worked example is given in Appendix 13.1.

13.3 Welded Joints
13.3.1 Introduction
Many metals (and some plastics) can be welded, but it there are often restrictions on the type of welding process that can be used. The ideal of fusion welding is that the joint is no weaker, or in any way inferior, to the joined materials.

Where a fabrication contains a number of welds it is essential that the design minimises shrinkage strains or high residual stresses can be present in joints and components which can lead to premature failure.

In the case of low carbon steels, the joint can in some instances actually be stronger than the joined steels. In practice many welding operations introduce defects which result in the joint properties being less than the theoretical indicated. The most common problem with fusion welded steel joints is hydrogen embrittlement leading to cracking. This may originate from damp coatings on consumable welding electrodes - it is essential that coated electrodes are stored in dry conditions. The other point to note is that many welding operations are carried out by hand and in these cases the quality of the joint is heavily dependent upon operator skill.

The carbon content of a steel has a major influence on it's weldability. Low carbon mild steel can be welded without difficulty, but for carbon contents above 0.2% much greater care is needed and in the case of high strength steels intended for equipment where fabrication by welding is very common, the carbon content is often limited to a maximum of 0.15%.

Aluminium and many of its alloys can be welded, but there can be problems - such as the production of oxide films and weld metal porosity, which can be avoided by using inert gas shielded processes. It is often necessary to carefully match the electrode composition to the alloy being joined.

13.3.2 The Design of Fillet Welds

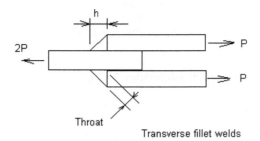

Transverse fillet welds

The first diagram shows the widely used transverse fillet weld. This is assumed to be of length 'l' perpendicular to the plane of the diagram. The size of the fillet is equal to the leg 'h' of the largest inscribed isosceles triangle.

The common method of analysis assumes the weld to be cut through at the narrowest point, the 'throat', see second diagram. Any outward 'bulge' due to weld metal build up is ignored. The stress, Sx, on the weld throat is resolved in the normal and shear directions, giving Sn and Ss.

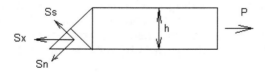

Stresses on weld throat

The throat area: $A = hl\cos45 = 0.707hl$

$Sx = P / A = P/0.707hl$

Resolving Sx into the normal and tangential components gives:

$Sn = Sx \cos 45 = P/hl$ and $Ss = Sx \cos 45 = P/hl$

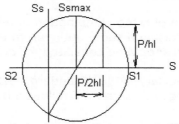

Mohr's circle diagram of stresses on fillet
weld throat

These stresses can be combined as shown in the Mohr's circle in the above diagram to give:

$S_1 = (P/2hl) + ((P/2hl)^2 + (P/hl)^2)^{0.5} = 1.618P/hl$ and

$S_{smax} = ((P/2hl)^2 + (P/hl)^2)^{0.5} = 1.118P/hl$

While the equations above give good agreement with test results, for design purposes it is common to use a more elementary approach and assume that the average working shear stress is equal to the load divided by the throat area: $Ss = P/0.707hl = 1.414P/hl$

13.3.3 Fatigue Strength Reduction Factors

The following fatigue strength reduction factors are suggested in 'Arc Welding in Design, Manufacturing and Construction' - James F. Lincoln Arc Welding Foundation, 1939:

Location	K
Reinforced butt weld	1.2
Toe of transverse fillet weld	1.5
End of parallel fillet weld	2.7
T-butt joint with sharp corners	2

For a detailed discussion of the fatigue strength of welded structures see: 'Fatigue Strength of Welded Structures', by S J Maddox, Abington publishing, 1991. ISBN 1 85573 013 8.

13.3.4 Classification of Welding Electrodes

BS 639 uses a rather complicated combination of letters and numbers, some compulsory and some optional, to classify electrodes. The standard should be consulted for details.

The American Welding Society (AWS) Standard A5.1 uses a less complex notation starting with a prefix E followed by 2 sets of digits:

> E: Electrode

> xxx Two or three digits indicating the tensile strength in 10,000 psi units

> xx Two digits indicating the coating type and application.

13.4 Offset Loads

The same approach can be used for designing a bolted or welded joint subject to an offset load.
An example in Appendix 13.2, below, illustrates determining the stresses in an array of 6 bolts and should be studied at the same time as the description below is read.

The offset load is replaced by an equivalent direct force through the centre of area of the bolt array or welds plus a torque about the centre of area of the bolt array or welds.

The direct force will give rise to a uniform shear stress depending upon the total cross section area of the bolts or welds. For welds the minimum area is normally used, ie throat x length rather than plate thickness (h) x length.

It is assumed that the torque about the centre of area will give rise to a shear stress which is proportional to the distance from the centre of area of the bolts or welds. The procedure for calculating this stress is similar to that for calculating the shear stress in a circular shaft subject to torque. The polar second moment of area about the centre of area of the bolts or welds is required, this is determined using the parallel axes theorem and as can be seen from the example, the contribution of the bolt second moments of area about their own axes is normally small compared to the 'area x (distance)^2' contribution and consequently the former is sometimes ignored. The shear stress on each bolt due to the torque contribution can then be determined from the formula:

shear stress = torque x max. radius / polar second moment of area about centre of area of bolt array.

For a number of welds the polar second moment of area of each weld about its own centre of area can best be found by using the perpendicular axes theorem and then using the parallel axes theorem to find the polar second moment of area of the weld about the centre of area of all the welds.

The final stage is to draw (or sketch) the vector diagrams adding the shear stress contributions due to the direct load and to the torque.

13.5 Brazed Joints

Brazed joints are very different to welded joints and the method of their design must also be different.
In the case of welded joints the key dimensions are length of weld and the throat, both of which are frequently clearly visible. A brazed joint does not normally form a consistent fillet, it forms by filling a narrow gap between the two heated components by capilliary action - which means the brazing alloy has to efficiently wet the surfaces. The strength of the joint depends not only on the area of wetted surface but also on the separation of the surfaces.

The data below shows the force needed to pull apart a nominal 12.5 mm diameter shaft brazed 12.5 mm into a nominal 12.5 mm diameter tube with brass heated to 950°C in a molten cyanide / carbonate / chloride salt bath.

Diametral clearance	0.025mm	0.051	0.076	0.10	0.127	0.153	0.204	0.254	0.38	0.508
Load N	100000	125000	108000	102000	106000	99000	* 75000	* 85000	31000	33000

* In these two tests one of the steel components failed before the joint.

This data suggests that the gap needs to be between about 1/80 and 1/16 mm for the highest strength. It is however likely that other filler metals with different mechanical properties might require different gaps for optimum strength. Suppliers of filler metals should be able to give advice.

There are a number of different types of brazing alloys covering a temperature range from about 650°C to 1000°C. The lower temperature filler metals, usually based on silver, are sometimes referred to as 'hard solders' and have brazing temperatures up to about 820°C. Higher temperature filler metals, with brazing temperatures above about 830°C are copper based.

To enable the filler metal to wet the surfaces to be joined, it is essential that the surfaces are thoroughly cleaned immediately before brazing and the appropriate flux used to prevent oxidation during heating.

13.6 Adhesive Joints
13.6.1 Types of Adhesives
A wide range of 'adhesives' is now available for a many engineering applications. These include not only bonding, but also sealing (functioning instead of, or as a part of a gasket) and thread locking (preventing nuts and bolts working loose).
An important consideration in the use of polymeric adhesives is that they are good at dissipating energy which can significantly reduce noise, vibration and harshness (NVH) which is an important consideration in vehicle structures.

For engineering applications requiring the highest strength, adhesives are used well below (at least 50°C below) their glass transition temperatures, examples include epoxies and certain acrylics. Other adhesives for less critical applications include:

> Contact adhesives - a solution or emulsion containing an elastomeric adhesive is coated onto both components to be joined (the adherends) the solvent is allowed to evaporate and the two components brought into contact. Rubber cement is an example.

> Pressure sensitive adhesives - are very low modulus elastomers which deform easily under low pressure, assisting them to wet surfaces. When the substrate and adhesive are brought into contact, van der Waals forces maintain the bond. These are often supplied as tapes.

> Hot melt adhesives - become liquid when heated, wetting the surfaces, then cooling to a solid polymer.

> Anaerobic adhesives - cure in the absence of oxygen and are widely used for preventing threads from loosening, for keeping bearings in place and for applications where an interference fit or some other fixing would otherwise be needed to keep components in place.

Structural thermosetting adhesives are normally available in two-part formulations that are mixed prior to use and which then cure in a time that depends upon the temperature.

One-part formulations are also available (the resin and hardener - a cross linking agent) but these normally have limited shelf life and must be stored at low temperatures.

13.6.2 Design of Adhesive Joints

Design procedures have been developed for the aircraft industry but more generalised procedures for other engineering applications are not widely available.

Good design requires that adhesive joints are loaded in shear and not in tension. Lap shear joints are widely used, however it is important to note that for design (A) below, increasing the length of the overlap will not result in a proportionate increase in the joint strength. This can be deduced by considering the forces, stresses and strains in the two components at the ends of the glue line. The shear stress in the glue line will be significantly greater at the ends of the glue line than in the middle.

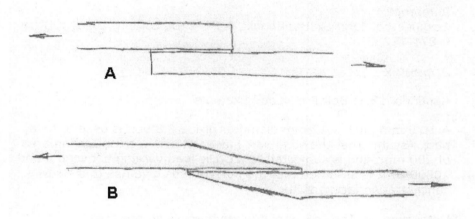

To achieve a good strength from a large overlap requires a design such as (B) where the components are tapered which gives a much better transfer of stresses and strains between the components and the glue line and results in a more uniform shear stress along the length of the glue line.

The table below shows the shear strength ranges of some popular adhesives. It must be noted that for adhesive joints cleanliness is critical and for some adhesives the component separation must be controlled within specified limits for a top quality joint. Leading suppliers are able to give detailed advice about applications.

Adhesive type	Lap joint shear strength, MPa, room temperature
Synthetically designed hot melt	0.7 - 7
PVA emulsion (white glue)	1.5 - 7
Cyanoacrylate	7 - 14
Anaerobic acrylic	7 - 14
Modified phenolic	14 - 28
Epoxy (unmodified)	10 - 28
Epoxy (rubber modified)	20 - 40

Reference
'Engineered Materials Handbook', ASM, Desk Edition, 1998, ISBN: 0-87170-283-5.

Appendix

Appendix 13.1: Bolt Pre - Load Example

A 1.75 mm pitch x 12 mm diameter grade 8.8 bolt is used to fix a part. Assume that the steel part has an effective cross section area of 200 mm^2 and is subjected to a cyclic load varying between 0 and 20000 N. It is assumed that the bolt threads give rise to a stress concentration factor of 3.

Determine: a) The FoS of bolt when there is no pre-load.
b) The minimum required pre-load, F_o to prevent loss of compression.
c) The FoS for the bolt when the pre-load, F_o = 22000 N.
d) The minimum force in the part when the pre-load is 22000 N.

Solution:
From BS 6104, Pt 1, 1981, Table 6, the ultimate tensile load of this size and type bolt is given as 67,400 N. The bolt core area is 84.3 mm^2
The UTS is 800 MPa and we assume that the fatigue endurance strength of smooth polished specimens (S_e') is half the UTS, ie 400 MPa. A fatigue endurance strength reduction factor of 0.33 (1 / stress concentration factor) is applied to give the fatigue endurance strength of the bolt, S_e = 133 MPa.

a) FoS with zero pre-load.

To determine the FoS the mean stress and the stress amplitude, are plotted on a modified Goodman diagram. With no pre-load the entire load is carried by the bolt. For a load varying between zero and 20000 N, the mean is 10000 N and the amplitude is 10000 N.

The mean stress, S_m = 20000 /(2 x 84.3) = 118.6 MPa also = the stress amplitude, S_a

When these are plotted on the modified Goodman diagram, the point A falls above and to the right of the line, outside the safe zone, the design is unsafe, the FoS, based on the UTS, is given by the ratio of the lengths of the lines OB / OA (if the diagram were drawn to scale) or algebraically from the modified Goodman diagram:

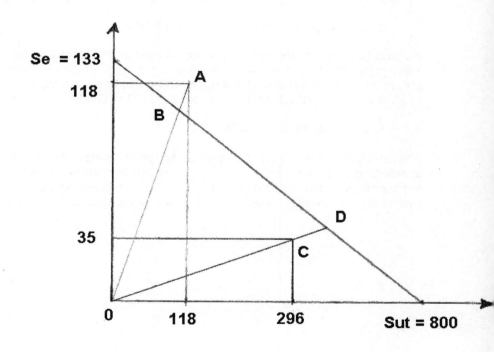

1 / FoS = (mean stress / S_{ut}) + (stress amplitude / S_e)

1/FoS = (118.6 / 800) + (118.6 / 133) = 1.04

FoS = 0.96

b) The minimum F_o required to prevent loss of compression.
For bodies of equal length and equal modulii, the spring constants are proportional to the csa. The csa of the bolt is 84.3 mm^2.
When the part has zero compression:

$$F_o = k_p P_{max} / (k_p + k_b) = 200 \times 20000 / 284.3 = 14070 \text{ N}$$

c) Find the FoS in the bolt when $F_o = 22000$ N

$$F_{b \text{ average}} = P_{average} k_b / (k_p + k_b) + F_o$$

$$F_{b \text{ mean}} = (10000 \times 84.3 / 284.3) + 22000 = 24970 \text{ N}$$

$$\text{stress}_{mean} = 24970 / 84.3 = 296.1 \text{ MPa}$$

$$F_{b \text{ amplitude}} = k_b P_a / (k_p + k_b) = 84.3 \times 10000 / 284.3 = 2965 \text{ N}$$

$$\text{stress}_{amplitude} = 2965 / 84.3 = 35.17 \text{ MPa}$$

Plotting this on a scale diagram would show point C is inside the 'safe zone', the bolt now has a FoS greater than 1, shown graphically by the ratio of the lengths OD / OC, or algebraically:
$$1 / \text{FoS} = (296.1 / 800) + (35.17 / 133) = 0.634$$

FoS, design factor = 1.58

The effect of the pre-load is to greatly reduce the magnitude of the alternating force and stress in the bolt (which is normally much more critical) while increasing the mean bolt force and stress (normally less critical) resulting in the bottom diagram.

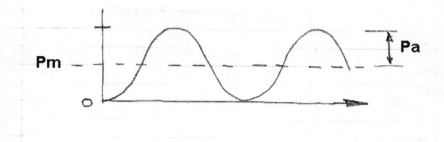

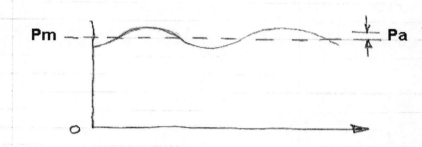

d) The minimum pre-load in the part when the bolt pre-load, F_o = 22000 N.

$$F_{p\,min} = k_p\,P_{max} / (k_p + k_b) - F_o$$

$$F_{p\,min} = (200 \times 20000 / 284.3) - 22000 = -7930\ N$$

Appendix 13.2: Stress in an Array of Bolts Subject to an Offset Load

The approach to this problem is explained with the aid of the diagram below:

Note that the full area of the 8 mm diameter bolt is used in calculating the area subject to shear as the unthreaded portion of the bolts should extend beyond the interface of the two components to be joined. Where more than 1 component is to be joined, the unthreaded portion should extend across all the interfaces. When appropriately tightened the interface friction will normally prevent direct bearing forces between the bolts and plates.

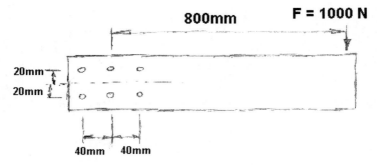

800mm   **F = 1000 N**

20mm

20mm

40mm   40mm

Bolt $\phi = 8\,mm$, $1.25\,mm$ pitch, 8.8 grade

Each bolt area $= \dfrac{\pi\,(8)^2}{4} = 50.26\,mm^2$.

τ_d due to direct load, F

τ_t due to torque $0.8\,F$

$\tau_d = \dfrac{Force}{6\,Area}$

$\tau_d = \dfrac{1000 \times 4}{6\,\pi\,(0.008)^2} = 3.3\,MPa$

$\tau_t = \dfrac{T\,r}{J\,array\ of\ bolts}$

Using parallel axis theorem, J_i bolt:

$$\dfrac{\pi\,d^4}{32} + Area\,(distance)^2$$

First term is usually much smaller than the second so:

The stresses can be combined using a vector diagram:

$$J_{total} = \frac{2\pi (0.008)^2}{4} \times (0.02)^2 + \frac{4\pi (0.008)^2 (0.02^2 + 0.04^2)}{4}$$

$$= 40.22 E-9 + 402.1 E-9$$

$$= 442.3 E-9 \ m^4$$

$$\gamma_t = \frac{0.8 \times 0.04472}{442.3 E-9} = 80.9 \ MPa$$

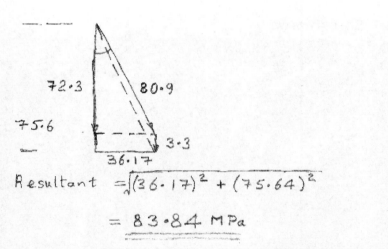

$$\alpha = \tan^{-1}(0.5)$$
$$\alpha = 26.56°$$

20mm
40mm

72.3   80.9
75.6
            3.3
   36.17

$$Resultant = \sqrt{(36.17)^2 + (75.64)^2}$$

$$= 83.84 \ MPa$$

By inspection of the sketch it can be seen that the two right hand bolts are subject to the highest stresses. The vector sum diagram above, is for the top right hand bolt, however it can be seen that the bottom right hand bolt has the same resultant stress magnitude.

The stresses generated are well below the UTS of the material used for grade 8.8 bolts

14 Cylinder Head, Air Flow, Valve Train Design, Valves, Stresses in Valves and Stresses due to Impact Loading - Valve Bounce

14.1 Cylinder Head
14.1.1 Introduction
The cylinder head contains contains the inlet and exhaust passages between the manifolds and the valves. As a general rule the passages should be as short as possible, as straight as possible with no changes in cross section and have smooth bores. However when using poppet valves, which are the norm on 4 stroke engines, there is inevitably some disturbance of the passage due to the valve guide and stem.

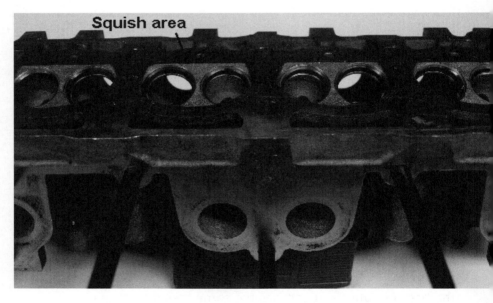

Squish area

In Figure 14.1, above, of a Rover 'K' Series cylinder head, it is possible to see through the inlet passages which are nearly straight. It is also possible in this view to see that the inlet valves are a slightly larger diameter than the exhaust valves. The exhaust valve passages end on the side of the cylinder head closest to the camera.

The other feature of this 2 valve head is the flat sector area just the far side of the valves in the picture. When the pistons approach tdc on the compression stroke, the mixture is forced out of this part of the cylinder at high speed causing swirl improving the mixing of fuel and air and facilitating good combustion.

The cylinder head also has to house the valve mechanism, including the cam shaft(s).

Figure 14.2, above, shows parts of the cylinder head of a Ford engine with two overhead camshafts, showing parts of the camshaft that operates the exhaust valves, and the tappets under the cams. Two of the brackets that hold the cam shaft in place have been cut away. Parts of the cut away cam shaft cover can also be seen.

14.1.2 Materials for Cylinder Heads

Cast grey iron was the original material used for cylinder heads however apart from large diesel engines, where it is still widely used, the advantages of sand cast aluminium alloys mean that these are now the norm for car engines. The key advantages of aluminium are good thermal conductivity, ease of casting and of machining compared to grey iron. The good thermal conductivity is critical for petrol engines as this assists in keeping the combustion chamber cool, which means that it is easier to design out local hot spots that can cause pre-ignition or 'knocking'. Consequently petrol engines with aluminium cylinder heads can have higher compression ratios than those with cast iron heads, producing higher bmep and better efficiency. LM25 or similar alloys are frequently used, see Chapter 9.6.5 for further details.

Two areas of the cylinder head where aluminium alloys are not ideal are the valve guides and the valve seats. To prevent wear problems it is common for brass or bronze valve guide inserts to be fitted. Constant impact of the valve head with the valve seat means that hard inserts must be fitted to prevent valve seat recession. Inserts are commonly a grade of 'Stellite', which is a cobalt based material, see Chapter 9.13. The inserts are an interference fit and are cooled to facilitate fitting.

The sealing of the cylinder head to block is difficult as the joint has to seal high pressures and hot gases from combustion and the separation of the bolts is something like 10 times the bolt diameter rather than the recommended 6 times (see the previous chapter). Consequently sealing the head and block joint often involves using a sophisticated multi layer thin sheet metal gasket.

14.2 Types of Valves
During the evolution of the petrol and diesel engine a variety of valve systems were developed and used. About the only configuration that enjoyed wide use in the past that is not now seen is the sleeve valve arrangement which was widely used on aero-engines. During the Second World War half of the aero-engine power available to the RAF had sleeve valves. Now all IC engines use poppet valves, sometimes described as 'a penny on a stick'. There is however still considerable variation in the details of the actuation arrangements, in most cases these details are needed as part of a variable timing system, normally only provided for the inlet valves.

14.3 Arrangement of Valves
The arrangement of the valves in the cylinder head depends on their number, size and the shape of the combustion chamber.

Figure 14.3, above, shows the arrangement of the 2 inlet and 2 exhaust valves in the cylinder head of a Ford engine. This valve arrangement makes it easy to have a central spark plug, which can be seen in the central threaded hole and this position minimises the flame path.

To minimise the wear on the valve stem and valve guides it is desirable to have the opening force acting as near as is possible directly down the valve stem. This can be provided by having a cylindrical tappet that slides in the cylinder head, the cam (or rocker) acts on the upper face of the tappet and the tip of the valve stem is in contact with the underside of the top face of the tappet. If the cam acts directly on the top of the tappet then a shallow cylindrical spacer or shim is normally provided in a pocket on the top or underside of the top of the tappet, different thicknesses of these shims are available to provide for adjustment of the valve clearance, see figure below. However this is a rather tedious way of adjusting the valve clearance as a certain amount of dismantling of the camshaft is necessary if 'adjustment' (i.e. fitting a different thickness shim) is needed.

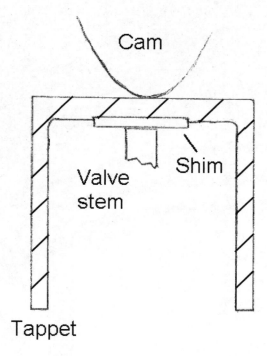

This arrangement was used in early car diesel engines during the 1980s.

This configuration does have the advantage that sideways forces generated by friction on the cam face are supported by the side walls of the tappet, not by the valve stem / guide. While this helps to reduce friction and wear between the valve stem and the valve guide or cylinder head, it does not completely eliminate this potential problem.

The cylinder head is normally made from a aluminium - silicon casting alloy, whereas the valve stem is a medium carbon steel (in the case of valves which have stainless steel or special alloy heads - these are usually friction welded to the stems). Stainless steel valves - used for inlet valves, which run cooler - may be one piece forgings. In any event none of the valve stem materials are recommended for sliding directly on aluminium. Where tapets are used which prevent sideways loading then the performance of valves operating directly in the aluminium alloy head may be just about acceptable, however it is normally better (although more expensive) to provide brass or bronze bushes which are pressed into the aluminium alloy head then the bores are normally reamed to the required size to take the valve stem.

The camshaft support bearings are commonly lubricated by direct oil feed and oil coming out of these bearings runs along the camshaft and provides slash lubrication for valve train components. It is common to put an 'O' ring or plastic guard over the valve stem to avoid excessive oil running down the valve stem to the guide, which may not matter when the components are new, but after some wear when the valve stem - valve guide clearance has increased, excessive oil could be drawn into the engine leading to unacceptable emissions and possibly to excessive oil consumption.

14.4 Valve Materials and Manufacture - for further information see section 9.11

Both inlet and exhaust valves are subjected to elevated temperatures and standard constructional steels do not have sufficient corrosion or wear resistance or high temperature strength. For inlet valves valve steels such as EN 51 (3% Ni), En 52 (3.5% Si, 8.5% Cr) and En 59 (2% Si, 1.4% Ni and 20% Cr) have been used. Exhaust valves operate at significantly higher temperatiures, some parts exceeding 750°C and special alloys such as 21-4N and 21-4NS are used.

One type of exhaust valve that was used in piston engine powered aero-engines and racing engines was the hollow stem valve that was half filled with sodium or sodium potassium alloy. Although solid at room temperatures, at operating temperatures the alloy would melt and as it reciprocated, the molten alloy inside tended to not to and was therefore effective at transferring heat from the hot end near the valve head to the cooler end, where in the case of air cooled aero engines the heat was removed by passing air.

Because the valves close very rapidly there is impact loading of the valve seat. The aluminium cylinder head is not able to withstand this and hard valve seat inserts, often made from 'stellite' - a cobalt alloy, are shrink fitted into the cylinder head.

The properties required of valve heads, resistance to hot corrosive gases and of valve stems, to be able to resist wear when reciprocating in a valve guide, mean that it is effective to use different materials for the head and for the stem. A heat resisting stainless steel or alloy is used for the head and a medium carbon steel is used for the stem. Both parts are axisymmetric and the materials used are sufficiently similar to enable them to be friction welded together. This process involves holding one part stationary, rotating the other in a chuck then pushing the one against the other which generates heat at the interface and expels surface oxides out of the joint. Rotation is stopped an the contact force maintained till the joint cools. This process is well suited to mass production and for small components such as these cycle times will be well under a minute. HGV axle shafts are also manufactured in this way with cycle times of about 1 minute.

14.5 Air Flow Into Combustion Chamber
As the pressure drop across the inlet valve is often small, the flow, for convenience, is assumed to be incompressible. At high engine revs. the pressure drop may well be 20 - 25 % of atmospheric pressure and in many engines this pressure drop, and consequent loss of power is the factor limiting the maximum engine speed. Assuming incompressible flow the velocity past the open inlet valve is given by the equation:

$$v = (2 \, g \, h)^{0.5} = (2 \, p/D)^{0.5}$$
where p is the pressure differential driving the flow, D is the fluid density and h is the height of the column of fluid to generate the same driving pressure.
To obtain the volume flow rate, multiply the velocity, v, by the cross section area, A and the coefficient of discharge, C_d.
Generally there is little point in having the area around the periphery of the open valve:
$$h \; 3.14159 \; (d_{valve})^2/4$$
significantly greater than the cross section area of the inlet port or inlet tract.
Where h = valve lift, d_{valve} = diameter of the valve and V the volume flow rate.
$$V = (2 \, p/D)^{0.5} \, C_d \, h \, 3.14159 \, (d_{valve})^2/4$$
However the if edges of the valve head and seat are sharp, the coefficient of discharge will vary at different valve openings and mixture velocities as the mixture jet will not always fill the opening,

but will break away from one or both surfaces to form a free jet. In general it is best from a flow viewpoint to round all corners on the valve and seat. Typically C_d will vary between 0.6 and 0.8. Additional information is given in Chapter 7 and reference 14.1.

14.6 Variable Valve Timing

For many years valve timing was fixed, however in the last quarter of the 20th century the advantages of variable valve timing were realised and car engines started to be fitted with variable valve timing for the inlet valves. Early systems did not change the period that the inlet valve was open, but shifted the phase of the opening period relative to the crank position. This was achieved either by having an intermediate casing (with vanes on the inside) driven by the timing belt. Inside the casing, on the end of the inlet camshaft, was a short shaft with some vanes attached. Oil under pressure is supplied to alternate spaces between the vanes from the camshaft and by varying the oil pressure supplied the two sets of vanes can be rotated relative to one another against a return spring. This changes the phase of the inlet camshaft relative to the crankshaft.

An alternative method 'VarioCam' used by Porsche involved the inlet valve camshaft being driven from the exhaust valve camshaft by a chain which was longer than the minimum needed and the slack was controlled by a plunger tensioner system which shifted the play from one side of the chain run to the other, changing the phase of the inlet camshaft relative to the exhaust camshaft and crankshaft.

The most sophisticated system currently in use is probably the Porsche 'VarioCam Plus'.
Readers are recommended to look at the picture on the Porsche web site, the description below is based on that on the site.

There is a two-stage lift mechanism on each inlet valve consisting of an electro-hydraulically switchable tappet. Each of the 12 tappets has two concentric lifters which can be locked together by means of a pin. When the tappets are locked, the outermost ring – which is driven by two large profile cams – is in direct contact with the valve. When the pin is removed, the innermost lifter – operated by a smaller cam lobe – has sole influence over the amount of valve lift. The timing of each valve is steplessly controlled by means of an electro-hydraulic rotary vane adjuster at the head of the corresponding camshaft.

To improve response when starting from cold, VarioCam Plus increases the amount of lift and retards the timing of the valves. At medium revs and minimal load, the valve lift is lowered and timing advanced to minimise fuel consumption and emissions.

To achieve maximum power and torque, the valve lift is increaased.

14.7 Stress Concentrations in Engine Valves.
An axisymmetric model of a typical engine valve was analysed with FEA.

The valve was constrained in the 'Y' direction by the edge defining the valve seat.

The valve had 3 circumferential grooves near the top of the stem to hold the collet and spring retainer, 0.0015 units diameter in a stem diameter of 0.008 units with a valve head diameter of 0.040 units and a total length of 0.1 units).

Where the stem joined the head, a 0.0075 unit radius was used,
The model assumed that the load in the positive 'Y' direction was applied around the top semi-circular groove in the stem.

The theoretical tensile stress in the stem was: 1.989 MPa.

They key results from the FEA von Mises stress plot are shown in the sketch below:

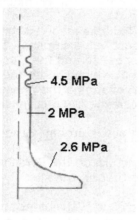

These von Mises stress results give the stress concentration factors shown in the table below. Also shown in this table are stress concentration values calculated from a maximum principal stress plot (not shown).

Location	Stress concentration based on von Mises stresses	Stress concentration based on maximum principal stresses
Bottom groove	2.25	3
Blend of head with stem	1.3	1.6

Note that the stress concentration in the middle groove was slightly lower than in the bottom groove.

It should be noted that some published curves for a single groove in a round bar in tension gave values of 1.6 for the stress concentration value, but a formula published in Roark, (6th Ed) reference 14.2, gave a value of 2.6 for a single groove in a round bar in tension.

These differences illustrate the importance of checking information from all sources carefully and the need to exercise engineering judgment, even when there is information and data available.

14.8 Impact Loads - Stresses Occurring During Valve Bounce
14.8.1 Introduction
This takes a simple approach based on data from a Ford Fiesta engine. The worst case scenario is examined - where valve bounce is occurring and the valve closing is driven totally by the valve spring and the cam has no moderating contact.

14.8.2 Assumptions

- Valve spring stiffness is about 6 N/mm
- Valve lift is 6.5 mm
- Valve stem diameter is 5 mm
- Valve stem length is 70 mm
- Mass of valve is 33 g
- Mass of spring is 25.5 g, use 1/3 of this, 8.5 g
- Mass of both colletts 1.1 g
- Mass of cap 8.2 g
- Mass of tappet and spacer 35.5 g
- Total reciprocating mass of valve etc. is 86.3 g

14.8.3 Calculations

As an approximation it is assumed that the average valve closing force exerted by the spring is 50N. In reality he force will not be constant as the spring exerts a decreasing force as it lengthens as the valve closes.

NB: Typical maximum valve accelerations are higher than the value calculated below - the valve springs have significant compression when fitted and generate a higher force than used in the example below. This means that the stress calculated is low and may well be exceeded in a real engine should valve bounce occur. The high stresses explain why failure of the valve train can happen rapidly when valve bounce occurs.

Using: Force = mass x acceleration, this gives the acceleration of the closing valve, driven by the spring, to be:
$50/0.0863 = 579$ m/s^2

Determining the velocity of impact using:

$v^2 = u^2 + 2as$,
$v^2 = 0 + 2 \times 579 \times 0.0065 = 7.5319$ (m/s)^2 gives: v = 2.74 m/s

Convert this to a drop height problem, determine the height of drop needed to give rise to a velocity of 2.74 m/s
Again use: $v^2 = u^2 + 2as$,

$\qquad 7.5319 = 0 + 2 \times 9.81 \times s$,
$\qquad$ So equivalent drop height is: s = 0.3839 m

The strain energy in a bar subject to tension or compression is given by:

$$U = (sigma)^2 AL/2E = W^2L/2AE$$

where W is the load, A the cross section area of the rod stem and L its length.

It is assumed that the valve assembly of weight P falls from a height h (0.3839 m in this case) and the valve head is stopped instantaneously (this will not actually be the case) when the seat on the head of the valve hits the valve seat insert in the cylinder head. Decelerating the colletts, cap, tappet, spacer, one third of the mass of the valve spring and one third the mass of the valve stem (the effective mass of a spring in a dynamic system is one third of the actual mass, see chapter 10) requires a force that results in a slight elastic stretching of the stem, by a small amount, delta, ð. The loss of potential energy through P falling freely through the height h, is equated to the work done by the equivalent static force P_E that would produce the same static deflection.

The weight of the components stretching the stem (assuming that the mass of the stem is $3.14159 (0.005)^2 0.07 \times 7800/4 = 10.72$ g, use one third $= 3.57$g) is $9.81(3.57 + 8.5 + 1.1 + 8.2 + 35.5) = 0.558$ N

$$P(h + ð) = P_E ð/2 = U,$$
ð is very small compared to h and can be ignored on the left hand side of the above equation.

Also $P_E = A E ð/L$, so

$$Ph = A E (ð)^2/2L \text{ and substituting values gives:}$$

$$0.558 \times 0.3839 = 3.14159 \times (0.005)^2 \times 200E9 (ð)^2/(4 \times 2 \times 0.07)$$

$$(ð)^2 = 7.639E\text{-}9m, \text{ so } ð = 87.4E\text{-}6m$$

substitute this value of ð in: $P_E = A E ð/L$, gives

$$P_E = 3.14159 \times (0.005)^2 \times 200E9 \times 87.4E\text{-}6/(4 \times 0.07) = 4903 \text{ N}$$

Substitute this value of P_E into sigma $= P_E/A$ gives

$$sigma = 4903 \times 4/(3.14159 \times (0.005)^2$$

$$sigma = 250 \text{ MPa.}$$

This is a very rough calculation but it gives some indication of the high stresses that can arise when valve bounce occurs. For comparison, a slowly applied load of 50 N results in a stress of 2.55 MPa. In normal operation the maximum stresses that the valve springs would exert on the valve stem might be about 6 times this value, say 15 MPa, then allow for a stress concentration factor of 2.5, this gives a maximum stress of 38 MPa. A stress of 38 MPa in a medium carbon steel valve stem is well below the fatigue endurance strength, however once valve bounce occurred and allowing a stress concentration factor of 2.5 and the valve stem stress goes up to 635 MPa. This value is above the yield stress of a medium carbon steel (about 350 MPa depending type and processing) which is often used for valve stems. Once valve bounce occurs, valve failure can occur very quickly.

References
14.1 'Internal Combustion Engines', C R Ferguson and A T Kirkpatrick, John Wiley and Sons, 2nd Ed., 2001, ISBN: 09780471356172.
14.2 'Roark's Formulas for Stress and Strain', W C Young, McGraw-Hill International Editions, 6th Ed., 1989, ISBN: 0-07-100373-8.

15 Transmission Systems

15.1 Introduction

The following topics are considered in this chapter:

Gears, Toothed belts (commonly called timing belts), Chains, V - belts, Multi - V - belts and Clutches.

The important features of the first five of these are summarised below:

System	Gears	Chains	Toothed belts	V - Belt	Multi - V
Centre distance	Critical	(1)	(1)	(1)	(1)
Speed Ratio	Exact	Exact	Exact	Few % slip	Few % slip
Cost	Low to High	Medium	Medium	Low	Low
Installation	Needs care	Intermediate	Intermediate	Easy	Easy
Power Capacity	Low to very high	High	Medium	Medium	Medium
Lubrication	Usually needed	Essential	Avoid oil etc.	Avoid oil etc.	Avoid oil etc.

Note - (1) Not critical with an idler.

There are 30+ British standards on gears and their manufacture, about 10 on belts and belt drives and a few on chains.

Metal gears almost invariably need lubrication, lightly loaded plastic gears, frequently run with very little or no lubrication.

Not only is the centre distance critical for gears, but their axial alignment must also be good. Thermal expansion must be considered in high power density systems.

Gears must be manufactured to close tolerances.

Gears used in high load density applications are invariably hardened and tempered. The smaller gear (the pinion) is normally harder

than the larger gear (the wheel). Higher hardness provides greater load carrying capacity.
Pairs of gears should not have an integer ratio, but should have a 'hunting tooth' to give even wear.

Even with excellent accuracy of manufacture and installation, high power gear systems may well give off significant noise.

To transmit loads smoothly, helical gears must be used (more than one tooth is then always carrying the load) this results in end thrust, which must be accounted for in bearing selection.

Chains are usually quite difficult to fit if they do not have a connecting link. Although some authorities frown on the use of connecting links, the speed and load rating is the same for chains whether they have a connecting link or not.

At very high speeds, oil/grease is thrown off gears and chains and special care is needed to ensure the supply of the correct quantity of lubricant.

Oil must be kept away from V and multi V belts.
Some V belts are 'notched' to reduce the bending stresses generated when they are bent round pulleys while only causing a small reduction in contact area and torque transmission capability. Multi V - belts typically have 4 shallow 'Vs' to provide adequate friction area and the wedging effect of the 'V', while having a shallow depth to keep bending stresses lower than in a belt with a single V.

15.2 Gears
15.2.1 Introduction
When mating gear teeth are designed to produce a constant angular velocity ratio during meshing they are said to have 'conjugate action'. To provide this an 'involute' type profile is almost universally used for tooth forms.

There are two modes that are important causes of gear failures. Bending stresses (leading to tooth breakage) which are a maximum at the tooth root and compressive stresses (leading to pitting) that are a maximum on the tooth face. Because tooth loading is cyclic, both of these mechanisms are of a fatigue nature. The design of gears needs to counter both of these potential failure modes. An important part of providing the resistance to the high contact stresses is to use gears of appropriate hardness. The lower the levels of impurities in a material, the better it is normally able to resist fatigue.

15.2.2 Gear Tooth Nomenclature

Pitch circle diameter (pcd): For two meshing gears these are the diameters of the discs that would transmit the same velocity ratio by friction (if there was no slipping) as the gears.

Module, m: this indicates the tooth size and is the number of mm of pitch circle diameter (p.c.d.) per tooth. For gears to mesh, their modules must be equal.
Gear ISO standards and design methods are now normally based on the module.
EG if a gear of module 3 has 16 teeth, its pitch circle diameter is: 3 x 16 = 48 mm.

Diametral pitch, P: is the number of teeth per m or mm of gear pitch circle diameter.
P = 1/m

Circular pitch , p: is the distance from one point on the pitch circle of one tooth to the corresponding point on the adjacent tooth, measured around the pitch circle. pP=3.14159

The first diagram shows the tooth geometry for the ISO basic rack in terms of module 1 size teeth; PI means 3.14159

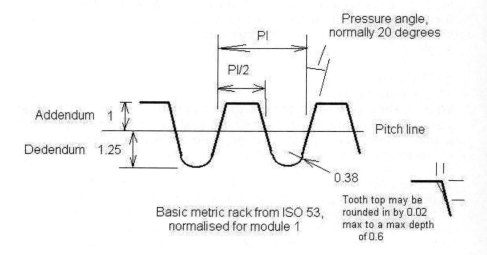

Basic metric rack from ISO 53, normalised for module 1

The diagram below defines some of the terms used for helical gearing.

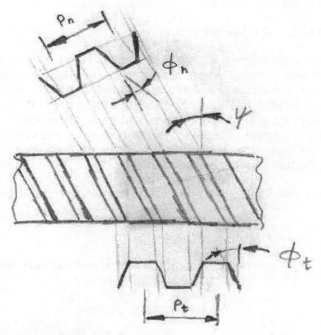

Helical gear nomenclature

The angle psi is the helix angle.
The transverse circular pitch, in the plane of rotation, is: p_t (usually called the circular pitch).
The normal circular pitch, perpendicular to the tooth axis, is: p_n
The normal pressure angle, phi_n is different from the transverse pressure angle, phi_t and these are related by the equation:
cos(helix angle) = tan (normal pressure angle)/tan(transverse pressure angle).

15.2.3 Loads on Teeth

The tangential force on the teeth can be found from:

W_t = 60H/(3.14159.d.n) where:

W_t = transmitted load, N

H = power, W

d = gear diameter, m

n = speed, rev/min.

Bending Stresses - The Lewis Formula

Although this was published in 1893, it is still very widely used for assessing bending stresses when designing gears. The method involves moving the tangential force and applying it to the tooth tip and assuming the load is uniformly distributed accross the tooth width with the tooth acting as a simple cantilever of constant rectangular cross section, the beam depth being put equal to the thickness of the tooth root (t) and the beam width being put equal to the tooth, or gear, width (b_w).

The section modulus is $I/c = b_w t^2/6$ so the bending stress is given by:

$$sigma_{bending} = M/(I/c) = 6W_t L/(b_w t^2) \text{ eqn.1.}$$

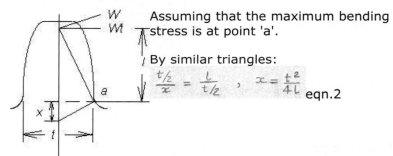

Assuming that the maximum bending stress is at point 'a'.

By similar triangles:

$$\frac{t/2}{x} = \frac{L}{t/2} \quad , \quad x = \frac{t^2}{4L} \quad \text{eqn.2}$$

Rearranging eqn.1 gives:

$$\sigma_b = \frac{6W_t L}{b_w t^2} = \frac{W_t}{b_w} \cdot \frac{1}{t^2/6L} = \frac{W_t}{b_w} \cdot \frac{1}{t^2/4L} \cdot \frac{1}{4/6}$$

Substitute the value for 'x' from eqn.2 and multiply the numerator and denominator by the circular pitch, 'p' gives:

$$\sigma_b = \frac{W_t \, p}{b_w \left(\frac{2}{3}\right) x \, p} \quad , \quad \text{let } y = \frac{2x}{3p}$$

$$\sigma_b = \frac{W_t}{b_w \, p \, y}$$

This is the original Lewis equation and 'y' is called the Lewis form factor which may be determined graphically or by computation.

Engineers often now work with the 'diametral pitch', 'P', $P = \pi/p$ and $Y = \pi y$ or the 'module', 'm', which is 1/diametral pitch = 1/P

Then sigma$_{\text{bending}}$ = $W_t P / b_w Y$ where Y = 2xP/3

Written in terms of the module:

   sigma$_{\text{bending}}$ = $W_t / (b_w m Y)$

The Lewis form factor considers only static loading, it is dimensionless, independent of tooth size and is a only a function of tooth shape. It does not take into account the stress concentration that exists in the tooth fillet.

The Lewis formula is generally limited to pitch line velocities up to 7.6 m/s and based on tests (in the 19th Century) on cast iron gears with cast teeth, C G Barth suggested a modification involving a velocity factor, K_V.

   In SI units this was $K_V = 3.05/(3.05 + V)$

For cut or milled teeth the Barth equation (in SI units) is often modified to:
   $K_V = 6.1/(6.1 + v)$, giving

   sigma$_{\text{bending, allowable}}$ = $W_t / b_w m Y K_V$

NB Recent Changes in Barth Equation
In about 2000 the AGMA (see below) re-defined the dynamic factor, K_V, as the inverse of that originally proposed by Barth, above. Consequently it is greater than 1 (and called K_V' here) and the expression for the allowable bending stress becomes:

   sigma$_{\text{bending, allowable}}$ = $W_t K_V' / b_w m Y$

For a full depth tooth with a 20° pressure angle, Y varies between 0.245 for a gear with 12 teeth to 0.471 for a gear with 300 teeth. (0.485 for a rack).

It is common for spur gears to be designed with a face width of between 3 and 5 times the circular pitch.

American Gear Manufacturers Association (AGMA) Code

Some key points from the AGMA approach to gear design are shown below.

AGMA have published graphs of allowable bending stresses and allowable surface contact stresses as a function of the Brinell hardness for some grades of through hardened steel.

Grade 2 steels, that have higher allowable stresses, are more closely specified than grade 1 steels.
The AGMA approach is commonly used and contains further refinements in addition to the information above, it also includes detailed guidance about materials.
A number of modifying factors are included in the AGMA code:

K_a = application factor - depends on the type of power source

K_s = size factor - increases above 1 for a module, m, of 6 mm or greater.

K_m = load distribution factor - depends mainly on face width.

K_v = dynamic factor - depending upon tooth accuracy, loads greater than the transmitted load may be generated.

Contact Stresses

These are determined by Hertzian contact stress analysis. The maximum pressure in the (rectangular) contact zone when two parallel cylinders are pressed together is given by:

$$P_H = E'\left(\frac{W'}{2\pi}\right)^{0.5}$$

$$E' = \frac{2}{\frac{1-\nu_a^2}{E_a} + \frac{1-\nu_b^2}{E_b}}$$

where E' is the effective modulus of elasticity.

W' is the dimensionless load = $w'/(E'/R_x)$

w' is the load per unit width = normal load/gear width and

$1/R_x$ = 2((1/pinion dia)+(1/gear dia))/sin(pressure angle)

The same modifying factors are again used with the contact stresses that were used with the bending stresses.

sigma$_{compressive}$ = $p_H(K_a\ K_s\ K_m/K_v)^{0.5}$

Depending upon the heat treatment, the maximum bending stresses for hardened gears can be in the range of 200 - 360 MPa and the maximum compressive stress 500 to 1200 MPa.

An example calculation is included in Appendix 15.1

15.2.4 Forces on Helical Gear Teeth
As the teeth on helical gears are inclined to the axis of the gear, the tooth force generates an axial or thrust load in addition to the radial force and the tangential force (which is the only one that does useful work). The tooth load can be resolved in the three directions as shown below:

Forces on helical gear teeth

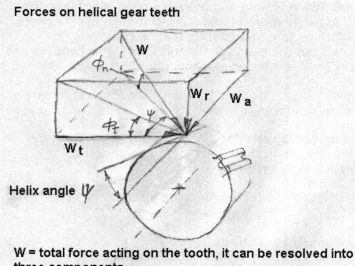

W = total force acting on the tooth, it can be resolved into three components

W_t = Tangential component, the only one that does useful work, used in power transmitted calculations.

$$W_t = W \cos \phi_n \cdot \cos \psi$$

$$W_r = W \sin \phi_n, \quad \text{radial component}$$

$$W_a = W \cos \phi_n \cdot \sin \psi, \quad \text{axial or thrust component.}$$

15.2.5 Stresses in helical gear teeth
When calculating the stresses in helical gear teeth, the Lewis form factor for the 'virtual number of teeth' needs to be used rather than that for the actual number of teeth. This is because on looking along a tooth on a helical gear the apparent radius of the gear is greater

than that of the gear blank (the cross section is an ellipse). The 'virtual number of teeth' is found by:

virtual number of teeth = actual number of teeth /(cosine of the helix angle)^3

15.2.6 Supplementary notes on Stresses in Gears

It should be noted that using the simplified version of these methods (including only K_v) on gears in automotive gear boxes gives high stresses, particularly for 1st gear. Gears for car gear boxes are manufactured to a high degree of accuracy, to keep noise levels low. The velocity correction factor, K_v, from the Barth equation, is over 100 years old and probably gives a conservative factor compared to that appropriate for modern high quality gears. Using all the AGMA factors - and noting that 'Y' the Lewis form factor is NOT used but the geometry factors J or I, (for bending and compressive stresses) are included, should give a more useful answer.

Note that 1st gear may be designed for a limited life as it so rarely operates under maximum load.

The minimum number of teeth for a gear is normally 13, as any fewer means that the tooth roots will have to be undercut, significantly weakening the teeth.

An example calculation of helical gear tooth strength is given in Appendix 15.2.

15.2.7 Torque Acting on a Gearbox

As the input and output torques associated with a gearbox are normally not the same, some 'holding' torque will be needed to prevent the gearbox rotating. This is illustrated in the diagram below:

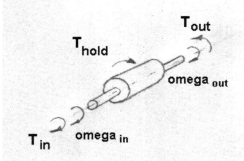

It is assumed that the input and output shafts are rotating in the same direction.

The diagram considers torques acting on the gearbox. The torque on the input shaft exerts a torque on the gearbox in the same direction as the direction of rotation of the input shaft.

The output shaft is applying a torque to the load, there is an equal and opposite reaction torque on the gearbox. The reaction torque on the gearbox from the output shaft is in the opposite direction to the direction of rotation of the output shaft.

As a gearbox is normally used to produce a change rotational velocity, omega_{in} will not be equal to omega_{out}. If it is assumed that the gearbox is 100 % efficient (a good quality gearbox may be 95 % efficient) power in = power out, so:

$$\text{omega}_{in}\ T_{in} = \text{omega}_{out}\ T_{out} \text{ so}$$

$$T_{out} = \text{omega}_{in}\ T_{in}/\text{omega}_{out}$$

Considering rotational equilibrium of the gearbox:

$$T_{in} + T_{hold} = T_{out}$$

$$T_{hold} = T_{out} - T_{in}$$

$$T_{hold} = [\text{omega}_{in}\ T_{in}/\text{omega}_{out}] - T_{in}$$

$$T_{hold} = T_{in}[(\text{omega}_{in}/\text{omega}_{out}) - 1]$$

15.2.8 Bending in Shafts with Helical Gears

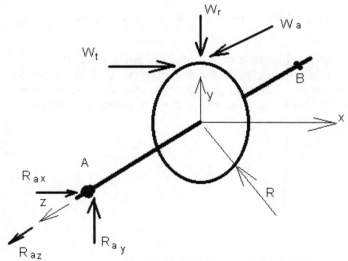

Forces on a shaft with a helical gear attached

Reactions at A and B in the x and y directions are found by summing forces in the x direction and taking moments about the y axis, then by summing forces in the y direction and taking moments about the x axis.

All the reaction to the axial force W_a will be carried at one end, depending upon the bearing arrangements. The axial force will cause tension or compression in the shaft and as it is not acting co-axially with the shaft centre line, it will also cause a bending moment about the x axis, in the y - z plane, see diagram below:

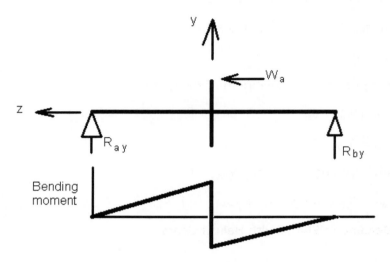

Bending moment about x axis due to axial force - variation along shaft

The general form of the bending moment diagram due to the transmitted load (which is replaced by an equal parallel force acting through the shaft centre and a torque rotating the shaft equal to R W_t) causes bending about the y axis in the x - z plane, see below:

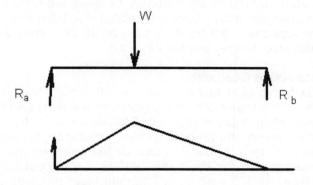

General shape of bending moment diagrams due to transmitted and radial forces

This is also the general diagram for the bending moment caused by the radial force, W_r, about the x axis in the y - z plane.

15.2.9 Lubrication of Gears
During operation the teeth are sliding against one another, so to prevent wear lubrication is normally essential for heavily loaded gears. Even though a gearbox may have an efficiency of 97%, where considerable power is being transmitted, 3% loss as heat generated within the gearbox, may necessitate the provision of some type of forced cooling.

15.2.10 Acceleration of a Geared System
The derivation of the expression for the equivalent inertia of a geared system is shown in Appendix 15.3.

15.2.11 Summary of Design Issues
Bending and breakage of teeth at root, usually fatigue failure due to cyclic loading. This situation can be made worse even by slight misalignment.

Surface of teeth pitting due to cyclic compressive stresses.

To maintain high efficiency and ensure the noise levels are low with highly loaded gears, it is essential that the shafts carrying meshing gears maintain the intended separation and accuracy of parallelism. This will involve not only assessing the stresses in the shafts carrying the gears but also the deflections of the shafts. As well as the stiffness of the shafts carrying the gears, the stiffness of the gear box should also be checked. This is particularly important in automotive gear boxes where the shafts are not very long and have a reasonable diameter, but the gear box will almost certainly be made from aluminium and will probably be designed for a minimum mass. But aluminium alloys have only about one third the stiffness of steel (and less than cast iron) so such an aluminium gear box design should also be checked for deflection.

15.2.12 Automotive Gearboxes

Modern automotive gearboxes use gears with helical teeth and unlike gears with straight cut teeth, gears with helical teeth can not be readily moved in and out of mesh. Consequently all the gears are in constant mesh and an arrangement similar to the simplified diagram below is used. In the diagram all the gears on the input shaft are integral with the shaft and all those on the output shaft are able to freewheel. Engaging or changing gear involves sliding the synchroniser in the appropriate direction.

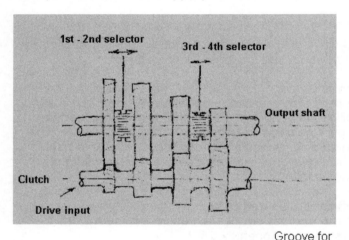

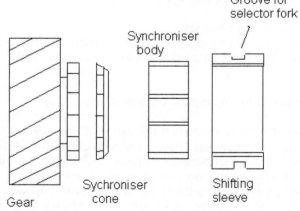

Simplified synchromesh system

The gear synchroniser consists of a shifting sleeve, synchroniser

body, 2 cones or rings (1 shown in diag.) and (not shown) 3 blocker bars, balls and springs.
The synchroniser body bore is splined to the output shaft.
The shifting sleeve is splined to the synchroniser body. Sliding a selctor towards either gear presses a sychronising cone against the freewheeling gear and changes its speed to match that of the sychroniser and output shaft. Once the speed is sychronised the shifting sleeve can slide accross transmitting drive from the gear via teeth on the side of the gear to the shifting sleeve then to the synchroniser and via it's splined hub to the output shaft.

Automatic Gear boxes are usually based on a series of epicyclic gear groups. Each gear group will have one or more brakes or clutches that can hold or release parts of each gear group. Changing gear is effected by releasing one brake in one gear group while applying another brake to the appropriate gear group. The brakes are normally operated by hydraulic systems controlled by electronics which in modern systems takes information from the engine management system.

Originally automatic gear boxes were not satisfactory in sports and other cars where drivers wished to exploit their potential good performance. About 20 years ago Porsche introduced the 'Tiptronic' gearbox which included an accelerometer and used this to modify gear changing depending upon whether the car was travelling in a straight line or cornering. This was a significant step forward and offered satisfactory gear changes in a wider range of driving situations while still maintaining the option of almost full manual operation.

A more recent development in automatic gearboxes has been the dual clutch system, which is like having two gearboxes in one, whereby even ratios run through one clutch and the odd ratios run through another. This enables the management system to preselect the next ratio that the driver is likely to need and when the change is needed it involves releasing the engaged clutch and engaging the other one. Porsche in 2008 introduced their dual clutch 7 speed automatic 'PDK' gearbox option which is rated very highly by people who have driven cars fitted with this gearbox.

Epicyclic gear groups have two important advantages:
i) It is possible to have a greater ratio than is feasible than with a single pair of gears.
ii) The load on any individual tooth pair is reduced because it is shared between a number of tooth pairs equal to the number of planet gears carried by the spider.
Automotive epicyclic gearboxes normally have 3 planet wheels on each spider but in aircraft engine gear boxes it is normal to have 5

or 7 planets on each spider which facilitates high transmission loads while retaining a compact, lower weight construction.

15.3 Chains

Chains consist of a series of links (side plates) connected by pins. The chain is able to transmit high tensile forces while still being able to articulate round driving and driven sprockets.

Most chains are 'roller' chains which have a roller on each pin to help reduce friction, however lubrication is essential as the roller will be rotating slightly with respect to the pin as the chain moves onto and off the sprockets. Dirt and other extraneous matter can seriously shorten the life of a chain and full enclosure is desirable. Some chains for motorcycle drives are provided with seals between side plates and rollers which helps prevent the ingress of dirt, but at the expense of extra friction.

Roller chains are classified by pitch, the distance between corresponding parts of adjacent links, and by their width. The first one or two digits indicate the pitch of the chain in 1/8 of an inch units (1/8 of 25.4 mm).

Roller chain is also available in 'duplex' and triplex' form, ie with 2 or 3 strands side by side.

Many other types of chain are in use, a common variation is to have side plates with brackets attached which are widely used for conveyor belts.

The approximate tensile strengths of some sizes of roller chains is given in in the table below:

Chain number	Pitch, mm	Pitch, inches	Average tensile strength, kN
25	6.35	1/4	4.1
35	9.525	3/8	9.3
40	12.7	1/2	16.5
60	19.050	3/4	37.8

In the past 30 years, many transmission applications that were performed by chains have been taken over by toothed belt drives. Advantages of belts include lower noise levels, especially when partly worm (though this means there is no audible warning of impending failure), lower cost and less vulnerability to minor dirt ingress.

Although many petrol and diesel engines now use toothed belts to drive their camshafts, several engines in 'up market' cars continue to use chain drives.

Manufacturers publish detailed information about the capabilities, requirements and ratings of their chains.

15.4 Toothed - or Synchronous - Belts

There are four common standard sizes of toothed belt and these are summarised below:

Pitch, mm	Total belt depth, mm	Tooth depth, mm
5	3.8	1.9
8	5.4	3.2
14	9.7	6.0
20	14.5	8.3

As well as the above sizes a 9.5 mm pitch with a total belt depth of 5.8 mm and 20 mm wide is often used for camshaft drives in small and medium automotive engines. Such belts have a tensile strength of about 6 - 8 kN.

To ensure that the belts function satisfactorily they must be correctly tensioned and no attempt should be made to stretch a belt, they are very stiff in tension and if sufficient force was exerted to stretch a belt the reinforcement would certainly be damaged. A widely published rule of thumb when fitting belts to camshaft drives is that the tension should be such that it is just possible to twist the belt through 90° using a finger and thumb in the middle of the longest run. This is obviously not a rigorous substitute for a proper tension gauge!

15.5 'V' Belts

A key feature of 'V' belts is that they do not contact the bottom of the pulley grooves but are wedged between the inclined sides of the pulleys, increasing the normal force and therefore the available friction generated driving force.
A wide range of sizes of 'V' belts are available and although these are not much used in automotive engineering, they are very widely used in industry to transmit drives from electric motors to pumps, compressors, etc. Where the power is too much for a single belt, multiple large belts, often up to 10 or more, are run side by side in multi groove pulleys.
For alternator drives on automobile engines a shallow multi V belt is widely used, the shallow depth gives reduced bending stresses compared to the conventional deep single V belt.

Appendix 15.4 includes the theory and an example calculation for a belt drive.

15.6 Clutches
15.6.1 Introduction

The plate clutch is used in automotive and industrial service to connect and disconnect the transmission of rotation / torque / power.

In the picture above, the housing on the left is bolted to the engine flywheel, with the clutch plate assembly, on the right, sandwiched between the pressure plate (the annular component reflecting the light on the left) and the flywheel (not shown in this picture, bolted to the end of the crankshaft - see picture in Chapter 11). As assembled the clutch plate rotates with the housing and flywheel, transmitting drive to the gerarbox via the splined bore. To release the clutch a thrust bearing pushes the inner ends of the fingers of the diaphragm spring which releases the spring pressure on the pressure plate.

In conveyor systems it is common to fit a clutch designed to slip and warn the operator if a jam occurs so corrective action can be taken before expensive gearboxes or conveyor belts fail.

15.6.2 Theory

To determine the torque transmitted it is necessary to make an assumption about the pressure distribution over the friction surfaces. For perfectly aligned new surfaces, it could be assumed that the pressure is uniformly distributed over the entire surface. However once the system has had some use, a better assumption is that the rate of wear is uniform over the friction surfaces. As a first approximation it can be assumed that the wear rate is proportional to the product of the velocity of sliding and the pressure. Since the sliding velocity is proportional to the radius r to the annular element dr, the following can be written:

wear = k p r, since the wear is constant for the entire face, the maximum pressure will occur at the inner radius, r_i hence wear = k p_{max} r_i

Eliminating wear and the constant, k, gives the pressure at any radius, p

$$p = p_{max}\, r_i/r$$

The total force Fn which must be exerted by the actuating spring, is found by multiplying the element area 2 x 3.142 x r x dr, by the pressure and integrating over the surface. This gives

$$Fn = 2 \times 3.142 \times p_{max}\, r_i(r_o - r_i)$$

The torque is found by multiplying the force on the element by the coefficient of friction, f, and the radius, and integrating over the area. This gives:

$$T = 3.142 \times f \times p_{max} \times r_i\, (r_o{}^2 - r_i{}^2) = 0.5\, f\, (r_o + r_i)F_n$$

Single plate clutches have lining on both sides of the plate. Multiple plate disc clutches have friction linings on both sides of alternate plates. The above gives the torque for a single face, thus this quantity must be multiplied by the number of friction faces to find the torque for the entire clutch.

15.6.3 Cone clutch

The cone clutch utilises the wedging action of the parts to increase the normal force on the lining for a given spring force, thus an increase in the tangential friction and the torque results. Uniform wear is assumed. Values of included semi - angle vary from about 12° upwards. Smaller angles can lead to jamming and a jerky take up.

Lining Pressure

Typical lining pressures (in N/mm^2) and dry coefficients of friction are shown below:

Material	Working Pressure	Coefficient of friction
Moulded materials and sintered metals	1 to 2	
Cast iron on cast iron	1 to 1.7	0.15 - 0.2
Steel on cast iron	0.8 to 1.4	0.2 - 0.3
Bronze on cast iron	0.5 to 0.8	
Wood on cast iron	0.4 to 0.6	0.2 - 0.25
Cork on metal	0.05 to 0.1	0.35
Asbestos blocks on metal	0.25 to 1.1	0.4 - 0.48

For clutches running in oil the coefficient of friction will typically be in the range 0.05 to 0.15.

Appendix 15

15.1 Example - Gear Tooth Strength Calculation

Note: Slightly differing values for the Lewis form factor, Y, may be found according to which book you use to obtain the information. The tooth root fillet radius is given in some articles as 0.3 times the module and as 0.38 m in others, this latter value has been used in the example below.

A spur gear with full depth teeth has a 20° pressure angle and is made from AISI 1020 as rolled.

The gear is module 3, has 16 teeth and is 30 mm wide (face width, b_w). Use a design with a fos of 3 based on yield strength.

If the gear is operating at 1200 rpm in a moderate application:

a) What power can be transmitted?

b) Based on an infinite life in bending, what power can be transmitted.

Solution (a): Moderate implies that the gear can be rated on the yield strength: 210 MPa (from published data tables) using a fos of 3 gives an allowable bending stress of 70 MPa.

Diameter of gear is no. of teeth x module = 16 x 3 = 48 mm.

The pitch line velocity: v = 3.14159 d n = 3.14159 x 0.048 x 1200/60 = 3.016 m/s.

Velocity factor (Barth eqn.): K_v = 6.1/(6.1 + v) = 6.1/9.116 = 0.67

Lewis form factor for 16 teeth: Y = 0.276

$\text{sigma}_{allowable} = W_t/(b_w\ m\ K_v\ Y)$ .. re-arrange and substitute

If the face width, b_w and the module, m are in mm, then sigma is in MPa

Tangential force: w_t = $\text{sigma}_{all}\ b_w\ m\ K_v\ Y$ = 70 x 30 x 3 x 0.67 x 0.276 = 1165 N

Power = W_t v = 1165 x 3.016 = 3.51 kW

Solution (b): Assume $S_e' = 0.5\ S_{ut} = 0.5$ x 380 = 190 MPa

Factors reducing smooth test piece fatigue strength (section 4.5.3.2) S_e':

Surface factor: $k_a = a\, S_{ut}^b$

Assuming the steel is hot rolled: a = 57.7, b = -0.718 so

$k_a = 57.7(380)^{-0.718} = 0.811$

Size factor: $k_b = (d/7.62)^{-0.1133}$

A value is needed for 'd', effective rotating diameter, d_e

Suggested d_e for a rectangular beam is: $d_e = 0.808(h\,b)^{0.5}$ see section 4.5.3.2.

Where h and b are height (depth) and width of the beam.

The width of the beam (tooth) is 30 mm

The beam height is the tooth root thickness t.

From section 15.2.3, eqn. 2, $x = t^2/(4\,L)$ and $Y = 2 \times P/3$

where P = diametral pitch, L is the tooth depth and

from 15.2.2 L = addendum + dedendum = m + 1.25 m = 2.25 x 3 = 6.75 mm

Diametral pitch, P = 1/m = 0.333 so

$x = 3\,Y/2P = t^2/4L$

$t^2 = 3\,Y\,4\,L/2P = 3 \times 0.276 \times 4 \times 6.75/(2 \times 0.33)$

$t^2 = 33.87,..\ t = 5.82$ mm

$d_e = 0.808(5.82 \times 30)^{0.5} = 10.68$ mm

$k_b = (10.68/7.62)^{-0.1133} = 0.962$

As loading is bending, $k_c = 1$

As there is no special information about loading, assume normal temperatures, so $k_d = 1$

Miscellaneous effects factor, k_e, needs to include:
Unidirectional bending only
Stress concentration and notch sensitivity.

For unidirectional bending: $sigma_a = sigma_m = sigma_{max}/2$

Using the modified Goodman relationship:

$(S_a/S_e') + (S_m/S_{ut}) = 1$

$S_a = S_m$, solve above:

$(S_a S_{ut}/S_e' S_{ut}) + (S_a S_e'/S_e' S_{ut}) = 1$

$S_a(S_{ut} + S_e') = S_e' S_{ut}$

$S_a = S_e' S_{ut}/(S_e' + S_{ut})$

Replace S_a by $sigma_{max}/2$ and S_e' with $0.5 S_{ut}$

$sigma_{max} = 2 \times 0.5 S_{ut}^2/(1.5 S_{ut}) = 0.67 S_{ut} = 1.33 S_e'$

For stress concentration: fillet radius = 0.38 m = 1.14 mm

$r/d = 1.14/5.82 = 0.195$, D/d is very large.

From published data: $K_t = 1.6$

Use notch sensitivity on this.

From published data for this material and radius, q = 0.6

$q = (K_f - 1)/(K_t - 1)$

where K_t is the theoretical or geometric stress concentration factor and K_f is the reduced actual stress concentration taking account of the material notch sensitivity.

$K_f = 1 + q(K_t - 1) = 1 + 0.6(1.6 - 1) = 1.36$

$1/K_f = 1/1.36 = 0.735$

k_e = correction for unidirectional loading x $1/K_f$

$k_e = 1.33 \times 0.735 = 0.978$

Combining all the fatigue strength reduction factors:

$S_e = k_a k_b k_c k_d k_e S_e'$

$S_e = 0.811 \times 0.962 \times 1 \times 1 \times 0.978 \times 190 = 145$ MPa

With a fos of 3, $sigma_{all} = 145/3 = 48.3$ MPa

$W_t = sigma_{all}\ b_w\ m\ K_v\ Y = 48.3 \times 30 \times 3 \times 0.67 \times 0.67 \times x0.276 = 804.3$ N

Power $= W_t\ v = 804.3 \times 3.016 = 2.43$ kW.

15.2 Example Helical Gear Calculation

A pair of helical gears with parallel axes transmit 75 kW with the pinion rotating at 600 rpm. The gears have pressure angles of 20°, a helix angle of 30° a module of 8 and a face width of 60 mm. The teeth are full depth, with 32 on the pinion and 44 on the gear.

Find the tooth bending stress.

Solution: Diameters of the pinion and gear wheel are:

8 x 32 mm and 8 x 44 mm, ie 256 mm and 352 mm.

The pitch line velocity = 3.14159 d n /60

= 3.14159 x 0.256 x 600/60 = 8.042 m/s

Use Barth equation for velocity factor:

$K_v = 6.1/(6.1 + v) = 6.1/(6.1 + 8.04) = 0.431$

Transmitted load: w_t = Power/velocity

$w_t = 75000/8.042 = 9326$ N

Because of the helix angle, phi, the force bending the teeth is greater than w_t

By resolving: $w_b = w_t/\cos(phi)$

$w_b = 9326/\cos(30) = 10770$ N

The Lewis formula for bending including the velocity factor:

$sigma_{bending} = w_b/(K_v\ b_w\ m\ Y)$

The Lewis form factor must be determined for the virtual number of teeth, N', as these are helical gears:

$N' = N/\cos^3(\text{phi})$

$N' = 32/(\cos 30)^3 = 49.27$

From tables: Y = 0.398, substituting values:

$\text{sigma}_{bending} = 10770/(0.431 \times 60 \times 8 \times 0.398) = 130.8$ MPa

Although this is quite a low stress, no allowance has been made for cyclic loading.

15.3 Determination of the equivalent inertia of a geared system - Acceleration of a Geared System

A pinion: A, moment of inertia I_a radius r_a drives a gear B, moment of inertia I_b and radius r_b.

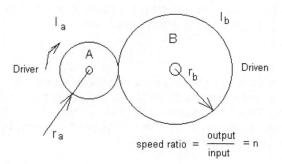

Simple gear system

If it is assumed that the system is 100% efficient, omega_a and omega_b are the angular velocities of A and B, then
work rate in = work rate out so:

Torque$_a$ omega$_a$ = Torque$_b$ omega$_b$ so
omega$_b$ / omega$_a$ = n = Torque$_a$ / Torque$_b$

If a torque M is applied to pinion A to accelerate the system then:
alpha$_a$ and alpha$_b$ are the accelerations of A and B respectively.
The acceleration ratios: alpha$_b$ / alpha$_a$ = n

The torque on A to accelerate only A is: I_a alpha$_a$
The torque required on B to accelerate only B is: I_b alpha$_b$ = I_b n

alpha_a

Therefore the torque on A to accelerate only B is: $n^2 \, I_b \, \text{alpha}_a$

So total torque on A to accelerate A and B :

$$= I_a \, \text{alpha}_a + n^2 \, I_b \, \text{alpha}_a$$
$$= (\, I_a + n^2 \, I_b \,) \, \text{alpha}_a$$

The quantity:

$$I_a + n^2 \, I_b$$

may be regarded as the equivalent moment of inertia of the gears referred to shaft A. This principle may be extended to any number of wheels geared together (and shafts, drums components fixed to them) the moment of inertia of each wheel/shaft in the train being multiplied by the square of it's speed ratio relative to the reference wheel. Thus hoists, etc can be reduced to an equivalent moment of inertia at the motor shaft or drum shaft.

Care must be taken when using equivalent inertias in problems where the efficiency (eta) of the gearing is given. If the efficiency of the gearing is eta then the torque required on A to accelerate B is $n^2 \, I_b/\text{eta}$ so the equivalent inertia of A and B becomes

$$I_a + (n^2 \, I_b)/\text{eta}$$

To find the gear ratio which gives the maximum acceleration, an expression for alpha is found in terms of n, I_a, I_b, resisting and accelerating torques etc. This expression for alpha is then differentiated with respect to n and this is then equated to zero, ie: d alpha/dn = 0. This is then solved for n.

15.4 Belt Drive Theory and Example Calculation

Theory

Note that in the example below the belt is assumed to be flat. Most belts now have a 'V' cross section. The V belt does not run on the bottom of the belt groove, but the sides wedge into the sides of the pulley. If the semi-included angle of the V groove is B, then the theory below needs modifying as the maximum friction force is no longer F = mu R, (where mu is the coefficient of friction) but becomes:

$$F = mu \; R \; \cosec(B) = mu \; R \; /[\sin(B)]$$

A 'V' grooved pulley is the equivalent of having a flat pulley with a coefficient of friction mu cosec(B).

In the theory below it is assumed that the element of belt subtends a small angle and when resolving radially, sine of half the small angle is approximately equal to the angle in radians and (resolving in a tangential direction) the cosine is approximately equal to 1.

$(T+dT)\cos\frac{d\theta}{2} - F - T\cos\frac{d\theta}{2}$ — tangential

as $d\theta$ is small, $\cos d\theta \approx 1$

$dT = F$, when belt is on point of slipping: $F = \mu R$, so $dT = \mu R$

Radial:

$(T + dT)\sin\frac{d\theta}{2} + T\sin\frac{d\theta}{\theta} - R = 0$

for small angles, $\sin\theta \approx \theta$

$$T\,d\theta = R$$

$$\frac{dT}{\mu} = T\,d\theta$$

$$\frac{dT}{T} = \mu\,d\theta$$

$$\int_{T_2}^{T_1}\frac{dT}{T} = \mu\int_{0}^{\beta}d\theta \qquad \text{giving: } \ln\left(\frac{T_1}{T_2}\right) = \mu\beta$$

$$\text{or}\quad \frac{T_1}{T_2} = e^{\mu\beta}$$

Example

A 600 watt alternator produces full output at 1000 revs. per minute and has an overall efficiency of 70%.The alternator pulley has a diameter of 40 mm, the coefficient of friction between the belt and pulley is 0.3 (assume the belt and pulleys are 'flat') and the angle of wrap of the belt around the pulley in 140°.
Determine: (i) the minimum values of the belt tension T_1 and T_2 that will provide the necessary output and (ii) the maximum normal pressure between the belt and the pulley if the belt is 6 mm wide.

The first part of the solution ignores the centrifugal effects, these arise because the belt is moving in an arc of a circle as it goes round the pulleys and some of the tension is needed to cause the belt to move in a radius as opposed to in a straight line.
The maximum normal pressure between the belt and the pulley will be just before the belt leaves the pulley on the tight side.

Alternator

$$\text{Power in} = \frac{600}{0.7} \text{ watts.}$$

$$\text{Power} = \text{Torque} \times \omega$$

$$\frac{600}{0.7} = (T_1 - T_2) r \, \frac{2\pi \, 1000}{60}$$

$$T_1 - T_2 = \frac{60 \times 600}{0.02 \times 1000 \times 2\pi \times 0.7}$$

$$= 409.3 \text{ N}$$

$$\frac{T_1}{T_2} = e^{\mu\beta} = e^{0.3 \times 2.443}$$

$$T_1 = T_2 + 409.3$$

$$\frac{T_2 + 409.3}{T_2} = e^{0.733} = 2.081$$

$$T_2 + 409.3 = 2.081 \, T_2$$

$$T_2 = 378.6 \text{ N}$$

$$T_1 = T_2 \times 2.081 = 787.9$$

$$F = \mu R$$

$$\text{Pressure} = \frac{Force}{Area} = \frac{R}{w\,r\,d\theta}$$

Tangentially: $(T + dT) - T = F$

$$dt = F = \mu R$$

Radially: $R = (T + dT)\frac{d\theta}{2} + T\frac{d\theta}{2} = T d\theta$

$$\text{Pressure} = \frac{T d\theta}{w\,r\,d\theta}$$

Max pressure is where T is max.

$$P_{max} = \frac{T_1}{w\,r} = \frac{787.9}{5 \times 20}$$

$$= 6.56 \ N/mm^2$$

$$= 6.56 \ MPa.$$

In the following section the effects of centrifugal force are considered. The diagram below shows the the forces acting on the belt while it is moving without transmitting any torque, hence the belt tension is constant, T_c, due only to centrifugal effects. In the example it is assumed that the mass per unit length of the belt, m, is 0.5 kg/m.

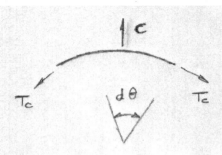

centrifugal force due to small element: $m r d\theta \omega^2 r = m r^2 \omega^2 d\theta$

Resolving radially:

$$m r^2 \omega^2 d\theta = 2 T_c \frac{d\theta}{2}$$

$$T_c = m r^2 \omega^2$$

Adding effects, radially:

$$(T + dT)\frac{d\theta}{2} + T \frac{d\theta}{2} = R + C = R + m r^2 \omega^2 d\theta$$

tangentially: $(T + dT) - T = \mu R$

$$dT = \mu (T - T_c) d\theta$$

$$\int_{T_2}^{T_1} \frac{dT}{T - T_c} = \int_0^\beta \mu \, d\theta$$

$$\frac{T_1 - T_c}{T_2 - T_c} = e^{\mu \beta}$$

Power transmitted
$$= \left[(T_1 - T_c) - (T_2 - T_c)\right] \omega r$$

$$T_1 - T_c = (T_2 - T_c) e^{\mu \beta}$$

$$\text{Power} = \left[(T_2 - T_c)(e^{\mu \beta} - 1)\right] \omega r$$

in example:

$$T_c = m r^2 \omega^2$$

$$= 0.5 (0.02)^2 \left(\frac{2\pi \, 1000}{60}\right)^2$$

$$= 2.2 \, N$$

$$\text{Power} = \frac{600}{0.7} = \left[(T_2 - 2.2)(2.081 - 1)\right] r \omega$$

$$\frac{600}{0.7} = (T_2 - 2.2)(1.081)(0.02) \frac{2\pi \, 1000}{60}$$

$$T_2 - 2.2 = \frac{600}{0.7} \times \frac{60}{2\pi \, 1000 (1.081) 0.02}$$

$$= 378.59$$

$$T_2 = 380.79$$

$$T_1 = (T_2 - T_c) e^{\mu \beta} + T_c$$

$$= (378.59) 2.081 + 2.2$$

$$T_1 = 790.05 \, N$$

In this case as the belt mass per unit length is quite small and the belt speed is low, the centrifugal effects are negligible.

16. Carburettors, Fuel Injection, Sensors and Actuators.

16.1 Background to Automotive Fuel Systems

For the first 80 years of the automobile, the petrol / air mixture was formed by a carburettor. Despite considerable improvements over the years it was becoming clear by the late 1970s that the carburettor was nearing the limits of its capabilities and the increasing requirements for improved economy and reduced exhaust emissions indicated that a better way of providing the mixture was needed.

Some fuel injection systems exercising control by a combination of mechanical and electronic devices had been developed by the late 1970s, but it was the developments in electronics in the 1980s and 1990s which lowered the costs of these systems and led to their widespread introduction, so that now there are virtually no new petrol powered cars sold in the developed world that do not have fuel injection and an engine management system.

Diesel engines have always used some type of injection system to force the fuel into the cylinders against the high pressure generated by the compression stroke. This used to involve carrying the fuel into the cylinder in a high pressure air blast which was able to carry oil droplets or powdered coal. Modern systems use positive displacement pumps which deliver diesel fuel at pressures of 200 Bar (10MPa) or more, generally higher pressures assist with fuel atomisation which in turn assists combustion.

Fuel injection systems, both petrol and diesel, operate on the basis of supplying fuel to the injectors at a constant pressure so the volume injected will be proportional to the time the injector is open.

16.2 Carburettors

16.2.1 Introduction

Although fuel injection is widely used in new cars and large motor cycle engines, there are large numbers of small and medium sized petrol engines made with carburettors powering small and medium sized motor cycles and a wide range of industrial and DIY equipment from cement mixers to lawn mowers and an understanding of the principles on which carburettors operate and are designed is important.

The function of a carburettor can be split into 3 stages:

- i) delivering the correct proportions of air and liquid fuel for combustion on a continuous basis while accounting for varying operating conditions.
- ii) Atomising (or breaking up) the liquid stream into a very fine spray and mixing it with the air stream.
- iii) Providing the latent heat of vaporisation to the liquid so the mixture can form a homogeneous vapour in readiness for ignition.

It is the first stage of the function which causes the most difficulties and some of the reasons for this are summarised below:

- i) The properties of the air and petrol are very different, air is a compressible gas and petrol is a liquid with much higher density (with much higher inertia) which is incompressible under the conditions of interest.
- ii) The actual demand for mixture is only during the induction stroke, which in a four stroke engine is approximately 1/4 of the time for each cylinder.
- iii) The air:fuel ratio needs to be varied according to operating requirements, hard acceleration and full power requires a rich mixture, for cruising a lean mixture is desirable to improve fuel economy.

Although a basic carburettor can be designed without difficulty, requirement (iii) varying the air:fuel ratio adds a considerable degree of complication.

There are two basic types of carburettor: constant venturi choke, where the orifice area is kept constant and the pressure difference or depression is varied while the other is the constant vacuum where the orifice is varied to meet demand while the depression remains approximately constant.

16.2.2 The Constant Choke Jet Carburettor The basic constant choke jet carburettor, see below, functions by having a fixed diameter jet placed at the narrowest point in a venturi and the fuel level is controlled by an adjacent float chamber to be a few mm below the jet. Air in the induction pipe accelerates as it goes through the venturi, this causes a drop in pressure which draws the petrol up out of the jet and it breaks up into a fine stream of droplets in the air stream. Assuming the throttle is open, the greater the engine speed, the greater the air speed through the venturi, the larger the depression and greater the flow rate of the petrol through the jet. To slow the engine down, the throttle is closed, this causes virtually all the pressure drop to occur across the throttle and the pressure drop across the jet is then very small reducing the flow rate of petrol from the jet orifice which reduces the power the engine is producing.

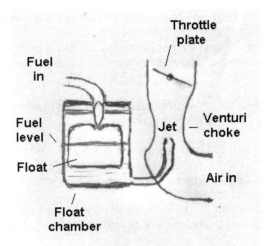

The flow of fuel from a single jet increases in proportion to the velocity of the air flowing through the venturi, but the density of the air falls as the velocity increases. This means that the mass flow of air increases more slowly than the fuel mass flow rate. Hence if the mixture is very slightly lean (say an air mass flow rate to fuel mass flow rate of 15:1) at part open throttle, then when the throttle is opened to double the air mass flow rate, the fuel mass flow rate will have increased by a factor of about 2.5 giving a rich mixture with an air fuel ratio of 12:1. This variation is not acceptable and one or more compensating jets are normally included to provide better control of over the range of engine speeds while providing appropriate variation depending upon engine load.

16.2.3 The Constant Vacuum Carburettor

In one version of the constant vacuum carburettor a tapered needle is held in the bottom of a cylinder which is integral with a piston which is free to slide in a suction chamber.
The suction chamber has a vent passage connecting it to the downstream side of the carburettor. Assuming the engine is running with the throttle almost closed, there is a small pressure drop through the carburettor and a large pressure drop across the throttle. If the throttle is opened, the pressure drop across the throttle reduces and there is briefly a larger pressure drop across the carburettor. This pressure drop is communicated to the suction chamber above the piston, the piston and cylinder rise, increasing the area available for the air being drawn into the engine increasing the air mass flow rate. At the same time the tapered needle is

drawn up through the jet, this provides a greater area for the fuel to flow through and the fuel flow rate increases. Hence the volume of mixture reaching the engine increases and the power produced increases. The motion of the piston is damped with an oil filled dashpot to prevent to rapid movement of the piston (which on opening the throttle would give a lean mixture when a rich mixture was needed). It is possible to vary the characteristics of the carburettor by supplying needles with different profiles. For example a needle with a larger diameter around its mid length, will result in a leaner misture for flow rates when the larger diameter portion is emerging from the jet. However other compensating devices are needed for more sophisticated requirements.

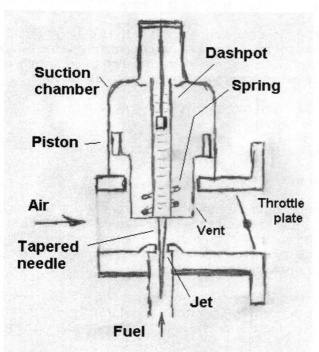

Over the years many devices have been developed to improve the capability of carburettors to cope with the diversity of requirements including compensating jets, air bleeding arrangements and accelerator pumps. While these have improved the capabilities of carburettors, it has been at the expense of significant complication.

16.2.4 Carburettor Design Principles
Stating from the Bernoulli equation and assuming there is no change in level:

$$V_1^2/2 + p_1/D_1 = V_2^2/2 + p_2/D_2$$

It is assumed that the fluid is incompressible and so the density, D, will remain unaltered and that the initial velocity is zero so:

$$V_2{}^2 = 2(p_1 - p_2)/D$$

so the velocity of fuel emerging from the jet or air through the venturi choke is given by:

$$V = (2 p / D)^{0.5}$$ where p is the depression (pressure drop) across the jet or venturi.

The volume flow is given by $v = A_{eff} (2 p / D)^{0.5}$

where A_{eff} is the effective cross section area of the jet, this is smaller than the physical cross section area as the coefficient of discharge of the jet will be less than 1, typically 0.6 - 0.8 for most carburettor jets. To include this C_d, the coefficient of discharge is introduced and A = actual jet or venturi area.

The depression in most fixed choke carburettors during normal running - in terms of fluid height - is approximately in the range of 100 to 500 mm of water column, corresponding to air speeds of 40 to 85 m / s. The petrol speeds are much lower, about 1 - 2.5 m / s.

To obtain the mass flow rate, the volume flow rate must be multiplied by the density, D:

$$\text{Mass flow rate} = A\ C_d (2 p / D)^{0.5} D$$

$$\text{Mass flow rate} = A\ C_d (2 p D)^{0.5}$$

When the engine is running, the air and petrol orifices, the venturi choke and jet, are subjected to the same depression and if the relative areas are suitably chosen, having regard to the densities of the two fluids, air and petrol will flow into and through the venturi in suitable fixed proportions.

If it is assumed that the C_d values for the jet and venturi choke are similar and that the density of petrol is about 750 kg/m^3, that of air at normal temperature and pressure is 1.28 kg/m^3 and that the stoichiometric ratio for air to petrol is 14.7:1:

Mass flow rate Air = $A_{choke}(2 p D_{air})^{0.5}$ = 14.7 x Mass flow rate of petrol = 14.7 x $A_{jet}(2 p D_{petrol})^{0.5}$

$$A_{choke} / A_{jet} = 14.7 (2 p D_{petrol})^{0.5} / (2 p D_{air})^{0.5}$$

Substituting values the relative areas of the air venturi choke to petrol jet should be:

Area of venturi choke / Area of jet = $(14.7 / 1) \times (750 / 1.28)^{0.5}$ = 356.

The high speed of the air stream through the venturi choke breaks up the stream of petrol as it emerges from the jet into fine droplets. This provides the required degree of atomisation of the fuel.

To maximise the power produced by an engine, the maximum mass of air (and fuel) need to be drawn into the engine so it is desirable that the air drawn in is as cool as possible. To facilitate this the air intake is normally outside the engine compartment, sometimes under a wheel arch.

To prevent icing up in cold temperatures carburettors may be fitted with some heating device. In the case of water cooled engines this is usually provided by a branch taken from the main engine cooling system.

16.2.5 Carburettor Materials
Petrol is corrosive, particularly towards steel. Most carburettors are manufactured either form brass or from a magnesium / zinc die casting alloy. The use of such alloys, which are easy to machine, also facilitates the drilling of fine passages needed for the compensating systems that are included in many carburettors.

For many years cars had steel petrol tanks coated on the inside with lead (referred to as 'tern plate') to enable them to resist corrosion promoted by petrol. Increasingly now plastic petrol tanks are used in cars as it is easier to mould plastics into odd shapes needed to make efficient use of the limited space in modern compact cars.

16.3 Fuel Injection - Petrol Engines
16.3.1 System Basics
The fuel injectors in most petrol engines are situated in the inlet manifold and spray fuel droplets towards the back of the inlet valve, the airflow should then carry the droplets past the open valve and into the cylinder. The fuel supply to the injectors in these systems will typically be at pressure in the range of 0.2 - 0.5 MPa.
A small number of petrol engines use gasoline direct injection (GDI) where an injector is situated in each cylinder and fuel is injected directly into the cylinder near the end of the compression stroke. This requires a much higher injection pressure than is needed for injection into the inlet tract.
The primary control on the mass of fuel to be injected is the mass flow rate of air into the engine. Although the stoichiometric ratio for air to petrol is about 14.7:1 this in practice needs to be changed significantly for starting, running while the engine is warming up and accelerating (made richer) and economical cruising (made leaner) and for coasting with the throttle closed no fuel is injected until the engine revs. drop below about 1600 rpm. To achieve this a

number of sensors provide data for a microprocessor and this is used either to directly calculate the required fuel flow rate or the data is compared with an operating 'map' and the signal to open the injector for the appropriate length of time is produced and sent to the injectors.

Early fuel injection control systems or engine management systems - e.g. Bosch L Jetronic - consisted of a bulky box of discrete electronics. This system used a hinged flap, lightly spring loaded, in the inlet tract to measure the air mass flow, however this in itself introduced a pressure drop which slightly lowered the engine efficency and more modern systems (e.g. Bosch LE Jetronic) use hot wire anemometry to compute the air mass flow as this does not cause a significant pressure drop. The electronics are now much more compact.

Some current systems do not measure the actual air flow directly but use closed loop control involving exhaust gas analysis with a lambda oxygen sensor and combining the readings from this with readings from other sensors (and possibly comparing readings with a map) to determine the quantity of fuel to be injected.

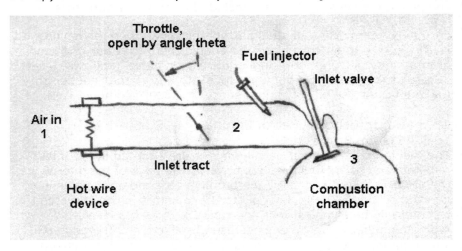

The key components of the inlet tract are shown above.

Lambda Closed Loop Control
In Europe, Japan and the US using closed loop control of the engine management system for vehicles fitted with three way catalytic converters has proved to be a very effective way of meeting current low emission requirements for CO, NO_x and HC. The excess air factor, lambda, is the ratio of the actual air:fuel ratio to the stoichiometric air:fuel ratio. Operating with a lambda = 1 within the very narrow limits of + or - 0.005 is most effective for minimising

pollutants. This requires a lambda oxygen sensor upstream of the catalytic converter and sometimes a second sensor downstream of the converter.

Lean Burn - Closed Loop Control for lambda greater than 1
Engine operation under lean burn conditions with closed loop control has the advantage of reduced fuel consumption, particularly when the engine is non-throttled. However to maintain low emissions requires the fitting of catalytic converters which are able to reduce NO_x during lean burn operation. The lean misfire limit (LML) for spark ignition engines in the lean burn range is approximately 1.7 regardless of engine design measures. Year 2007 air cooled Harley Davidson motorcycles run lean. They are not fitted with catalytic converters but are fitted with a lambda sensor in each exhaust pipe close to where they exit from the cylinder heads. The potential disadvantage of running an air cooled engine lean is that there is significantly less cooling due to fuel vapourisation and there is some information suggesting that these engines run at about 20°C hotter than when running on a near stoichiometric mixture. Obviously this is highly dependent upon other operating conditions such as load and ambient conditions.

16.3.2 Fuel Injection - Diesel Engines
Modern diesel engines use a common rail system which separates the functions of pressurising the diesel fuel and injecting the fuel into the cylinders. A high pressure pump supplies fuel to the common rail, which acts as an accumulator, at a pressure of up to about 1600 bar. Some injectors are operated by magnetic solenoids, however more recently operation by piezo electric crystals has been introduced and developed. The latest arrangements enable very accurate control of the injection process including splitting it into more than one injection per combustion cycle. The use of the high pressures means that fine droplets are formed facilitating better combustion and reducing particulate emissions. Good combustion and smoother running are also aided by the very close control exerted over the injection process. The components in such systems have to be manufactured to very close tolerances and the fuel must be free from contamination. The lubricity of the diesel fuel, which is limited, is also important in ensuring the systems perform correctly.

16.4 Sensors
16.4.1 Introduction
As mechanical systems become more sophisticated there is increasing need to provide efficient control. This normally requires a combination of:

- sensors - to monitor conditions, loads, speeds, inputs (eg throttle position)
- microprocessor with software - to process the data to provide optimal settings for the present conditions and demands - eg what fuel flow through the injectors for the measured engine speed, temperature, throttle position etc.
- amplifying circuits - to provide the appropriate power to the actuators - eg the appropriate volts / amps to operate the fuel injectors
- actuators - provide the required force, torque, rotation, etc., needed to operate other components within a system.

General areas of application include:

- i) monitoring and information
- ii) back up and safety
- iii) part of the main operating system

These different uses have differing requirements, in (i) failure will probably not be catastrophic, it might be in (ii) and (iii). In (ii) the system may be idle for long periods of time, but reliable operation is vital when needed, eg automobile airbag actuating systems.

Automotive sensors are assigned to one of 3 reliability classes according to the application:

- Class 1: Steering, brakes, passenger protection
- Class 2: Engine, drive train, suspension, tyres
- Class 3: Comfort and convenience, information, diagnostics, theft deterrence

The following sections briefly examines the main types of sensor:

16.4.2 Position Sensors
The are commonly based on the resistance of a length of film or coiled wire. These may be straight for linear measurement or circular for angular measurement. The variation in resistance between one end of the wire or track and a moving wiper allows the position of the wiper to be accurately determined.

16.4.3 Velocity and RPM sensors

These are often based on electromagnetic effects. A common type of inductive sensor uses a bar magnet with a soft iron pole pin which has a coil around it. When the teeth on a ferromagnetic ring gear move past the sensor, a fluctuating voltage is generated in the coil proportional to the rate of change of magnetic flux, this is proportional to the speed that the teeth are moving past the device. The frequency of the fluctuation is equal to the frequency at which the teeth are moving past the device.

This type of sensor has often been used in conjunction with the starter ring on car engine fly wheels to provide engine speed indication and a second device is normally used to provide ignition timing information.

16.4.4 Acceleration Sensors

The majority of these are based on piezo electric devices. When a piezo electric crystal is put under fluctuating stress (direct or shear) a voltage is generated between opposite faces. In an accelerometer one or more piezo crystals are used to support a small inertial mass within the casing. When the casing is subject to acceleration, the inertial mass tends to remain stationary and as it moves with the casing, the accelerating force is translated through the piezo crystal generating a voltage across the crystal faces. This usually needs amplifying. This type of device only responds to fluctuating accelerations.

These types of device are widely used for:

Application	Range
Knock control - providing a signal for the engine management computer to adjust the ignition timing	1 - 10g
Airbag deployment, seat belt tensioner - passenger safety	50g
Suspension control - passenger comfort and handling	1 - 10g

ICE are usually at their most efficient if the ignition is as far advanced as possible without causing pre-ignition of the mixture or 'knocking'. One or more accelerometers may be fitted to the cylinder head, their output monitored and knocking will be immediately detectable as a massive increase in vibration. Some engine management strategies advance the ignition timing until knocking is detected then retard it till it stops then advance it, continually repeating this procedure to maintain efficient operation.

16.4.5 Pressure Sensors
Pressure measurement can be by diaphragm deflection or force sensor.

16.4.6 Flow Measurement
In spark ignition engines air flow is the primary control parameter. For small ratios of maximum to minimum flow rates (eg 10:1) the pressure drop across a fixed orifice may be used. However in car engines the ratio of the maximum to minimum flow rates is much greater than 10:1. For these types of application a variable flap device can be used. Air being drawn past the flap causes it to open, the rotation of the flap being monitored by a suitable potentiometer. The voltage drop across the potentiometer can then be used to determine the air flow. This type of device has the disadvantage of partially obstructing the airflow and lowering the engine efficiency slightly and not being able to respond to very rapid fluctuations.
A mass flow meter that offers virtually no resistance to the flow and has no moving parts is the hot wire or hot film device. A closed loop control device maintains a constant temperature differential between the hot fine platinum wire or thin film resistor and the passing air. The engine management system converts the signals into mass flow. This system has a fast response rate, in the millisecond range, however it can not recognise flow direction, so strong pulsations in the inlet manifold can cause substantial measuring errors.

16.4.7 Torque Sensors
Torque is measured either by measuring the angle of twist of a length of shaft or by measuring the stress in a portion of shaft.

16.4.8 Temperature Sensors
In motor vehicles temperature sensing (with contact thermometers) is normally done by utilising the sensitivity to temperature variation of electrical resistance materials. These may have a positive (PTC) or negative (NTC) temperature coefficient. The following types of devices are in use:

- Sintered ceramic resistors (NTC) thermistors, made from heavy metal oxides and oxidised mixed crystals.
- Thin film metallic resistors (PTC), integrated on a single substrate wafer together with two temperature neutral trimming resistors, can give extreme precision.
- Thick film resistors, pastes with high specific resistance and positive and negative temperature coefficients are often employed as sensors for compensation purposes.

16.4.9 Lambda Oxygen Sensors

Lambda Oxygen Sensors are used in the closed loop control of vehicle engine management systems, see section 16.3. For use close to lambda = 1, sensors are based on zirconium dioxide which operate on the principle of a galvanic oxygen concentration cell. The cell uses a solid electrolyte whose ceramic is made from zirconium dioxide and yttrium oxide, with platinum electrodes on both surfaces, which separates the exhaust gas from the surrounding air. This ceramic is an oxygen ion conductor and a voltage is generated across the electrodes depending upon the partial pressures of oxygen in the exhaust gas and in a reference as per the Nernst Law.

To give accurate readings the sensor must be in thermodynamic equilibrium with the gas and to aid rapid warm up and accurate operation, sensors may be electrically heated.

To measure the oxygen content of exhaust gases from burning lean mixtures, a more complex configuration is used and if a broadband lambda sensor is required a device which is a combination of the conventional and lean mixture sensor is used.

16.4.10 Other Sensors

Optical sensors are used to detect raindrops on car wind screens and then to automatically operate wipers. Optical devices are also used to trigger washing of head lamp glass when dirt buildup warrants.

Developments in miniature solid state devices means that the range of sensors available is increasing and as their use increases, prices drop, making them more attractive.

The developments in thick and thin film technologies have made it possible to manufacture a range of largely silicon based devices. Micro machining has made it possible to produce beams and diaphragms that are required for strain gauges, accelerometers and pressure gauges, at the chip level.

16.5 Actuators

16.5.1 Introduction

Actuators are the final elements in a control system. They receive a low power command signal and energy input to amplify the command signal as appropriate to produce the required output. Applications range from simple low power switches to high power hydraulic devices operating flaps and control surfaces on aircraft; valves, car steering, etc.

16.5.2 Types of Actuator

Actuators may be grouped in a number of ways:

- Electromechanical
- - electromagnetic - exploits the mutual attraction of soft ferrous materials in a magnetic field. The device has one coil which provides the field energy and the energy to be transformed. The attractive force is unidirectional so a return device of some type is needed, often a spring. Relays or solenoids based on this principle are widely used in cars to switch a range of electrical equipment with a current demand of more than about 10 amps - fans, head lights, horn, wipers.
- - electrodynamic - based on the (Lorenz) force generated when a current carrying conductor (often in the form of a coil) is held in a magnetic field. DC motors are frequently used as part of an actuator system.
- Fluid mechanical
- - pneumatic. A common device is the pneumatic cylinder
- - hydraulic. A common device is the hydraulic cylinder

Key features of pneumatic and hydraulic systems are summarised below:

Feature	Hydraulic actuators	Pneumatic actuators
Medium	Fluid, can be oil, oil/water mix (non flammable) or water + corrosion inhibitors - virtually imcompressible - viscosity heavily temperature dependent	Usually air - compressible - separate lubrication probably required. - viscosity fluctuations not important
Pressure range	Up to about 30 MPa - 200 MPa for diesel injectors	Up to about 1 MPa
Applications	Positioning with high load rigidity and precision in closed loop control systems	Devices with lower power and force / torque requirements, positioning by mechanical stops in open loop systems.

In most applications fluid mechanical actuator drives are in the form of hydrostatic energy converters. These operate on the displacement principle converting the pressure energy of the fluid into mechanical work and vice - versa. Automotive brakes are an important example.

The hydrodynamic transformer works by converting flow energy (kinetic energy of the moving fluid) into mechanical work. An important automotive application is the hydrodynamic torque converter used in place of a clutch (although it also multiplies the torque) in most vehicles fitted with an automatic gearbox.

Other types of actuator may be based on the piezoelectric effect and and the behavior of shape memory alloy wire or strip.

16.5.3 Current Trends

A significant trend is the move away from hydraulic to electrical devices. This is driven partly by the desire to have cleaner systems (no hydraulic fluid) and making integration with other (normally electrical) control systems easier to achieve. New cars are often now fitted with electric power assisted steering rather than the hydraulic system that was the only system available till recently. Developments are progressing with electrical assistance of car braking systems. This trend to electrical systems is also present in the aviation industry, but the very high power densities and forces required from some actuators mean that this will be more difficult.

References

'Automotive Handbook', Bosch, 5th ed., 2000, ISBN: 0-7680-0669-4.